ENVIRONMENTAL INFLUENCES

✳ ✳ ✳

THIRD OF A SERIES ON

BIOLOGY AND BEHAVIOR

BIOLOGY AND BEHAVIOR 3

Environmental Influences

Proceedings of a conference under the auspices of

Russell Sage Foundation and The Rockefeller University

David C. Glass, *Editor*

PUBLISHED BY *The Rockefeller University Press*

AND *Russell Sage Foundation* NEW YORK 1968

LIBRARY OF CONGRESS
CATALOG CARD NUMBER 68-56103
PRINTED IN THE UNITED STATES OF AMERICA

Preface

THERE IS a marked and growing concern among social scientists about the effects of environmental factors on biological mechanisms of behavior. One example is the recent work with small mammals on environmental stress and adrenal and gonadal functioning. Correspondingly, many biological scientists call attention to the fact that a comprehensive human biology cannot omit one of man's more striking characteristics — his social nature. Although the interdependence of the organism and its environment has long been recognized, the systematic study of environmental effects on biological functioning and the behavioral consequences has received less attention than it deserves. On April 21–22, 1967, Russell Sage Foundation and The Rockefeller University sponsored a conference on environmental influences on behavior. The meetings were held in Caspary Auditorium on the Rockefeller campus in New York City. This was the last in a series of three conferences on biology and behavior. The aim of the series was to strengthen the dialogue between the biological and social sciences, and to stimulate a *rapprochement* between the two disciplines in order that future work in each field might be undertaken in fuller recognition of the other.

The present volume contains fifteen papers that were delivered at the two-day conference. The first volume was published in the fall of 1967 and dealt with the topic of neurophysiology and emotion. The second volume contained the proceedings of the conference on genetics and behavior, and was published in the spring of 1968. The ultimate goal of all three books is to disseminate information that will foster understanding of behavior through research that rises above the limitations imposed by narrow specialization.

The evening paper of the present conference was delivered by

v

Professor René Dubos on "Environmental Determinants of Human Life." One of the more important themes of this paper is reflected in the following excerpt: "Since the human genetic pool remains essentially the same from one generation to the next, its phenotypic expression represents the responses to the total environment and the ways of life, which are continuously changing." Professor Dubos develops this idea by giving detailed consideration in his paper to the consequences for human biology of some of the environmental forces that are most characteristic of the modern world, including the urban environment with its multitude of stresses and uniquely demanding phenotypic adaptations. He concludes that: "While there is no doubt that man can function and reproduce in a completely artificial environment, it is probable that alienation from nature will eventually rob him of some of his important biological attributes and most desirable ethical and esthetic values." In other words, man can adapt to a stressful environment, but these adaptations have indirect effects which are deleterious to biobehavioral functioning. Recent work in Professor Dubos' laboratory shows such effects in infrahuman species.[1]

Further support for Dubos' position comes from experimentation with human subjects in my own laboratory at the Rockefeller.[2] We have been able to show that individuals pay a "psychic cost" for adaptation to aversive noise stimuli, the nature of this cost being reflected in lowered tolerance for postadaptive frustrations. We have also been able to show that, when the individual is given control over the noise, the cost of adaptation is reduced, so that frustration tolerance is not appreciably lowered following the adaptive process. Research of this kind underscores the need for taking sociopsychological factors into account in analyzing biobehavioral adaptations to environmental stress. The results of such research have far-ranging implications for city planning, urban redevelopment, and indeed the entire problem of environmental change.

The topics discussed during the two days of the conference dealt with specific social- and physical-environmental effects on behavior. The complete text of each paper is included in this volume. The morning session of the first day was concerned with early nutritional deficiencies and later mental performance. It was concluded that malnutrition is one of the contributing factors to poor social background, poor physical growth, and inadequate mental functioning. A number of empirical studies suggest that children with a history of early malnutrition are educational risks. Normal adaptive functioning requires a normal environment, adequate nutrition, and a normal genetic constitution.

The afternoon session considered early social deprivation in non-human primates and its implications for human behavior. The papers uniformly emphasized a comparative perspective, underlining the view that an understanding of human behavior and development can be aided by systematic examination of primate behavioral development. Viewpoints merged toward the belief that environmental and social events during the first few weeks of life may be vital to the development of the infant. While the precise nature and duration of this critical period in human infancy is yet to be specified, it was generally believed that very early unsatisfied social and physical needs present serious and often irreversible obstacles to later development.

On the second day, the morning session was devoted to discussion of the effects of social isolation on human learning and performance. Social interaction (i.e., the mere presence of others) was found to have a facilitative effect on performance, whereas social isolation has an inhibitory effect. It was concluded that this finding needs qualification, for there is other evidence showing that humans tend to isolate themselves from further stimulation after a high degree of social interaction. Additional social contact may actually lower rather than raise performance level. It would appear that human and infrahuman animals seek an optimal level of arousal which varies from environment to environment and from species to species.

The final session of the conference was addressed to research on cultural deprivation and its effects on higher mental functioning. Recent research shows that differences in behavior and mental organization, such as that between middle-class and lower-middle-class children, does not emerge until after two years of age. Data suggest that every child requires a set of schemata to interpret experience; distinctive events to promote the development of such schemata; perception of a model whom the child views as possessing attributes he values; a set of goals promoted by people the child admires; and, finally, some degree of certainty about the occurrences of each day. Some children are deprived of all or most of these ingredients, and it is this group which is customarily considered "culturally deprived."

To summarize: the conference ranged over a variety of environmental influences on behavior, including nutritional deficiencies and mental development and functioning; the effects of social deprivation on intellectual performance and social behavior among human and infrahuman species; and the influence of cultural deprivations on human cognitive development and organization. It was concluded that neither social nor biological determinants of behavior can be emphasized to the relative exclusion of the other.

We would like to thank Dr. Orville G. Brim, Jr., President of Russell Sage Foundation, and Dr. Detlev W. Bronk, President of The Rockefeller University, whose joint efforts and support made the conference possible. We also want to thank Dr. Carl Pfaffmann, Vice President of The Rockefeller University, and Dr. Donald R. Young, Visiting Professor at the Rockefeller and formerly President of Russell Sage Foundation. Both men were instrumental in conceiving and implementing the idea of a conference series on biology and behavior. Our gratitude also goes to the following men who served as chairmen of the various sessions: Professors Paul Weiss and Alfred E. Mirsky of the Rockefeller; Professor Stanley Schachter of Columbia University; and Professor Francis H. Palmer of the City University of New York.

Russell Sage Foundation was established in 1907 by Mrs. Russell Sage for the improvement of social and living conditions in the United States. In carrying out its purpose, the Foundation conducts research under the direction of members of the staff or in close collaboration with other institutions, and supports programs designed to develop and demonstrate productive working relations between social scientists and other scientific and professional groups. The program in biology and the social sciences represents one such activity which was undertaken jointly with The Rockefeller University.

I would like to express my gratitude to Mr. William Bayless of

The Rockefeller University Press and to Mrs. Betty Davison of Russell Sage Foundation for their assistance in organizing the conferences, publishing the proceedings, and arranging for promotion and distribution. I would particularly like to thank Mrs. Helene Jordan of The Rockefeller University Press, who performed valuable editorial work in bringing the present volume to publication. Finally, I would like to pay tribute to one of the contributors, Professor Richard H. Walters, who died soon after the conference. He will long be remembered by his former colleagues at the University of Waterloo (Canada) and by the larger psychological community for his valuable contributions to the study of behavior.

DAVID C. GLASS
Russell Sage Foundation and
June 17, 1968   The Rockefeller University

Contents

Preface   DAVID C. GLASS   v

EARLY NUTRITIONAL
DEFICIENCIES

Nutritional Deficiencies and Mental Performance in
Childhood
           JOAQUÍN CRAVIOTO   3

Behavioral Changes Caused by Malnutrition in the
Rat and Pig
           RICHARD H. BARNES   52

Sociocultural Factors in Nutritional Studies
           EDWARD A. SUCHMAN   61

INFRAHUMAN STUDIES OF
SOCIAL ISOLATION

Early Social Deprivation in the Nonhuman Primates:
Implications for Human Behavior
           WILLIAM A. MASON   70

The Crucial Nature of Early Experience
           LEON J. YARROW   101

The Social Environment of Infant Macaques
           PETER MARLER and ANDREW GORDON   113

Communication of Affects in Monkeys
           I. ARTHUR MIRSKY   129

CONTENTS *continued*

SOCIAL IMPLICATIONS OF EARLY ENVIRONMENTAL INFLUENCES

Environmental Determinants of Human Life
RENÉ DUBOS   138

REINFORCEMENT AND INTERPERSONAL RELATIONS

The Effects of Social Isolation and Social Interaction on Learning and Performance in Social Situations
RICHARD H. WALTERS   155

Indifferent Exteroceptive Stimulation and Reinforcement
D. E. BERLYNE   185

The Construction and Selection of Environments
WILLIAM KESSEN   197

Social Conditions, Physiology, and Role Performance
P. HERBERT LEIDERMAN   202

THE EFFECTS OF CULTURAL DEPRIVATION

On Cultural Deprivation
JEROME KAGAN   211

When is Infant Stimulation Effective?
URIE BRONFENBRENNER   251

Perception, Cognitive Maps, and Covert Behavior
LEONARD S. COTTRELL, JR.   257

References   267

Index   289

ENVIRONMENTAL INFLUENCES

Nutritional Deficiencies and Mental Performance in Childhood

JOAQUÍN CRAVIOTO

DISCUSSION

Behavioral Changes Caused by Malnutrition in the Rat and Pig
RICHARD H. BARNES   52

Sociocultural Factors in Nutritional Studies
EDWARD A. SUCHMAN   61

"Protein-calorie malnutrition of early childhood" is a phrase used in the medical literature to cover the whole range of mild to severe clinical and biochemical manifestations of deficient intake and/or utilization of animal food-stuffs and carbohydrates.[46]

Studies of several communities with a high prevalence of malnutrition have shown three sets of factors that appeared to be associated with infant malnutrition. First are both the quantity and the quality of the food ingested by the child. Second are features of health and disease that may indirectly affect nutritional status and weight gain. Among these, infections play a major role. Third are those influences of a more general social character that include such things as family relationships, social and economic status, educational background, and patterns of child care.[23,29,62]

The cause of malnutrition is highly complicated because of the number of interrelated variables that produce it. To give an idea of the difficulties introduced by this multiple causation, it might be

JOAQUÍN CRAVIOTO Department of Nutrition II. Hospital Infantil de Mexico, Mexico, D. F.

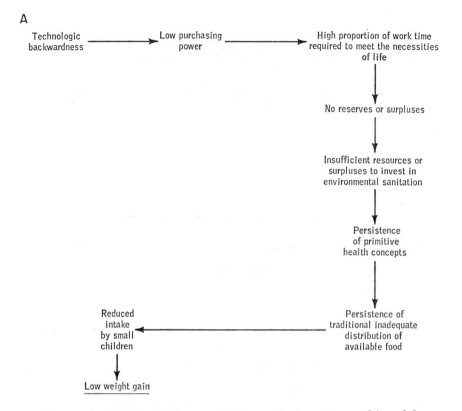

A

Technologic backwardness → Low purchasing power → High proportion of work time required to meet the necessities of life

↓

No reserves or surpluses

↓

Insufficient resources or surpluses to invest in environmental sanitation

↓

Persistence of primitive health concepts

↓

Persistence of traditional inadequate distribution of available food → Reduced intake by small children

↓

Low weight gain

FIGURE 1 A–B (see facing page)   Interrelations among biosocial factors and low weight gain.

enough to show that in a preindustrial social setting the small infant can fall into a clinical picture of malnutrition in at least four ways, as illustrated in Figures 1A–D (pp. 4–7).

Animal experiments have shown that protein malnutrition, particularly early in life, produces permanent organic modifications, especially in total length, length of lower limbs, dentine composition, and proportion of muscular tissue present in the adult.[57,58,64,79,80]

Studies on the recovery of children with advanced chronic malnutrition seem to confirm the results obtained in animal studies. A child who has recovered from severe malnutrition is shorter and his general skeletal development is retarded in comparison with that of individ-

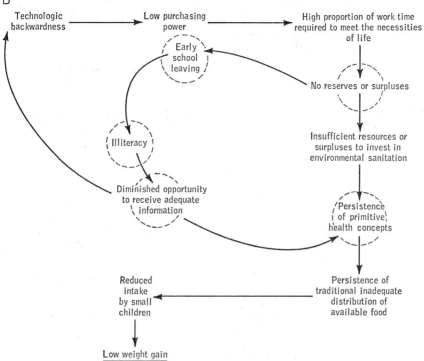

B

Technologic backwardness → Low purchasing power → High proportion of work time required to meet the necessities of life

Early school leaving

No reserves or surpluses

Illiteracy

Insufficient resources or surpluses to invest in environmental sanitation

Diminished opportunity to receive adequate information

Persistence of primitive health concepts

Reduced intake by small children ← Persistence of traditional inadequate distribution of available food

Low weight gain

uals of the same age and ethnic group who have not suffered malnutrition.[1,6,15,21,30,41,45,53,59,65,66,73]

The effects of malnutrition are not restricted to diminished or altered body proportions. Apparently, malnutrition can arrest certain aspects of biochemical maturation and can also produce retrogressions to earlier age-specific patterns of functioning. For example, when water content and distribution in malnourished children are recalculated on the basis of the age indicated by the actual weight or height, it is apparent that both content and distribution are "normal" for a younger child. Similar conclusions can be reached when the data for fat absorption, plasma lipid concentrations, changes in proportions of alpha and beta lipoproteins, modifications of cholesterol concentrations in blood, and urinary excretions of creatinine are plotted against the age for height and/or the age for weight.[20,26] It is also of interest that, when vaccinated, children recovering from malnutrition respond

C

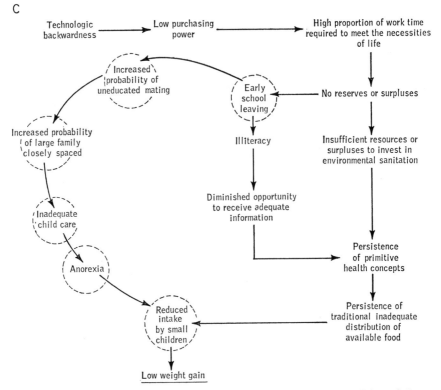

FIGURE 1 C–D (see facing page)   Interrelations among biosocial factors and low weight gain.

immunologically in much the same way as very much younger normal infants.[61]

Kumate, et al.,[52] found a diminution of about 20 per cent in the levels of hemolytic complement in 118 malnourished children. The decreases were similar for all four components determined (C′1, C′2, C′3, and C′4). They found a low, but statistically significant, correlation between the degree of malnutrition, estimated as the percentage of difference between the theoretical and actual body weights, and the level of complementary activity. Similar results were obtained by Ramunni and Moretti[67] and by Vasile.[78] Unpublished observations of Kumate at the Hospital Infantil de Mexico have also shown that 7-S gamma-2-globulin is reduced in severe malnutrition, with average values of about 400 milligrams as against about 1,000 milligrams in well-nourished controls.

D

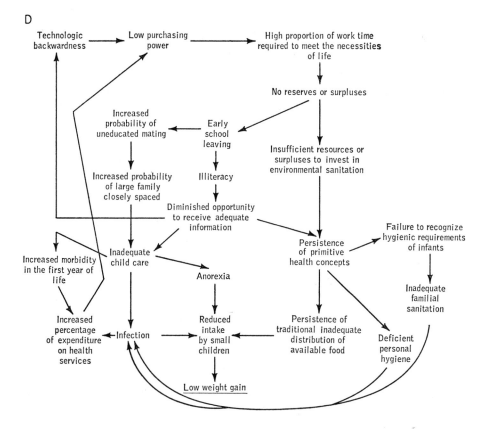

Free amino acid concentrations in blood plasma of children affected with either marasmus or kwashiorkor generally show an abnormally high ratio of phenylalanine to tyrosine.[24] A similar finding in urine previously reported by Cheung, et al.,[18] suggests the possibility of a defect in the enzyme system that metabolizes phenylalanine into tyrosine.[33]

The extent to which malnutrition can alter normal biochemical maturation in humans is perhaps best illustrated by Dean, who has been able to reproduce in malnourished preschool children the biochemical lesions most characteristic of the absence or marked lack of certain enzymes participating in the metabolism of the aromatic amino acids histidine, tyrosine, and phenylalanine — a phenomenon normally present only in the newborn infant.[31]

At present, more children survive severe protein malnutrition than die of it. In 1952, approximately 30 per cent of children with third-degree malnutrition died, but less than 5 per cent died during 1962–1964.[40] This is the result of better knowledge of the biochemical characteristics of malnourished children and better means for rapid diagnosis and assessment of the effects of treatment for severe dehydration and infections.

Nevertheless, we must remember that the problem of malnutrition does not end when a considerable number of deaths are averted. The majority of children afflicted by malnutrition do not die, most adults inhabiting the preindustrial areas of the world have not escaped malnutrition in one degree or another, and there will be survivors of this generation's malnourished children — all of which leads us to wonder about the permanent or transitory after-effects that may impair full development.

It is interesting for the student of human nutrition to realize that although impressive advances have been made during the past fifteen years in the clinical and biochemical aspects of protein-calorie malnutrition, only recently have pediatricians, public health workers, psychologists, and educators become concerned with the problem of a potential delay in mental development of afflicted children. The effects of dietary deficiencies upon higher nervous function in humans have not been systematically investigated, perhaps because infantile malnutrition has mistakenly been equated only with poor socioeconomic status.[34]

Food consumption surveys evaluating the nutritional status of high and low socioeconomic groups show marked differences in dietary intake on a per capita basis, but not enough emphasis has been placed on the findings that, in communities where infant malnutrition is highly prevalent, the preschool child does not receive the proper proportion of the total food available to the family.[4] In other words, traditional patterns often prevent preschool children from being fed, at the time most needed, adequate amounts of the nutrition foods consumed by older children and adults in the family. The ideas that combined to produce this dangerous pattern of intrafamilial food distribution are an integral part of the prevailing ideology concerning health and disease, life and death,[27] and are not restricted to the illiterate population. They are also found in many well-educated, middle- and high-income families eager to do their best for their children.

Awareness of this situation developed slowly because assessment of any residual damage to the central nervous system caused by protein-calorie malnutrition requires long-term observations. However, such studies, although difficult to design and carry out, are important both for the development of millions of the world's malnourished children and for the light they may shed on the neurophysiology and neuro-psychology of child development.

A longitudinal study seemed to be the only way to test for causal relationships, considering the complicated nature of the subject and the number of professional disciplines necessarily involved in the collection and analysis of pertinent information. Before engaging in the project, we attempted to find out if children malnourished at an earlier period in their lives would show significant differences from children who probably always had had an adequate diet. The work, on which I report here, was conducted from 1957 to 1965.

From the beginning, we were aware that the main limitation of these preliminary studies lay in treating malnutrition as an isolated variable outside of its social context. We know that food deprivation is only one item in the complex socioeconomic system, but, as I said before, the first step had to deal with a simple question: what differences, if any, can be found in children subjected to different risks of malnutrition, and for how long do they persist?

A concern with the behavioral development of infants and children in societies where malnutrition is prevalent makes it essential to have a baseline in order to estimate the level of initial behavioral organization. The work of Geber and Dean[37] and of Robles, et al.,[69] strongly suggests that the norms for psychomotor and adaptive development that have been derived from studies of infants in the United States and in western European countries are not applicable to the newborn in Africa or Mexico. Newborn infants in these preindustrial communities have been described as exhibiting remarkable levels of precocity in both motor and adaptive behaviors. However, the samples studied have never been clearly defined, nor have the children been homogeneous for age. Neither the study of Geber nor that of Robles has related behavioral findings to other indexes of development, such as body weight and length, nor have they described the prenatal and perinatal circumstances of the infants studied. As a consequence, it is not possible at present to know if precocity is, in fact, characteristic of representative infants in a preindustrial society or whether the phenomenon is only pseudoprecocity in certain functions associated with low body weight, neurological damage, or both.

In trying to provide answers for some of the questions surrounding this problem, we decided to study the behavioral organization in a defined population of newborns, representative of all such children born in a large maternity service in Guatemala, by relating behavior to weight and body length.[54] The 100 infants studied — 56 girls and 44 boys — were all normal newborns, the products of normal, spontaneous delivery, uncomplicated labor, and uneventful pregnancy. All were full-term, and consisted of all infants with such backgrounds born in the service during a thirty-day period.

All children came from families belonging to the middle and lower segments of the working class. Ninety-five of the children were of mixed Indian-European origin and the remaining five were of Indian stock. Since no identifiable behavior or growth differences distinguished these latter infants from the remainder of the sample, they were included in the study population.

Body weight and body length were determined by anthropometric examination, for which we used a finely calibrated scale and a standard adjustable headrest and footboard for measuring the length of the supine infant in full extension. Clinical normality of each child was determined by pediatric evaluation. Weight distribution for the total sample of infants studied is presented in Figure 2. Mean weight was 3,000 ± 310 grams. Weight values tended to be normally distributed. Seven infants were below 2,500 grams, with the lowest weight 2,040 grams. Twelve weighed more than 3,500 grams, and the maximum weight was 4,390 grams. Separate distributions by weight for boys and girls are presented in Figure 3. The distribution of body length for the whole sample is presented in Figure 4. Figure 5 shows the distributions of body length by sex.

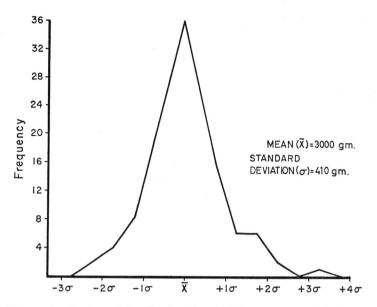

FIGURE 2 Body weight distribution of full-term normal infants.

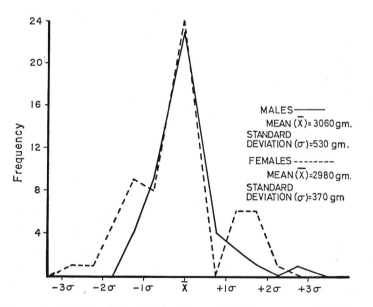

FIGURE 3 Body weight distribution of full-term normal infants according to sex.

Two experienced examiners used the Gesell scales to evaluate psychomotor and adaptive development.[38] Time of examination varied from 24 hours to 72 hours after birth; this variation was the product both of administrative circumstances and of the postnatal condition of the infant.

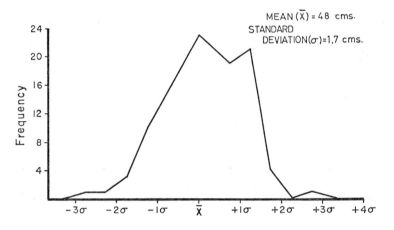

FIGURE 4   Body length distribution of full-term normal infants.

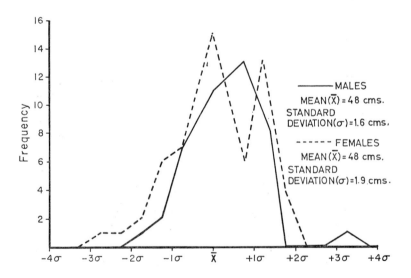

FIGURE 5   Body length distribution of full-term infants according to sex.

Psychomotor Development

The findings on psychomotor performance are shown in Figure 6. As may be seen, all of the children were advanced in their motor functioning. The lowest level of motor organization was at an estimated age level of 13 days; most of the children were three to five weeks above expectation for their age. Mean psychomotor performance in this sample was 24 ± 4.8 days.

A better appreciation of the organization of psychomotor functioning in these newborn infants can be obtained from Table I (p. 14). The items listed are not expected to be performed before the second month of age, so it is interesting to note that significant numbers of newborn infants behaved adequately on demands normally responded to by two-month-olds, with 90 per cent showing a good level of manual relaxation.

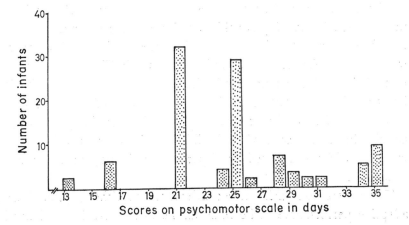

FIGURE 6 Frequency distribution of scores on *psychomotor* scale in 100 full-term normal newborn infants examined within 72 hours after delivery. The shapes of the two distributions are highly similar, with the girls over-all of slightly lower weight than the boys.

Table I

Organization of psychomotor functioning in full-term newborn infants according to sex

Items	Position	Percents passing each item	
		Females	Males
1 Lifts head, zone I, momentarily	Prone	48	41
2 Lifts head, zone I, persistently	Supine	9	14
3 Head predominately bobbing erect	Sitting	16	23
4 Head set forward, bobs	Sitting	18	18
5 Head in midposition	Prone	25	34
6 Head compensates ventral suspension	Prone	11	16
7 Lifts head, zone II	Prone	7	11
8 Lifts head, zone III	Prone	2	2
9 Hands opened or loosely closed	Supine	91	89

Adaptive Development

The distribution of adaptive development scores is shown in Figure 7. Precocity in adaptive skill was by no means as pronounced as that shown for motor development. The mean adaptive level in days was 7.8 ± 3.4. A more detailed view is shown in Table II. More than half of the children performed adequately on only two of the four items on the one-month scale. The most striking of these was the response to auditory stimulation, which resulted in clearly diminished activity in 95 per cent of the children. The other involved rattle-grasping, which was passed by 82 per cent of the boys and 62 per cent of the girls.

There were no significant sex differences for either psychomotor or adaptive performance. The relations between adaptive and psychomotor development were explored through analysis of the adaptive scores of the children who were most precocious in their psychomotor behavior. When all children who had psychomotor scores equivalent to those of 30-day-old infants were distributed in accordance with

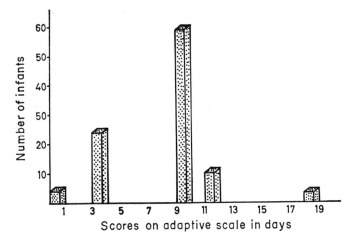

FIGURE 7   Frequency distribution of scores on the *adaptive* scale in 100 full-term normal newborn infants examined within 72 hours after delivery. Mean body length was 48 ± 1.7 centimeters. The shortest infant was 42 centimeters in length, and the longest 53.5 centimeters.

their levels of adaptive performance, a weak trend of positive association was found. Five of the high psychomotor performers were above the median for adaptive performance, eleven were at the median, and two performed below the median for the group. These associations are not statistically significant.

TABLE II

Organization of adaptive functioning in full-term newborn infants

	Items	Percents passing each item	
		Females	*Males*
1	D. Ring, Rattle: Regards vision only	5	2
2	D. Ring: Follows to middle lines	2	0
3	Ra: Drops immediately	62	82
4	Bell – r: Attends, activity diminishes	95	95
5	Ra.: Retains briefly	16	18
6	Ra.: Retains activity	7	14

Relations Between Behavior and Body Measurements

To analyze the relation between psychomotor performance and body measurements, we considered only those items of behavior in which the group exhibited variability. Items 1, 3, 5, 6, and 7 of Table I fulfilled this criterion. Accordingly, it was possible for a child to perform successfully on one to five of these items. The distribution of such performances is presented in Table III. As may be seen, half of the children passed at least one of the discriminating items.

The relation of the height or weight of these most precocious children to that of the remaining infants is expressed in Tables IV and V. Within the range of weights studied, no significant association existed. A similar lack of association was found between the bodily measurements of the child and his level of performance in adaptive development. However, it must be emphasized that the advanced level of psychomotor performance is not associated with an equivalent level of precocity in adaptive behavior.

It is difficult to argue in support of an ethnic explanation for precocity, because its presence seems to be associated with birth in a preindustrial society rather than with ethnic homogeneity. Such ethnically divergent subgroups as the East African infants studied by Geber and Dean,[37] the Nahoa Indians of the Mexican plateau,[69] the West Africans examined by Faladé,[34] and the Central American Indian-Caucasian group examined in the present study, all appear to have similar degrees of advanced psychomotor organization in the neonatal

TABLE III

*Number of discriminating items in psychomotor scale
passed by newborn full-term Guatemalan infants*

	Number of items passed				
	1	2	3	4	5
Number of children passing	19	7	10	10	4

Table IV
Relation of height to psychomotor precocity

		Height	
		Above median	Below median
Number of infants:	Most precocious	22	28
	Least precocious	28	22

$X^2 = 1.30$ Not significant

Table V
Relation of weight to psychomotor precocity

		Weight	
		Above median	Below median
Number of infants:	Most precocious	26	24
	Least precocious	24	26

period. Knobloch has summarized other difficulties associated with an ethnic interpretation, which need not be repeated here.[49]

Some suggestive evidence, particularly that deriving from studies on the offspring of animal mothers who have been differently stimulated during pregnancy,[77] directs our attention to environmental considerations as possible mechanisms producing early psychomotor precocity. In these studies, motor organization was significantly different in groups of neonatal animals born of mothers who had been stimulated differently.

It is possible that conditions of life in preindustrial communities, including the relation of the mother to heavy labor throughout the period of pregnancy, as well as the high status associated with being pregnant and therefore demonstrably fertile, may result in systematic alterations in fetal environment. This, in turn, could produce advanced levels of motor organization at birth. To test the hypothesis, studies might be designed using appropriate animal models and human infants from closely related ethnic groups in preindustrial and more advanced communities.

Quite apart from the sources for psychomotor precocity, we as yet have little understanding of its functional significance for the child, either in early infancy or in the course of later development. Intensive ecological and longitudinal studies of infants high in motor precocity and those relatively nonprecocious from preindustrial communities may provide information that would permit us to relate the phenomenon of precocity to growth, morbidity, and mortality in infancy. Such studies are in progress in our department.

Cross-sectional studies of motor and adaptive performance carried out in six different communities — two of typical mestizos, one of Zapotec Indians and one of Nahoa Indians in Mexico, and two of Cakchiquel Indians in Guatemala have shown that, soon after birth, infants tend to decline progressively in their Gesell test scores to a degree that places them below their European counterparts by the time they are eighteen to twenty-four months old.

Dean expressed the Gesell Developmental Quotients (Y) for a given age (x) on the basis of a scale on which 100 represents the performance of the "normal" North American or European child of the same age as the children being tested. By following this method, the relationship between quotients and chronological age could be described by a curve of the type $Y=ax-b$ for the total span of birth to 42 months, and a satisfactory approximation of this curve can be attained by fitting a series of straight lines over subsets of smaller age intervals. (Figures 8A–D, pp. 20 and 21)

In regard to body growth, even children who develop kwashiorkor later in their lives usually grow well during the first months of life. When the mother's milk no longer meets the infant's needs and suitable supplements are not added, weight and height increments begin to slow down. By the time the child is completely weaned, which for most areas of Latin America usually is between the eighteenth and the twenty-fourth month, height is practically stationary and weight may even show a slight decrease.

When the scores on motor and adaptive behavior were compared with actual weights and heights, a high degree of association was found. Table VI illustrates the significance of these associations. On the other hand, no statistically significant association could be demonstrated between developmental scores and per capita cash income,

TABLE VI

Values for empirical constants a *and* b. *Calculated for relation between percentage of theoretical adaptive or motor behavior and percentage of mean theoretical weight for age in rural children of Cakchiquel language group. (Equations of the form* $Y = a \pm bx$*, where* $Y = \%$ *of theoretical behavior and* $x = \%$ *of theoretical weight for age)*

Field of behavior	a	b	Statistical significance of prediction equation "F" Test
Motor	10.48	1.22	11.77*
Adaptive	65.92	0.42	5.79**

*Significant at 1% level
**Significant at 5% level

crop income, parental education, parental hygiene, or type of housing. Terman-Merrill scores of intelligence (Y) of rural preschool children aged 30 to 72 months appeared to be negatively correlated with the chronological age (x) of the children. The least-squares equation for the fitted straight line to this data was $Y = 1.37 - 0.86x$; standard error of fit = 13.

As before, body weight and height were found to be positively correlated with the intelligence scores of these children. Mathematical expressions of these associations showed that the intelligence quotient was equal to 0.79 times the "height age" in months, plus 12; or 0.51 times the "weight age" in months, plus 29; the errors of the fittings were 13 and 20, respectively (Figures 9A and B, p. 22). Because mental age shows a better association with height age than with chronological age, the data are interpreted as suggestive of a concurrent lag of so-

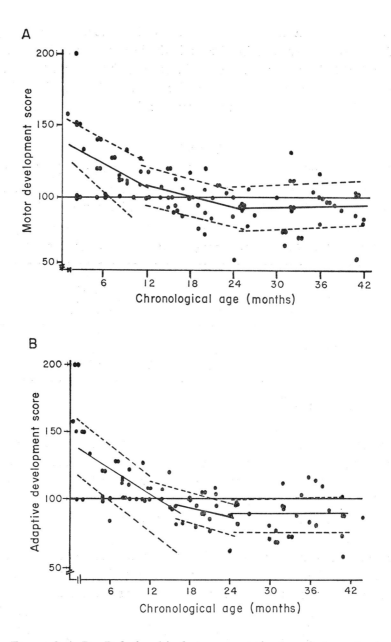

A

Motor development score

Chronological age (months)

B

Adaptive development score

Chronological age (months)

FIGURE 8 A–D Relationship between quotients and chronological age. Girls were somewhat shorter than boys, and the body-length distribution showed a significant tendency toward bimodality. (See facing page)

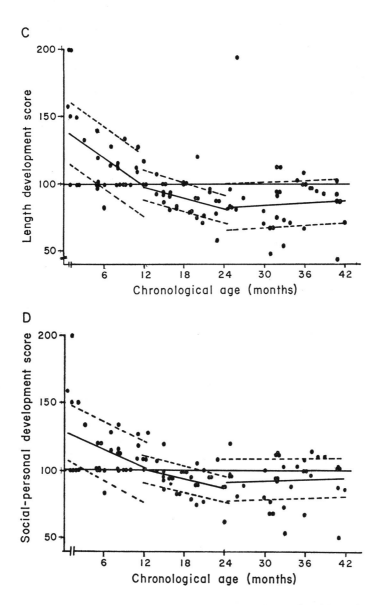

C

Length development score

Chronological age (months)

D

Social-personal development score

Chronological age (months)

matic and mental growth. An argument against the idea that the lower scores found in mildly to moderately malnourished children were solely because of cultural bias, as found in the Terman-Merrill test, is that a bias becomes more pronounced as the child grows older and goes to school.

Studies performed as part of a program (Operación Zacatepec) to establish quantitatively the factors determining the status of nutrition

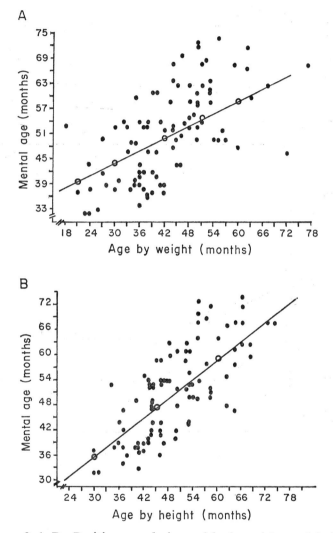

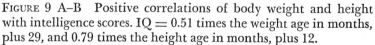

FIGURE 9 A–B   Positive correlations of body weight and height with intelligence scores. IQ = 0.51 times the weight age in months, plus 29, and 0.79 times the height age in months, plus 12.

in Mexican rural communities have indicated that the evolution of weight during the first five years of life may be described by three well-defined phases.[66] The first encompasses the four to six months following birth; these are characterized by weight gains similar to those shown by normal full-term infants born in highly industrialized countries. This phenomenon is most apparent when gains are not expressed as absolute values but as percentages of birth weight. The second phase extends from the sixth to approximately the thirtieth month. During this period, weight gains become progressively smaller, and reach their minimum between the eighteenth and the twenty-fourth month, after which they show a tendency to rise slowly but steadily. In the third phase, there is a return to incremental values normal for the chronological age.

Studies on experimental animals show that the magnitude and persistence of alterations caused by diet depends a great deal on the period of life in which they appear, so we have argued that the effects of malnutrition on mental development in the mature individual would vary as a function of the age at which malnutrition had been experienced. Accordingly, it could be predicted that psychological deficit resulting from severe malnutrition would be most profound if the stress took place during the first of the three age periods of growth, i.e., under six months of age.[28]

From all the children admitted to the Nutrition Ward of the Hospital Infantil de Mexico, those selected for study were the ones classified as suffering from third-degree protein-calorie malnutrition, as defined by the criteria of Gomez, et al.,[39] and Bengoa,[8] who include in that group all malnourished children with pitting edema, regardless of weight. Immediately after treatment of any infectious disease and correction of severe dehydration, the behavior of the children was assessed by the Gesell method. Tests were repeated at regular intervals of two weeks during the entire period the children were hospitalized. At the end of one year of study it was possible to analyze serial information obtained on six infants who were less than six months old upon admission, nine children between 15 and 29 months and five children between 37 and 42 months (Table VII, p. 24).

Results of the first test session are given in Table VIII, p. 25. It can

TABLE VII

Developmental quotients (Gesell) at the inception of study of
20 children suffering from severe protein-calorie malnutrition

	Chronological age (months)	Field of behavior (Developmental quotients)			
		Motor	Adaptive	Language	Personal-social
Sub-group I					
No. 1	3	67	67	67	33
2	4	25	25	25	25
3	5	20	20	20	20
4	5	20	60	20	20
5	6	33	33	33	33
6	6	33	33	33	33
Sub-group II					
No. 1	15	40	40	27	35
2	16	69	69	56	59
3	20	75	70	65	75
4	23	42	42	42	42
5	24	38	29	4	12
6	25	46	40	35	44
7	27	37	37	22	33
8	29	52	62	48	52
9	29	31	17	24	24
Sub-group III					
No. 1	37	57	49	57	81
2	37	40	49	35	35
3	38	39	39	37	37
4	41	7	7	7	7
5	42	26	26	31	26

be seen that, on the first examination, the 20 children exhibited a reduction in all developmental spheres explored by Gesell test stimuli. These findings confirm previous preliminary observations made of a small group of kwashiorkor children,[70] and are in agreement with similar reports from Venezuela[6] and Africa.[36]

In order to examine improvement in performance, data for each child were plotted against days of hospitalization. The shape of the

TABLE VIII

Certain characteristics of the children on admission to the study

	Chronological age (months)	Weight (kgs)	Percentage of mean theoretic weight for age	Height (cms)	"Age for height"
Sub-group I					
No. 1	3	3.25	57	56	2
2	4	2.24	35	50	0
3	5	3.25	46	50	0
4	5	3.86	55	57	2
5	6	3.10	42	56.5	2
6	6	2.89	39	56	2
Sub-group II					
No. 1	15	4.66	47	63	5
2	16	8.75	82	73	16
3	20	6.50	59	74	17
4	23	6.90	58	69	11
5	24	6.30	52	72	14
6	25	7.15	58	78	22
7	27	6.90	55	75	18
8	29	7.64	58	78	22
9	29	5.75	45	78	22
Sub-group III					
No. 1	37	8.62	62	86.5	31
2	37	5.90	45	78	22
3	38	10.40	72	83	28
4	41	6.38	43	78	22
5	42	5.99	40	71	13

curves suggested that the findings represented a series of linear functions. Data were therefore fitted to algebraic expressions of the form $Y = a + bx$. In the equation, Y represents the performance in terms of months of specific behavior, i.e., the age at which a normal child would receive the score found in the tested child; x is the number of days of treatment and the b is an empirical constant determined by the data. The constant b was calculated by the least-squares method for each group and for each field of behavior. Table IX presents the values of the regression equations thus obtained, and Figures 10A to C give the findings.

TABLE IX

Values of regression equations (from Y=a+bx). Table shows the relation between developmental quotients (Y) and days of treatment (x) in three groups recovering from advanced malnutrition.

Developmental quotient (months)	Age groups (months)					
	3–6		15–29		37–41	
	a	b	a	b	a	b
Motor	2.18	0.033	12	0.06	14	0.10
Adaptive	2.30	0.033	12	0.08	15	0.11
Language	2.0	0.033	9	0.05	15	0.07
Personal-social	2.11	0.033	10.5	0.07	16	0.11

The theoretical values of Y, predicted by the equations when x varied from 1 to 200, were determined and compared with the mean of the empirical values. In all age groups and fields of behavior the probability (chi-square test) was greater than 0.95 that there was no significant difference between the observed data and that of the prediction.

The equations and their corresponding graphs demonstrate that the rate of recovery from the initial deficit varies in direct relation to chronological age at admittance. The older the group the greater the value of the slope. Consequently, the difference between the chronological and mental ages, computed on the basis of psychological test behavior, diminished in all the children except those who were younger than six months when admitted to the hospital. The increment in mental age of this group was equal to the number of months expended in the hospital ward. In other words, in the youngest group the initial deficit remained constant throughout the observation period, which in some cases extended up to six and a half months. It is important to notice that progress in the first two weeks of treatment is so rapid that it appears unlikely that the differences between initial test performance and level of functioning at the end of treatment can

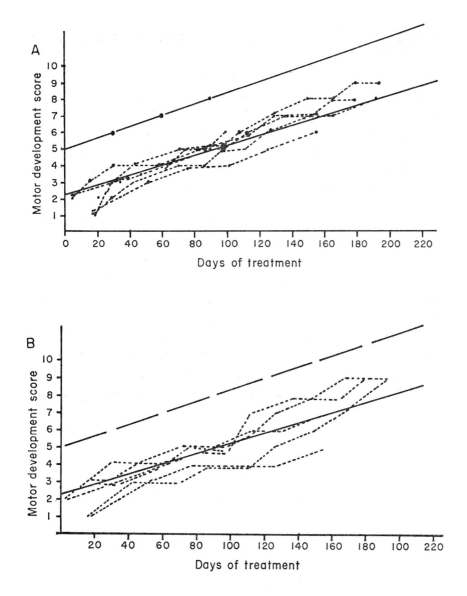

FIGURE 10 A–C Findings based on Table IX. Twenty-seven per cent performed at levels no greater than age expectancy. The remainder were, in the main, only moderately advanced, with 60 per cent functioning at a nine-day level and only 3 per cent behaving two weeks or more beyond age expectation. (Figure C, page 28)

be the result solely of the extra care and attention the children received in the hospital.

Among the general factors which contribute to the intellectual development of the child, those considered to be among the most influential are the educational level of the parents, especially of the mother, and the maternal attitude to the child's intellectual development. Knobloch and Pasamanick[49] have shown systematic variation of developmental quotients in relation to the level of maternal education, and have indicated that this relation is progressively more manifest as the child grows older. Similar findings of a direct association between the child and parent IQs have also been reported by Kagan and Moss.[47]

The influences of non-nutritional factors have not been taken into account sufficiently in studies of mental development of malnourished children. This is especially regrettable, as it is known that the great majority of these children have parents who are either illiterate or have a very low scholastic achievement. In a study designed to characterize the environment in which these severely malnourished children live, Martínez, Ramos-Galván and de la Fuente[56] found a great number of mothers who themselves had low intelligence quotients.

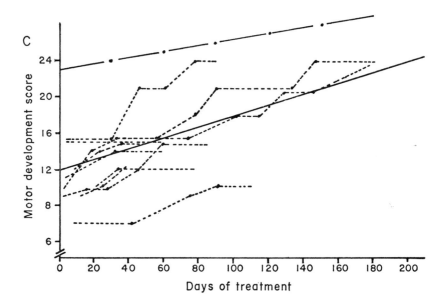

Furthermore, children suffering from protein-calorie malnutrition generally come from homes where economic pressure prevents the parents from providing adequate and varied intellectual stimulation for development. However, Stoch and Smythe,[76] in their semilongitudinal study of mental development in Cape Town, have reported that the parents of both well-nourished and undernourished children scored at very low levels on the Raven intelligence test.

Early diagnosis of mental subnormality in children can seldom be established, even in severely defective cases, because the assessment measures of intelligence at ages under 16 weeks bear little or no correlation with those made at subsequent ages.[7] After the first 16 weeks, the prediction of intellectual potential becomes somewhat more reliable, especially in those groups of individuals that lack a rich cultural environment. Thus, in summarizing the influence of certain variables on the prediction of later intelligence, Knobloch and Pasamanick[50] have come to the conclusion that it is necessary to abandon the concept that the level of motor development in infancy is an index which will predict the future intellect of the child. Clearly, accelerated motor behavior does not necessarily represent a superior intellectual potential, and even children with serious mental defects may exhibit a normal motor development. If intelligence is defined as the ability to cope with and adapt to new circumstances of life, and is reflected in the increasing complexity of the channels through which the child reacts to objects, it is probable that, as Knobloch and Pasamanick have suggested, the adaptive sphere is the area of behavior that can best serve as an analogue for later intelligence. The Gesell measures of adaptive functioning are concerned with the organization of stimuli, the perception of interrelationships, and the separation of the whole into its component parts, with subsequent resynthesis to permit solution of a new problem. As a result, they may provide valuable clues to the future course of intellectual development.

The persistence of low scores in adaptive behavior during rehabilitation of infants who have suffered protein-calorie malnutrition before the age of six months suggests more than a transient loss in intellectual capacity. It may be indicative of a potential reduction in functional level in later years. It is possible that the disordering of adaptive capacity in older groups of infants is a transient phenomenon and that the initial deficit will tend to be overcome if other relevant factors do not interfere.

The hypothesis of a potential permanent mental retardation seems to be supported by the findings of Cabak and Najdanvic, who have restudied a group of 36 malnourished Yugoslavian children 7 to 14 years after discharge from the hospital.[17] The results showed that none of those between 4 to 24 months had IQs above 110, and 17 per cent did not even reach an IQ of 70. This distribution of IQs is in marked contrast with the data reported by Stevanovic, who studied a well-nourished group with the same ethnic backgrounds and with fathers in similar occupations. He found that 32 per cent of the children had IQs above 110, and only 2 per cent had IQs below 70.

Our findings are also in agreement with the report of Barrera-Moncada,[6] who has described normal IQs in 20 rehabilitated children, all of whom had been more than two years and ten months of age when admitted to the hospital because of severe malnutrition. Similarly, Kugelmass, Poull, and Samuel found that improvement in the diet of undernourished children over two years of age was followed by an improvement of 18 points in the IQ.[51] The results obtained from adult volunteers by Keys, et al.,[48] point in the same direction: as age advances, the effects of nutritional deprivation on the central nervous system tend to disappear more rapidly. Although these studies are by no means definitive, the findings are in accord with the picture that is emerging from animal investigations of age-specific malnutritional effects in experimentally induced malnutrition.

STUDIES ON SCHOOL-AGE CHILDREN

Scientific testing for effects on the development of central nervous system function caused by either primary or secondary food deprivation at an early age in school children or in older individuals can, of course, be carried out definitively only by a longitudinal study. As I have said, we are currently engaged in such an investigation. However, the findings of a longitudinal study become available only after a long period, so we decided that a certain amount of pertinent in-

formation could be obtained through a carefully conducted cross-sectional retrospective study of neurointegrative organization in school children.

We planned to carry out a cross-sectional study of intersensory functioning in the total population of village primary school children. Detailed prior information indicated a significant prevalence of serious, acute, or prolonged malnutrition during infancy and the preschool years.[25] Previous studies[21,30] have demonstrated that differences in growth, particularly extremes of growth distribution, indicate exposure either to primary or secondary malnutrition. On this basis, a group of children representing the shortest 25 per cent was designated as that most likely to represent early malnutrition. The functioning of this group was compared with that of village children in the tallest quartile for age. Assuming all other factors to be equal, the latter were those with the least likelihood of having been malnourished earlier in life.

Clearly, at least three important variables must be controlled when height for age is being used as an index. The first is parental stature and, thus, familial factors affecting height. Therefore, it was necessary to obtain anthropometric information on parents, as well as on children.

A second is that small stature during the years studied may represent a general maturational lag, in the course of which both height and intersensory functioning may be subnormal. To control for this possibility, we studied a second sample of children of the same ages who exhibited equivalent differences in height but who probably had never suffered malnutrition.

Third, since no integrative capacity is unaffected by environmental influences, we collected comparative information on the social, economic, and educational status of the family of each child.

Intersensory organization was the indicator of neurointegrative development selected for study. This was done for two reasons. First, a growing body of evidence in comparative psychology, neurophysiology,[60] perception,[43] learning,[9] and developmental disturbance[44] points to the importance of intersensory organization as a basic mechanism underlying adaptive behavior. In considering this process, Sherrington[75] went so far as to argue: "[The] naive observer . . . would have expected evolution in its course to have supplied us with more various sense-organs for ampler perception of the world. . . . The policy has rather been to bring by the nervous system the so-called 'five' into closer touch with one another. A central clearing house for sense has grown up. . . . Not new senses but better liaison between old senses is what the developing nervous system has in this respect stood for." In addition, a variety of studies[9,10] indicate that the basic mechanism involved in primary learning (i.e., in the formation of conditioned reflexes) is the effective establishment and patterning of intersensory organization.

The second reason for using intersensory competence as an indicator stems from the work of Birch and Lefford,[13] which has shown that adequacy of intersensory interrelations improves as a clearly defined growth function in normal children between the ages of 6 to 12 years. In school children of the same ages as those we planned to study, they found that the interrelations among touch, vision, and kinesthesis improved in an age-specific manner, and resulted in developmental curves that were as regular as those for skeletal growth.

We replicated the rural study using an upper-class urban sample of school children who were most unlikely to have been undernourished, and whose variations in height would thus be unrelated either to primary or secondary malnutrition. The rural community study was ecological in its organization, and we sought to relate growth achievements as well as intersensory development to the social, economic, educational, and physical characteristics of the families from which the children derived. The stature of the urban group could be studied and, at the same time, growth and function of a socially differentiated rural group could be compared with a socially and economically homogeneous urban group. The number, age, and sex of children included in the study are shown in Table X.

Each child's social, cultural, familial, and economic background was obtained through individual interviews with parents, observation of child-rearing practices, detailed evaluations of housing and sanitary conditions, a census, and parallel anthropological studies.

We used the Birch and Lefford method[13] for studying intersensory

TABLE X
Age and sex distribution of the children studied

Age	Rural children			Urban children		
(years)	Boys	Girls	Total	Boys	Girls	Total
6	6	13	19	10	10	20
7	21	10	31	15	5	20
8	11	9	20	9	11	20
9	16	11	27	10	10	20
10	16	9	25	9	11	20
11	9	12	21	10	10	20

integration. Equivalence relationships among the visual, haptic, and kinesthetic sense modalities were explored for geometric form recognition. The term haptic is used here to describe the complex sensory input obtained by manipulating a test object, and involves tactile, kinesthetic, and surface movement sensations from the subjects' fingers and hands. The kinesthetic sense, in this study, refers to the sensory inputs obtained from the wrist, elbow, and shoulder joints and from the arm and shoulder musculature.

We used a paired-comparison technique to study intersensory equivalence in the perception of geometric forms. A form presented to one sensory system (standard) was compared with forms presented to another (variable). Thus, a visually presented standard was compared with a series of forms presented haptically or kinesthetically. Similarly, a haptically presented standard was compared with a kinesthetically presented series. On the basis of such examination, we could determine the existence of cross-modality equivalences and nonequivalences between the visual and haptic sensory systems, between the visual and the kinesthetic, and between the haptic and kinesthetic.

Eight forms, selected from the Seguin Form Board, were used for both visual and haptic test stimuli. They were a triangle, a hexagon, a square, a semicircle, a cross, a diamond, a star, and a circle, each inscribed 1/8 inch deep on a 4x5-inch linoleum block. For visual stimulation, the block was placed on a table directly in front of the subject. For haptic stimulation, the examiner placed the subject's hand on a block shielded from the subject by an opaque screen. The subject then actively explored the form. Kinesthetic information was obtained by shielding the subject's eyes from his preferred arm by a screen. A stylus, held in normal writing position, was placed in the subject's hand. The examiner gripped the stylus above the point at which it was held by the subject and moved the hand and stylus in the grooves inscribed in the linoleum block. The outline dimensions of the grooves were of the same size and shape as those of the blocks used for visual and haptic stimulation.

For all sensory modalities, the forms were always presented so that the long axes were parallel to the frontal plane of the subject. In a kinesthetic trial, the movement was always started at the topmost point of the figure and continued in a clockwise direction for the right hand and in a counter-clockwise direction for the left hand. In putting the subject's hand through the motion, a short pause (approximately one second) was made at each point at which there was a change of direction, and only one complete circuit was made.

All subjects were tested individually in a quiet room with just the examiner. To familiarize the subject with the forms, he was given the Seguin Form Board Test before beginning. The form board was presented with the cross in the upper left-hand corner as seen from the subject's position. With the subject watching, the eight pieces were stacked in three piles at the head of the board in a standard manner. The subject was instructed to put the blocks back in the right places. In effect, this task represented a visual-visual comparison series; the form of the block and the form of the depression on the Seguin Board were visually matched by the subject. Numbers and kinds of errors were noted by the examiner. No time score was obtained.

Following this preliminary test, a screen was placed on the table, and the following explanation was given: "In this next game, I am going to move your hand around like this." The procedure was demonstrated by moving the arm through a triangle, square, and circle. "You are to tell me if the shape your hand moves around is the same as the shape that you see in front of you. To make the game more interesting, I am not going to let you see which shape your hand is going to go around. I will hold your hand behind this screen." The task was then demonstrated with the subject's hand behind the screen. The circle was used as the visual standard test object, and the square, triangle, and circle as kinesthetic test objects. When the examiner was sure that the subject understood the nature of the task, the testing series was begun. The subject was asked for a judgment of "same" or "different" for each paired comparison presented. If the subject was doubtful, he was asked to guess. No repeat trials were given. No affirmations or corrections were made during the test period.

The instructions for the visual-haptic series were essentially the same as for the visual-kinesthetic, except for minor changes to make the wording appropriate to the haptic stimuli. In this series, the blocks were placed in the subject's hand out of his field of vision behind the screen. They were compared to the standard visual stimulus, which was a block placed in the subject's field of vision on the table before him. A judgment of "same" or "different" was elicited.

For the haptic-kinesthetic series, the instructions were again the same, with minor changes appropriate to the situation. In this series, however, the subject wore darkened goggles. The standards were the haptic stimuli, presented to the hand to which no kinesthetic stimulus was being applied. After comparison, the judgment of "same" or "different" was again elicited. Judgments were scored as right or wrong. Two kinds of error were distinguished—when nonidentical forms presented across modalities were judged as the same and when identical forms were judged as different.

The result showed that each of the pairs of intersensory relations tested improved with age in both the rural and the upper-class urban groups, and had the form of a logarithmic growth curve. As was the case for the New York suburban school children studied by Birch and Lefford,[13] the different pairings of sensory interrelations did not develop to the same degree or at the same rate. Visual-haptic integration was significantly more effectively organized at every age than were either visual-kinesthetic or haptic-kinesthetic interrelationships. In the rural group, for example, the error curve for visual-haptic integration reached an asymptote between the seventh and eighth years, and performance on this task was errorless after that age. In contrast, neither visual-kinesthetic nor haptic-kinesthetic integrative performances reached an errorless level of competence within the range of ages studied. A comparison of the data presented in Tables XI and XII, illustrated by Figures 11 and 12, show clearly that a simple modi-

TABLE XI

Mean and range of errors made in the recognition of identity between cross-modally presented identical forms by the sample of rural children studied

Age (years)	Sensory modalities tested					
	Visual-kinesthetic		Visual-haptic		Haptic-kinesthetic	
	Mean	Range	Mean	Range	Mean	Range
6	5	0–15	1.06	0–8	3.67	0–13
7	3	0–10	0.28	0–2	2.0	0–8
8	1.51	0–7	0.25	0–4	1.5	0–6
9	1.28	0–7	0	0	1.0	0–4
10	1.64	0–4	0	0	1.44	0–6
11	0.66	0–4	0	0	0.76	0–3

TABLE XII

Mean and range of errors made in the recognition of identical forms by a sample of upper-social-class urban school-age children

Age (years)	Sensory modalities tested					
	Visual-kinesthetic		Visual-haptic		Haptic-kinesthetic	
	Mean	Range	Mean	Range	Mean	Range
6	2	0–6	0.7	0–3	1.6	0–5
7	0.8	0–4	0	0	1.1	0–3
8	1.1	0–3	0.1	0–1	0.5	0–2
9	1.3	0–3	0.2	0–1	0.7	0–3
10	1.1	0–3	0.1	0–1	1.5	0–4
11	0.4	0–2	0	0	0	0–3

fication of a constant would result in the superimposition of the age-specific, mean-error curves of the rural and urban children.

The physical growth achievements, at each age level, of the most stunted and most fully grown 25 per cent of the rural and urban chil-

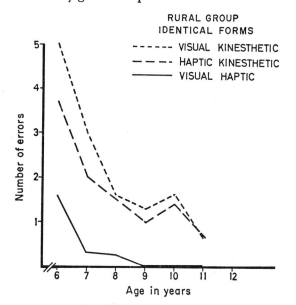

FIGURE 11   Results of integrative performances of rural children, based on data in Table XI.

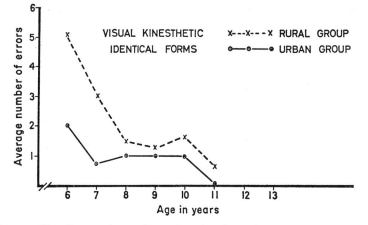

FIGURE 12   Comparison of rural and urban visual-kinesthetic integrative performances, illustrating data in Table XII.

TABLE XIII

Mean and range of height in centimeters of rural and urban school-age children at extremes of difference in stature

Age (year)	6	7	8	9	10	11
Rural children						
Lower quartile for height range	98 / 96–99.5	106 / 101–108	108 / 99–110	113 / 107–116.5	114 / 109–116.5	119 / 113–123
Upper quartile for height range	107 / 105–113	113 / 111.5–118	119 / 116–122	124 / 122–126	127 / 124–133	134 / 131–138
Urban children						
Lower quartile for height range	111 / 106–115.5	115 / 110–118	121 / 119–123	130 / 125.5–133	130 / 127–132	135 / 132.5–137.5
Upper quartile for height range	126 / 124.5–129	130 / 128.5–135	137 / 132.5–141	141 / 137–147	147 / 145–150	156 / 155–157

dren are presented in Table XIII, which shows that the shortest urban children were comparable in height to the tallest group in the rural sample (left).

When the intersensory performances of the children in the upper height quartile are contrasted with those of the children in the lower height quartile, only the rural children exhibited marked differences in intersensory integrative skills. These differences were present in all three combinations tested. They were particularly clear across the whole age span for errors of nonequivalence that were made when children misjudged identical forms presented across two modalities. Figures 13 and 14 summarize the data presented in Table XIV (p. 41).

Differences in the number of errors of equivalence made by the two height groups in judging nonidentical forms also tended to favor the

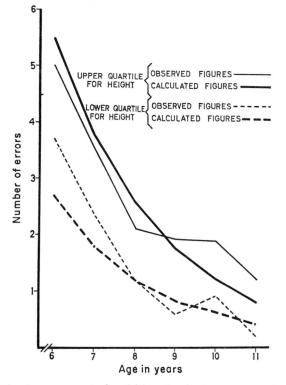

FIGURE 13 Summary of visual-kinesthetic data on rural children (identical forms) shown in Table XIV.

taller group of children. This difference was most notable in the performances of the youngest groups of children — the six-year-olds. This is seen in Figures 15A and B (p. 42), which present the data on the cumulative percentage of six-year-olds in the two height groups who made errors of equivalence, and clearly indicate the lag in development of intersensory competence that was present in the shorter children during the first school year.

When differences in height, as such, occurred in children who had not been nutritionally deprived, they did not result in differences in the rate of intersensory development or in the level of intersensory competence that was achieved at a given age (Table XV, p. 43).

Anthropometric information about the parents revealed that the height difference between the upper and the lower quartiles of the urban sample was mainly a reflection of family differences in stature. In the rural population, on the other hand, there was no significant association between the statures of parents and children.

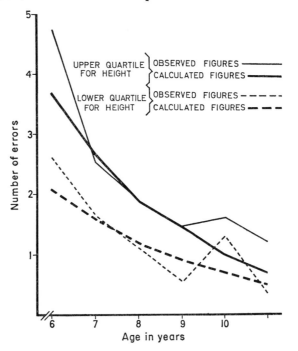

FIGURE 14 Summary of haptic-kinesthetic data on rural children (identical forms) shown in Table XIV.

TABLE XIV

Errors made in the recognition of identical forms by tall and short rural children

Age (year)*	Visual-kinesthetic quartile for height				Visual-haptic quartile for height				Haptic-kinesthetic quartile for height			
	Lower		Upper		Lower		Upper		Lower		Upper	
	N	Mean	N	Mean	N	Mean	N	Mean	N	Mean	N	Mean
6	9	5 (0–15)*	10	3.7 (0–9)	9	1.12 (0–6)	10	1.0 (0–8)	9	4.75 (0–13)	10	2.6 (0–8)
7	17	3.53 (0–10)	14	2.35 (0–5)	17	0.29 (0–2)	14	0.28 (0–2)	17	2.53 (0–8)	14	1.64 (0–3)
8	10	2.1 (0–7)	10	1.2 (0–3)	10	0.40	10	0.10	10	1.90 (0–4)	10	1.10 (0–3)
9	16	1.93 (0–7)	11	0.63 (0–3)	16	0	11	0	16	1.46 (0–4)	11	0.54 (0–3)
10	11	1.90 (0–4)	14	0.92 (0–4)	11	0	14	0	11	1.63 (0–5)	14	1.28 (0–6)
11	10	1.20 (0–4)	11	0.18 (0–1)	10	0	11	0	10	1.20 (0–3)	11	0.36 (0–2)

* Figures in parenthesis show range of errors. Age is given in completed years.
N=Number of children.

Since the height of the fathers in the urban group was related to that of their children, we decided to find out if a father's height made any significant contribution to his child's intersensory performance.

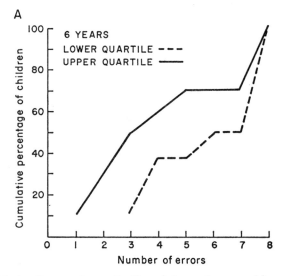

FIGURE 15 A   Proportions of tall and short six-year-old rural children making errors of equivalence in visual-haptic judgment.

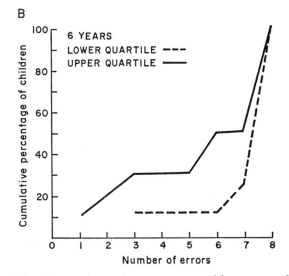

FIGURE 15 B   Proportions of same group making errors of equivalence in visual-kinesthetic judgment.

TABLE XV

Errors made in the recognition of identical forms by two height groups of upper-social-class urban children

| Age (year)* | Visual-kinesthetic quartile for height | | | | Visual-haptic quartile for height | | | | Haptic-kinesthetic quartile for height | | | |
| | Lower | | Upper | | Lower | | Upper | | Lower | | Upper | |
	N	Mean	N	Mean	N	Mean	N	Mean	N	Mean	N	Mean
6	5	2 (0–6)*	5	2 (1–4)	5	1.0 (0–3)	5	0.4 (0–2)	5	1.8 (0–5)	5	1.4 (0–3)
7	5	1.6 (0–4)	5	0 (0)	5	0 (0)	5	0 (0)	5	1.4 (0–3)	5	0.8 (0–2)
8	5	1.8 (0–3)	5	0.4 (0–2)	5	0.2 (0–1)	5	0 (0)	5	1 (0–2)	5	0 (0)
9	5	1.8 (1–3)	5	0.8 (0–2)	5	0.4 (0–1)	5	0 (0)	5	1 (0–3)	5	0.4 (0–2)
10	5	1.6 (0–6)	5	0.6 (0–1)	5	0 (0)	5	0.2 (0–1)	5	2 (0–4)	5	1 (0–4)
11	5	0.4 (0–2)	5	0.4 (0–1)	5	0 (0)	5	0 (0)	5	1 (0–3)	5	0.6 (0–2)

* Figures in parenthesis show the range of errors. Age is given in completed years.
N=Number of children.

We grouped fathers above or below the medium height for the sample and plotted the relation of the father's group position to the intersensory performance of the child. No significant association was found.

The only strong positive association relating to family background was between height of the child and educational level of the mother (Table XVI). When the mother's educational level was below the median for the sample of mothers studied, there was a greater likelihood that her child would be short. Conversely, if she was educated

TABLE XVI

Association between height of children and educational background of mothers

Educational background of mothers	Children in the lower quartile for height	Children in the upper quartile for height
Above the median for the total group	28	41
Below the median for the total group	41	26

Chi^2=5.78.
p<.02.

above the median, her child would probably be in the taller segment. It is of interest that no significant association was obtained between the father's educational status and the child's height.

We next turned our attention to auditory-visual equivalences. Recently Birch and Belmont[11] advanced the theory that auditory-visual integrative development follows an established age-specific course in school-age children in both suburban New York and Scotland, and that such development is related to over-all intelligence and to learning how to read. There is a possibility that such relationships may be more stable indicators of cross-cultural development than are such culture-sensitive instruments as intelligence tests. If this is the case, such measures may be useful in examining factors affecting neuro-integrative development in widely differing environments.

As a first step, we compared the developmental course of auditory-visual integration in middle-class Mexican and middle-class New York suburban school children.[12] The subjects were 66 boys and 114 girls, 6 through 12 years old, from a Mexico City school for intellectually normal and superior children of upper-middle-class families. Most of their parents were university graduates and were either in the professions or in business administration. The children showed a systematic increase in integrative ability from year to year, with the greatest single leap in skill occurring between the sixth and eighth years, the period at which learning to read is a central portion of the school curriculum.

The auditory-visual development of these children was then compared to that of 220 intellectually normal children in a suburban New York elementary school. This was accomplished by exploring their ability to equate a temporally structured set of auditory stimuli with a spatially distributed set of visual ones. The group consisted of 97 boys with a mean age of 8 years and 8 months; ages ranged from 5 years, 4 months to 12 years. The 123 girls ranged from 5 years and 3 months to 12 years and one month, with a mean age of 8 years, 7 months. There was almost no difference between the groups of 6- and 7-year-olds. Thereafter, although the developmental slopes in the two groups were parallel, the New York children increased in accuracy each year by approximately one point. The mean differences in any single year are not significant, but if the differences across the whole age range studied are cumulated, they become statistically significant at less than 5 per cent. No differences in auditory-visual competence were found between the tall and the short children in either cultural groups.

Evidence exists of differences among ethnic groups in form-perception and sensitivity to visual illusions[68,74,82] — differences that clearly indicate that the way of life affects sensory integrative functioning. Therefore, data obtained in the present investigation are interpreted as meaning that the auditory-visual integrative test is insensitive to the differences between the two cultures, and its developmental course is apparently unaffected by them.

As the next step, we studied auditory-visual capacity in children who had been exposed to malnutrition. In this way we hoped to extend our previous inquiries on the effect of malnutrition on neuro-integrative development. This time we included a new set of cross-modalities whose level of functioning seems to be directly related, at least at certain age-periods, with reading readiness and reading ability.[22]

We selected a total of 296 children, 141 boys and 155 girls, all of whom were individually examined for auditory-visual integrative ability. All were 7 to 12 years old and enrolled in the primary school of a rural village in southwestern Mexico. The degree of exposure to malnutrition prior to and during the school years was ascertained by the child's height in relation to the median for the total group of the same age and sex. The children were divided into two groups—the upper 25 per cent of the height group for each sex and age and the lowest 25 per cent.

The children were asked to identify a dot pattern that corresponded to a rhythmic auditory stimulus. The results showed that the ability to integrate auditory and visual information improves over the age-span tested, with the most rapid improvement occurring between the ages of 9 and 11. This improvement was present in both the tall and the short children. However, at each age level the mean performance of the taller group was higher than that of the shorter. This difference was most striking at 12 years of age, at which time the short group had a mean score of 6.1 correct responses in contrast to 7.5 correct for the taller group. Not only were the mean values for the two groups different; at all ages except age 9, the cumulative frequency curve for the tall group was superior to that of the short group; by age 12, 42 per cent of the taller children were making 8 or more correct judgments, with 30 per cent achieving perfect scores of 10. In contrast, only 9 per cent of the shorter children in this age group scored 8 or higher, and none made a perfect score. From all our data on neurointegrative functioning, two facts clearly emerge: in rural children, a difference in height is accompanied by a difference in intersensory integrative ability; in upper-social-class urban children, differences in height are not associated with differences in such ability. (Therefore, height cannot be considered a determinant of intersensory integrative organization. The only exception to this conclusion is when such differences in height are due to causes which directly affect intersensory integrative organization.)

The question remains whether the inadequacy in intersensory integrative performance in the rural children represents a reflection of malnutrition, or if both poor integration and growth differences are associated with more general subcultural differences, which may have contributed independently to differences in growth and intersensory functioning. These two alternatives can most readily be analyzed if they are considered diagrammatically as two consequential schema (Figure 16). In Scheme I, malnutrition and intersensory inadequacy

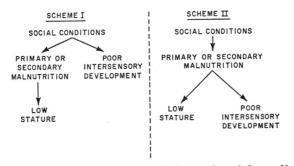

FIGURE 16 Possible schema for relations of social conditions to malnutrition, intersensory development, and stature.

are hypothesized to have independent origins in a background of social impoverishment. They bear no direct relation to each other, but are indirectly associated by a common antecedent. In Scheme II, the hypothetical causal sequence advances the view that social conditions result in malnutrition, which, in turn, causes short stature and poor intersensory integrative development.

Available evidence does not permit rejection of either hypothesis. However, it is possible to examine certain implications of each position with respect to the available data. If social impoverishment does indeed contribute to poor intersensory development, a significant association should have been found between short stature and such so-cial factors as depressed family income, poor housing, the proportion of income spent on food, personal sanitary conditions, and so on. Therefore, it was most striking to find, in the data of the present study, no significant association of neurointegrative function with any factor except the mother's educational level.

The positive relation of the mother's education to intersensory adequacy must be considered in association with the distribution of responsibility within the household — in particular with the relation of the mother to child care and child health. It is important to remem-ber that in this, as in many other rural societies in Latin America, the closeness of the child to his mother during the first years of life is not confined to physical contact, but the rules and practices of health and care in the household belong entirely to the woman's world. There is, therefore, a strong possibility that the better-educated female will rely less on the traditional methods of feeding and child care that are direct causes of improper diets in health and disease, particularly in early life.[19,81]

Although these findings cannot lead to an absolute rejection of the possibility in Scheme I, it appears more likely that malnutrition is one of the intervening variables between social background and poor physical growth and intersensory inadequacy. Obviously, a definite an-swer can be provided by long-range longitudinal studies, wherein it would be possible to control independently for all phases of environ-ment, including inadequate nutrition. Such a study is now in prog-ress, and hopefully will provide more direct tests of the alternative schema during the next decade.

If there is a strong possibility that malnutrition interferes with in-tersensory organization, a few words about the possible mechanisms of action may be relevant. Theoretically, malnutrition could act ei-ther directly, by interfering with the development of the central nervous system, or indirectly. To examine the second possibility first, three mechanisms are readily apparent:

1. Loss of learning time. During periods of malnutrition the child is less responsive to his environment and consequently learns less; at a

minimum, he loses a certain number of months, and therefore will probably show some long-term developmental lag.

2. Interference during critical periods of learning. Experimental evidence suggests that brain function is sequentially acquired and integrated into the total pattern of performance and experience. Timing is of the utmost importance, as each function makes its appearance chronologically and is apparently optimal in operation at that particular point. In other words, learning cannot be considered as simply additive. Rather, what appears to be most important is the correlation of the experimental opportunity with a given stage of development. These stages are known as "critical periods of learning."[16,71,72] Interruptions of these critical periods may be clinically evident immediately, but more often they do not show up until the child is older.

The exact timing of the critical periods has not been definitely established, but some useful information can be derived from an examination of the consequences of interference at different ages. Our own work showed that the deficit in mental age observed in severely malnourished infants under six months of age, as calculated from their psychological test behavior, was not corrected, whereas in older patients the rate of "catch-up" varied in direct relation to their chronological ages. The findings of Barrera-Moncada[6] in Venezuelan children and those of Keys, et al.,[48] in adults also point to a marked association between the persistence of later effects on mental performance and the period of onset and the duration of malnutrition.

3. Motivation and personality changes. To a considerable extent, the infant's reactions determine the mother's response.[32] Lack of response to stimulation and general apathy are two of the first effects of malnutrition. Apathy can provoke apathy and contribute to a cumulative pattern of reduced adult-child interaction. This has consequences for learning, for maturation, for interpersonal relations, and so on — the end result being a significant risk of backwardness in more complex learning.

Malnutrition also modifies the growth and biochemical maturation of the brain. The increase of cell cytoplasm, with the extension of axons and dendrites—one of the two main morphological processes associated with the growth of the human brain at birth—is largely a process of protein synthesis. It has been estimated that proteins multiply by more than 2,000 as the apolar neuroblast matures into the young anterior horn cell. Perhaps an easier way to grasp the magnitude of this process may be simply to recall that at the time of birth the human brain is gaining weight at a rate of 1 to 2 milligrams per minute, as calculated by brain weights recorded at several stages of gestation. (Changes in the central nervous systems of animals on inadequate diets have been documented by Lowry, et al.,[55] and Platt.[63] McCance and associates have shown gross alterations in the content of water and of several minerals[58] in the brain cells, and Flexner and associates[35] have advanced evidence that interference with protein synthesis in the brain produces loss of memory in mice.) Ambrosius[3] has reported that in severely malnourished children the normal relation between brain weight and total body weight is distorted. He and his associates have interpreted their findings as an indication of arrested growth of the central nervous system.

It may well be that the critical periods in behavior represent the responsiveness of the nervous system at a given stage of biochemical organization. If so, nutritional inadequacy may interfere with the staging and timing of the development of both brain and behavior. Two significant features of learning will be considered in this connection: formation of conditioned reflexes and the acquisition of academic skills.

In most conditioning situations, two stimuli, each belonging to a different sensory modality, must be integrated. For example, in classical salivary conditioning of dogs, a taste or touch stimulus is linked to an auditory or a visual one. If interrelations between the sensory modalities are inadequate, conditioning may be either delayed or ineffective. Therefore, if intersensory integration does not occur at normal age-specific points, inadequate primary learning may result.

Alekseeva and Kaplanskaya-Raiskaya[2] have found that protein deficiency often alters conditioned responses in young children. The capacity to elaborate new conditioned reflexes is said to be affected first, but even previously well-established reflex responses may be depressed or abolished. Birch and Lefford have reported that visual-motor control in design copying is dependent on visual-kinesthetic intersensory adequacy.[14] If, as Baldwin has pointed out,[5] such visual-motor control is essential for learning to write, it becomes apparent that inadequacy in visual-kinesthetic organization can interfere with this primary educational skill.

The less adequate development of auditory-visual integration in seriously malnourished children has a two-fold implication. First, it reinforces the possibility that neurological changes in animals experimentally fed on grossly deficient diets may have their counterparts in malnourished human populations. Second, it relates to the functional significance of such a neurointegrative lag. Learning to read requires the ability to transform temporally distributed auditory patterns into spatially distributed visual ones. Accordingly, if it is accepted that, for the beginner, reading is largely concerned with learning to recognize the symbols which represent spoken words,[42] a primary disturbance in the ability to integrate stimuli from the two critical sense modalities — hearing and vision — may increase the risk of his becoming a poor reader. Available evidence indicates that inadequacies in intersensory development may make the child fail to establish a normal background of conditionings in his preschool years and so be unable to profit from education in his school years.

If the data are interpreted in this way, we may predict that shorter children, whose height is a reflection of their earlier and sometimes continuing malnutrition, risk school failure because they cannot master primary school subjects. If, as field observations suggest, this prediction is valid, early malnutrition may be the starting point of a developmental path characterized by neurointegrative inadequacy, school failure, and subnormal adaptive functioning.

Behavioral Changes Caused by Malnutrition in the Rat and Pig

RICHARD H. BARNES

The studies that Dr. Cravioto has presented represent extremely thorough and critical investigations of the relationship between early nutrition and behavioral development. The careful and extensive collection of information that he and his colleagues have made, together with data on nutrition and growth from a variety of other sources, seem to offer good evidence that, in the rural population studied, increased body size is causally related to improved nutritional status. As a nutritionist, it seems to me that a crucial and most exciting problem is why, in such a homogeneous group, with limited but similar purchasing power and with limited but similar availability of foods, the child of one family is nutritionally superior to that of another.

One height correlate Dr. Cravioto has described — the level of the mother's formal education — may be related to certain sociological factors that contribute to the child's intellectual development. These sociological factors also may be related causally to the level of nutrition of the child; the latter, in turn, influences growth rate. Finally, the child's nutritional status may have been the factor that directly governed its neurointegrative development. Unfortunately, this type of reasoning leads to a jumble from which it seems impossible to extract the specific contributions of any single environmental factor, including nutrition.

One of the important ways in which the biological role of nutrition in behavioral development can be studied is with experimental animals. This has been my primary research interest in recent years, so I will feel much more at home discussing laboratory studies than

RICHARD H. BARNES Graduate School of Nutrition, Cornell University, Ithaca, New York

attempting an analysis of the studies with children that have been described. One point relating early nutrition to adult behavior that has been thoroughly established in many laboratories is that a partial deprivation of food, either during the nursing period or for several weeks immediately following weaning, will cause rats and mice to show unusual attitudes toward food for months thereafter. One well-known characteristic is their hoarding of food. We have extended these observations to both rats and pigs, and have been able to show that these animals have greatly enhanced drives for food if they have been underfed or malnourished in early life. Rats that had been malnourished in early life increased food consumption when they were forced to eat their daily allotment of food in a period of just one hour. After a few days' experience with this restrictive type of feeding, food intake was the same for the previously malnourished rats and the normal controls. However, one characteristic of the former groups did not disappear as long as the one-hour-per-day feeding schedule was followed — their highly excited behavior when the food cups were placed in the cages. This behavior could be quantitatively expressed by the large increase in food spillage.

We·have also been able to demonstrate an intensified drive for food in adult pigs that had been malnourished for a relatively short period in early life. These pigs were weaned from their dams at three weeks of age and for the next eight weeks were fed a diet containing only 3 per cent protein. They were then given a diet of normal composition for 9 to 12 months, when certain behavioral tests, including a specially designed food-attitude test, were made. For several months prior to the behavioral tests, the animals were given daily feedings equivalent to 2 per cent of their body weight. This amount was sufficient to permit good growth, but was less than the pigs would eat if fed ad libitum. They were transferred to individual pens, and a measured amount of food was dispensed each time the animal poked its snout in a special feeder. Thus the animals were changed from a restricted daily intake to ad libitum feeding, and automatic records of the individual feedings were taken 24 hours a day. The results for the first three days, starting four hours after the switch, are given in Table I. This table separates food intake for nights (7:00 P.M. to

TABLE I

	Control[1]			Malnourished[1]		
	Days			Days		
	1	2	3	1	2	3
Night 7 PM–7 AM	0	2	6	36	14	8
Day 7 AM–7 PM	32	18	20	42	30	28
Total	32	20	26	78	44	36

Food consumption pattern in pigs that had been malnourished and then rehabilitated with a diet of normal composition, but fed in an amount equivalent to 2 per cent of body weight daily. Food consumption was measured with a recording feeder starting 4 hours after the initial release of animals to completely ad libitum feeding. (From Barnes, R. H., I. M. Reid, W. G. Pond, and A. U. Moore[3])

[1] Expressed as gm/kg body weight.

7:00 A.M.) from days (7:00 A.M. to 7:00 P.M.). The previously malnourished pigs not only ate considerably more during these three days, but also followed a pattern of eating off and on throughout the night, in contrast to the rather infrequent night feeding for the controls.

These striking differences in food attitudes can be traced to early nutritional deprivations for both rats and pigs. They were not completely unexpected, because, as I have pointed out, many laboratories have shown that enhanced food drives and hoarding attitudes in adult rodents were the results of early food deprivation. Other investigators have noted decreased exploratory activity in adult rats that had been nursed in large litters. These are extremely interesting manifestations, and we have embarked upon a program to study in much greater detail the long-lasting results of early nutritional deprivations. At this time, I can mention only preliminary observations.

The behavioral characteristics of spontaneous exploratory activity in rats have been studied extensively at the Institute of Human Nutrition Research in Prague. One of the psychologists, Dr. Slavka Frankova, is spending a year in our laboratories at Cornell and is applying her techniques for measuring exploratory activity to rats that have been subjected to several forms of malnutrition from the first few days of life. A rat is placed in a box from which it cannot see, but in which it can be observed by, the investigator. The pattern of movements exhibited has been shown to be related to the current as well as the prior nutritional status of the animal. Dr. Frankova has been able to show a significant decrease in exploratory activity in rats only 10 days old that have been subjected to nutritional deprivations from the day of birth. Furthermore, rats that have been nutritionally rehabilitated following an early food deprivation continue to show this typical decrease in spontaneous activity months after their return to an adequate dietary intake.

A behavioral pattern in adult pigs that had been severely malnourished in early life also has been observed, and we believe it may be closely related to the altered spontaneous exploratory activity of previously malnourished rats. These pigs, which weigh 100 to 200 kilograms but were exposed to eight weeks of severe malnutrition when they were young, are much more difficult to handle than are the normal control animals. They are not mean-tempered; if anything, they are more gentle than the controls. However, it is most difficult to make the experimental pigs move out of their pens and walk into the adjoining laboratory, where they are weighed or subjected to various behavioral tests. The test procedures are not traumatic, so we believe that it is not fear of unpleasant surroundings. In fact, the animals are usually given a small amount of food when they are being tested and, as already pointed out, they have an enhanced drive for food. Nevertheless, the behavioral differences are striking, and it will be important to see if the characteristics exhibited by previously malnourished pigs show any similarity to the behavioral patterns of previously malnourished children in underdeveloped countries.

We are also studying learning behavior in malnourished rats and pigs. We have devoted considerable effort to developing nutritional procedures that cause severe protein-calorie malnutrition during the early life of the animals and in devising learning behavior tests that are applicable to the adults. We have had partial success in the former effort by nursing rats in large litters, weaning the young to a purified diet containing only 3.5 per cent protein, and continuing this protein-deficient regimen for 8 weeks. Figure 1 shows the growth depression that results from the combined pre- and post-weaning depriva-

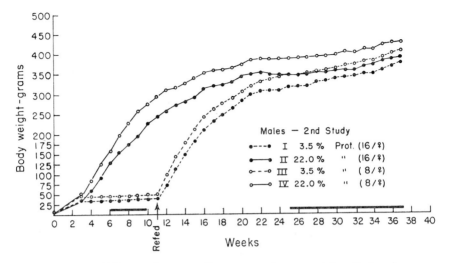

FIGURE 1 Effects of pre- and post-weaning nutritional deprivations and later nutritional rehabilitation on growth of rats. Weaning was at three weeks, and pre- and post-weaning deprivations are indicated by decreased growth rates during these periods. Stunting is shown by the lower body weights of the experimental animals from about the 25th week of life, when apparent growth potential has been reached, as is evident from the plateauing of growth curves. (From Barnes, R. H., S. R. Cunnold, R. R. Zimmermann, H. Simmons, R. B. MacLeod, and L. Krook[1])

tion and also the effects of either pre- or post-weaning deprivations alone. The permanent stunting of body size, which is essentially equivalent and results from all three forms of nutritional deprivations, is also shown here.

Learning behavior studied at about nine months of age, using a discrimination test in a Y-shaped water maze, has shown that the doubly deprived rats consistently made more errors than did the completely normal controls. In only occasional experiments have we seen a significantly poorer performance in rats that had been malnourished only by nursing them in large litters; in no study have we seen any effect caused only by the eight-week low-protein diet. It does seem clear, however, that the degree of stunting resulting from early malnutrition is not necessarily correlated with performance in learning behavior tests.

Severe protein-calorie malnutrition, which simulates in several respects conditions found in the human infant, can be developed in the new-born pig. This is accomplished by feeding a purified diet containing only 3 per cent protein, but a relatively high calorie intake that includes 24 per cent fat. This diet, together with two variations, is described in Table II. The first two columns show the normal con-

TABLE II

	1 Control "ad lib."	2 Control "restricted"	3 Low protein Low calorie	4 Low protein High calorie
Protein (casein)	24	24	3	3
Carbohydrate (glucose	73	73	94	73
Fat (corn oil)	3	3	3	24
Calories/100 gm	415	415	415	520
Protein calories, %	23	23	2.9	2.3
Food consumption	2–3% body wt.	pair fed⟵⟶ad lib.		ad lib.

Major components—minerals and vitamins added

Plan of dietary treatment groups for behavioral studies in pigs. (From Barnes, R. H., A. U. Moore, I. M. Reid, and W. G. Pond[2])

trol diet containing 24 per cent protein, which was fed either in an amount sufficient to provide good growth or in a restricted amount so as to prevent any growth during an eight-week experimental feeding period. The third column describes a very low-protein, but also low-calorie density diet, and the fourth a low-protein, high-calorie density diet. The consequences of feeding these diets to young pigs may or may not be related to protein-calorie malnutrition in the child, but there is no question that they do cause a varying degree of severity of protein-calorie malnutrition for the pig; the most severe is caused by the low-protein, high-fat diet, and the least severe by the normal diet fed in restricted quantity.

At the end of the eight-week experimental feeding period, the pigs receiving the low-protein, high-fat diet have extremely low total serum proteins, and the albumin levels are in the neighborhood of 1 per cent. They have slightly fatty livers and frequently there are gross signs of edema. They exhibit extreme apathy and their food consumption decreases considerably. Conditioned avoidance tests conducted in a shuttle box at the sixth to eighth week of the experimental diets have given the results shown in Table III. Judging by the numbers of avoidance and nonescape responses, the performance of the two groups fed the protein-deficient diets was inferior to that of the two groups receiving the control diet. The apparently poor performance of the pigs eating the control diet ad libitum was because they were too large for the shuttle box and tried to jump out of the box, rather than over the hurdle, to avoid the shock. This study was repeated with a larger shuttle box, and the two groups that had received the control diet, either ad libitum or in restricted quantity, again showed the same performance.

Pigs from the two studies were rehabilitated by feeding them a normal swine ration starting after they had eaten the three experimental diets in the four treatment groups for eight weeks. Approximately nine months after nutritional rehabilitation, classical Pavlovian conditioned response studies were conducted. Intensity of room light was used as the conditioned stimulus and an electric shock as the unconditioned stimulus. After a consistent conditioned response was established, attempts were made to extinguish the response by exposing the animal to the change in light intensity with-

TABLE III

Group	Diet	No. pigs	Response per pig in 30 trials		
			Avoidance	Escape	Non-escape
1	L. prot.-H. fat	8	1.3	19.6	9.1
2	L. prot.-L. fat	4	3.0	11.7	15.3
3	Control-Restricted	4	12.5	16.0	1.5
4	Control-Ad libitum	6	5.8	22.8	1.3

Conditioned avoidance response of pigs either fed an adequate diet ad libitum or subjected to 3 forms of dietary restriction from the third to the eleventh week of life. (From Barnes, R. H., A. U. Moore, I. M. Reid and W. G. Pond[2])

out an accompanying shock. We observed no difference in the developmental rate of the conditioned response in the four treatment groups. However, we consistently found differences in the rates at which the response was extinguished. Five of the eight pigs that had been made protein-deficient in early life did not extinguish the conditioned response in 30 trials, while all eight pigs that had received the control diet, either ad libitum or in severely restricted quantity, extinguished the response.

These studies, with both conditioned avoidance and with classical conditioning, show a difference in behavioral characteristics among groups of pigs that had been stunted to the same degree in early life. Figure 2, which shows the growth rate following nutritional rehabilitation, clearly illustrates the superior growth of the controls (Group IV) over the restricted controls (Group III). Yet behaviorally these

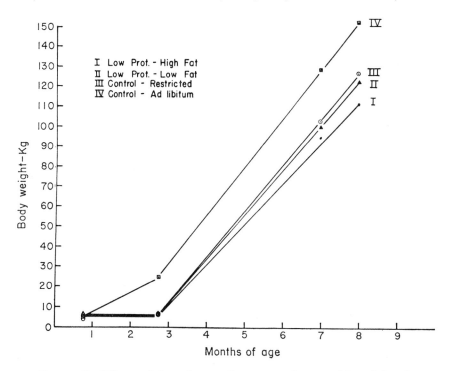

FIGURE 2   Effects of three forms of post-weaning nutritional deprivation followed by nutritional rehabilitation on growth of pigs. (From Barnes, R. H., A. U. Moore, I. M. Reid, and W. G. Pond[2])

groups were similar. As in the previous studies with rats, the results show that there does not need to be a correlation between the extent of growth retardation and behavioral development.

I believe that the studies with pigs and rats support the general conclusion that severe protein-calorie malnutrition in early life can have long-lasting, possibly permanent, effects upon learning behavior. As the severity of the malnutrition decreases, the variety of behavioral abnormalities and possibly the degree to which they are affected, decrease. Two types of protein-calorie malnutrition in the pig — that might be likened to kwashiorkor and marasmus — affect behavior in a manner that is interpreted as a retardation in the ability to learn. Behavioral abnormalities induced by more minimal nutritional deprivations in early life may be of importance, but their relationship to what can be described loosely as learning behavior is certainly not clear.

The animal studies that have been described here are obviously of a preliminary nature. However, they do illustrate how the experimental animal may help in elucidating the causal relationship of early nutrition to behavioral development in man. They also offer some hope of providing information as to the manner and the extent to which malnutrition may have a specific effect upon learning ability.

Sociocultural Factors
in Nutritional Studies

EDWARD A. SUCHMAN

To a social scientist, nutrition means the production and the distribution, as well as the consumption, of food. Malnutrition connotes a breakdown somewhere in this system — a dysfunctional sign of social pathology or disorganization that affects healthy growth and development or produces some form of disease. Such a breakdown can be the result of physical forces in the environment acting on the community as a whole, such as a drought or economic depression, or of folkways and mores, which affect the food habits or eating practices of the society.

From this point of view, nutrition offers an excellent example of the interdependence of man's physical, biological, and social environment — and of the importance of studying the effects of nutrition upon learning and behavior within the general context of social development. It makes little sense to view either half of the hypothesis that early nutritional deficiencies are related to retarded mental performance in childhood — the major thesis of Dr. Cravioto's paper — in isolation from all of the social forces surrounding and influencing both food intake and mental development.

Food has had a profound effect upon the structure and function of all societies. Its availability has determined where cities were to be built and how wars could be fought. The food consumption patterns of any society strongly reflect the social, economic, religious, and political forces shaping that society. Rituals and taboos surround the meanings of food and govern not only what may be eaten, but how and by whom it should be prepared, served, and, as waste, disposed of. Food, as a symbol, has been used to express friendship or enmity, good or evil, morality or guilt. Eating, as a function, has served to

EDWARD A. SUCHMAN   University of Pittsburgh, Pittsburgh, Pennsylvania bind groups together, to mark ceremonial occasions, to provide release from tension and stress.

Little wonder, then, that the changing of food habits has constituted one of the most stubborn areas for health action. As Cassel has noted in his analysis of the social and cultural implications of food and food habits, changing practices must take into account the significance of food for the group one hopes to reach. One must know what meanings the different foods have for the society and the individual, what purposes they serve, with what customs, beliefs, and statuses they are associated, and to what behaviors they are bound.[1]

It is against this background of social forces that one must appraise Cravioto's and others' attempts to study the relationship of malnutrition to behavior, especially when these also include deliberate intervention to remedy the situation. Stated in its most challenging form, one may ask: To what extent have these studies taken into account the large number of socioenvironmental factors inherently associated with deficient dietary intake, on the one hand, and mental or behavioral development on the other? We may conceive of nutrition as one independent or "causal" variable in a long chain of preceding and concurrent events that affect the dependent or "effect" variable of mental development. So interpreted, it is only one part of an ongoing process of physical and social growth conditioned by a wide variety of intervening variables that alter and modify the relationship positively and negatively. By way of illustration, we may posit that certain preceding variables such as social class or family eating patterns will affect the amounts and types of foods offered the child. This will influence his resistance to disease-causing agents or his interest in exploring his environment, which, in turn, will affect his physical, social, and mental development. Given this statement of the problem in terms of a multiplicity of "causes" and an interdependence of "cause-and-effect," we may now turn to Dr. Cravioto's study in an attempt to establish "confidence limits" within which we may accept his findings as valid and, perhaps more important, suggest ways of increasing the significance of such nutritional studies.

We begin by looking at the two possible explanatory models offered by Dr. Cravioto. In the first scheme he proposes that malnutrition *and* poor mental development are independent consequences of social conditions, with malnutrition leading to poor physical growth. This is what social researchers have customarily called a "spurious" association — that is, the observed relationship between malnutrition and mental development reflects only a common origin. There is no inherent causal connection between the two and, consequently, there is no reason to believe that a change in one would produce a change in the other. This model is represented by those research workers, for example, who would argue that poverty or social deprivation result in a poor diet on the one hand and, quite independently, retarded mental development on the other hand. Obviously, the acceptance or rejection of this model is crucial for any program designed to improve mental development. To the extent that this model is correct, one would attempt to change the underlying social conditions rather than the food intake. It becomes essential for those nutritional research workers who hypothesize that malnutrition is a cause of poor mental development to disprove this model. And, of course, this is the task undertaken by Dr. Cravioto in his chapter.

The second scheme proposes that social conditions affect malnutrition, which, in turn, leads independently to the two consequences of poor mental development and retarded physical growth. Given this model, a change in social conditions would produce a change in nutritional deficiency, which would have the twofold effect of better mental and physical development. However, this model also means that it should be possible to affect mental and physical development *solely* by changing diet without any modification of the underlying social conditions. Similarly, from this model, one could argue that any change in social conditions which did not also produce a change in food intake would *not* result in better mental and physical development. This is the model Dr. Cravioto undertakes to support with his research findings.

Before looking at these specific findings and their interpretation, it is worth pointing out that other important alternative schemes exist, reflecting the multiplicity of causes and interdependence of events between preceding, independent, intervening, and dependent variables discussed previously. First, it is possible that social conditions lead to a wide variety of other phenomena that may independently affect the nutritional status of the child, his mental development, and his physical growth. For example, social-class membership may lead to child-rearing practices, which separately and quite independently affect his diet, his exposure to learning opportunities, and his physical health and development. In this scheme, child-rearing practices become the crucial variable for both explanation and intervention. Another such variable might be infectious diseases, which also result from social conditions, but independently affect diet and the mental and physical development of the child.

Another model would stress the reciprocal action among social conditions, diet, mental and physical growth. In this explanatory scheme, malnutrition may be viewed as producing social conditions that interfere with the physical and mental growth of the child. For example, an inadequate diet may lead to greater susceptibility to disease; this would have its own consequences for physical and mental development. According to this model, malnutrition can affect physical and mental growth without any necessary connection between food intake and biological processes.

My own predisposition as a behavioral scientist favors that model which views diet as only one ingredient in a vast array of social conditions affecting mental and physical development, and which seeks not to isolate malnutrition as *the* explanation of retarded growth, but rather to demonstrate its contributing role in an interactional model of multiple causes and reciprocal relationships. Let us now turn to the evidence presented by Dr. Cravioto in favor of his Scheme II, in which malnutrition is viewed as a crucial intervening, or explanatory, variable between social conditions and the separate effects of poor intersensory development and low stature. This is not to say that Dr. Cravioto is unaware of the complexity of isolating "causal" factors by means of statistical correlational analysis, but only that, in my opinion, he is pressed, in his attempt to demonstrate the greater validity of Scheme II over Scheme I, to make questionable assumptions about the meaning of his operational indexes and the inferences to be drawn from his findings.

We begin with some of the major assumptions concerning his measures of social conditions, malnutrition, mental development, and physical growth. To study the effect of *social conditions*, Dr. Cravioto utilizes a comparison between middle- and upper-class urban children and a heterogeneous group of rural children. The assumption here is that social class as indicated by the socioeconomic status of the family would provide a necessary control for environmental forces not related to nutrition. While such a demographic control is unquestionably desirable, it is hardly adequate to test the independence of nutrition from such class-related factors as child-rearing practices, cultural stimulation, intrafamily relationships, eating habits, achievement motivation, and exposure to infectious diseases. Furthermore, the social-class comparisons presented are complicated by the fact that the upper-class group in this study was brought up under urban living conditions, while the lower-class group came from a rural background. I do not feel that social-class membership per se is an adequate measure of socioenvironmental forces affecting physical and mental growth, and strongly urge that studies attempting to separate dietary effects from social factors look directly for variations in such variables as cultural stimulation or child-rearing practices with the same degree of precision attempted in measuring nutritional intake.

In regard to the measure of early nutritional deficiency employed by Dr. Cravioto, this is perhaps the source of my most critical reservation. The only measure used is that of height. The major assumption is that short children had been subjected to early malnutrition while tall children had not. Differences in intersensory organization between tall and short children are then offered as proof that such differences stem from early nutritional deficiency. This is the major hypothesis to be tested and, it appears to me, there is simply too great an inferential leap from a correlation between height and performance on tests of intersensory organization to the conclusion that malnutrition has a direct and independent effect upon mental development. I feel strongly the need for a more adequate measure of early nutritional deficiency than present height — especially when this variable is the major factor under investigation.

Furthermore, the use of height as the index of malnutrition destroys its utility as a simultaneous measure of physical growth. How does one test the relationship between malnutrition and low stature, as indicated by Dr. Cravioto in both Scheme I and Scheme II, when low stature is taken as *the* index of malnutrition? Aside from the question of the adequacy of height as a measure of physical development, clearly one cannot use the same index to study both the independent and dependent variables in a hypothesis.

Finally, we come to the index of mental development — intersensory organization. This is perhaps the most sophisticated of Dr. Cravioto's measures, if not the only one. For this measure, we do have an interesting and apparently reliable and valid series of tests of mental performance. Certainly these tests are a major improvement upon the old-fashioned and highly culture-bound IQ tests, and do appear to relate more directly to mental growth. We can applaud their development. It still behooves us, however, to register our long-standing appeal for a broader definition of the behavioral dimension in studies of nutrition. We might characterize this as social development or role performance. Basically, it represents the ability of the individual to learn to respond to social stimuli in a way which enables him to carry out his social tasks in a competent manner. My hypothesis would be that malnutrition can retard the social learning of the child, impeding the development of personal relationships and role performance. To some extent, such social development will be directly allied to mental development. In fact, one might argue that the emphasis upon intellectual rather than social development reflects the value placed upon mental proficiency in American society. It may well be that in those nonindustrialized, underdeveloped areas where malnutrition is most likely to be prevalent, the intellectual development of the child is far less important or valued than is social development.

That this possibility of linking nutrition to problems of social development is not absent in Dr. Cravioto's thinking can be seen in his final attempts to relate early nutritional deficiency to school failure. There is every reason to believe that malnutrition as a form of sociocultural deprivation reflecting both environmental conditions and family dietary and child-rearing practices will leave its mark upon the ability of the child and adult to function in his various social roles. But, once again, I am forced to note the discrepancy between my emphasis upon nutrition as reflecting a significant social force and Dr. Cravioto's more limited concluding paragraph: "If the data are interpreted in this way, we may predict that shorter children, whose height is a reflection of their earlier and sometimes continuing malnutrition, risk school failure because they cannot master primary school subjects." This conclusion invokes all of the reservations we have noted previously in regard to the assumptions and inferences of the study under discussion.

I would like to conclude with a description of a research project now being developed in Guatemala under the auspices of the Institute of Nutrition of Central America and Panama, commonly known as INCAP, and directed by Dr. Cipriano A. Canosa. I have had the good fortune of serving on an interdisciplinary team of physicians, nutritionists, nurses, psychologists, anthropologists, and sociologists concerned with the design of this project. This research is proposed basically as a study of planned social change, in which research on the role of diet in mental and social development is used as the basis for designing an intervention program to test the ability of a food-supplementation program to affect mental and social growth.

The proposal begins with the following statement of the problem:

It is well known that malnutrition occurs as a result of the interaction of the child with his social, physical and biological environment. It is also known that the environment as a whole directly affects and modifies the mental development of an individual.

It has been postulated that children living in poor environmental conditions have different psychological development and behavior than children living in a better environment, and that these differences could be due to the effect of malnutrition. But it could also be due to the socio-cultural environment, or more likely to a combination of the socio-cultural environment and malnutrition.

The research design calls for two related studies — an ongoing prospective survey of two towns and an experimental food-supplementation program in a number of villages. Data will be obtained on sociocultural factors, as well as dietary surveys; biomedical studies, including clinico-nutritional examinations and neurological evaluations; epidemiological surveys of morbidity and mortality; and psychological tests. In all cases where necessary, specific tests will be designed for the particular population being studied. These data will be obtained at periodic intervals over a projected nine-year period to provide both baseline data and measures of subsequent changes and to permit an evaluation of the effects of the food-supplementation program.

In the "town" study, an initial survey of a representative sample of families will obtain basic data on such sociocultural variables as food values and eating customs, family organization and child-rearing practices, an epidemiological survey of family health status and illness behavior, a detailed dietary survey, psychological tests such as language, perception, memory, and learning, and various clinical examinations. These measures will be taken periodically over a span of two years. At this time, a food-supplementation program will be initiated, and the same measures repeated, comparing participating with nonparticipating families. In another community, similar baseline measurements will be obtained, but here a food-supplementation program will be carried out on a saturation basis.

The experimental design for the village study calls for comparing two groups of children six years of age and under, plus newborn infants entering each group, on a longitudinal basis over a six- to nine-year period. Children and mothers in the experimental villages would be provided a nutritionally adequate diet on a daily basis. A control group of villages would receive no nutritional supplement. Measures such as those listed above would be obtained for both experimental and control villages before and after the supplementation program.

Both programs would attempt to focus attention on the entire course of development of the child. At the earliest evidence of conception, the pregnant women could be subjected to periodic, routine, perinatal examinations and their nutritional status could be estimated. Information could be collected concerning delivery, and the newborn could be examined and studied thereafter by repeated clinico-nutritional, dietary, neurological, anthropometric, and psychological examinations, as well as bone X-rays of hand and wrist. At the same time, anthropological, sociological, and demographic data would be collected in a systematic manner.

For the purpose of this volume, the significant aspect in the design of this project is its firm adherence to an ecological framework, in which both physical and social environment are related to the mental, social, and physical growth of the child, and in which nutritional status is viewed as only one component of a system in dynamic equilibrium. The emphasis is upon the interactional effects of each of these components upon the others, with an awareness that changes in any part of the system, whether biological or social, require a new equilibrium or balance of forces. In such an approach, the problem to be studied is no longer one of deciding between alternatives, such as Scheme I or Scheme II of Dr. Cravioto, but of accepting and understanding the inherent interdependence of the relationship between biology and behavior.

Early Social Deprivation in the Nonhuman Primates: Implications for Human Behavior

WILLIAM A. MASON

DISCUSSION

The Crucial Nature of Early Experience
LEON J. YARROW   101

The Social Environment of Infant Macaques
PETER MARLER and ANDREW GORDON   113

Communication of Affects in Monkeys
I. ARTHUR MIRSKY   129

It has long been a hope that the nonhuman primates have something special to tell us as to why the experiences of infancy and childhood seem to hold unique importance for man. I believe that hope is well-founded, and it is my purpose here to consider how far we have come toward realizing it. Thus, it would be proper to regard what I have to say as a report of progress, and as a statement of possibilities.

My intention is, first, to consider different ways of approaching the nonhuman primates as a resource for studying human problems; second, to describe some general trends of primate behavioral development; third, in the light of these trends, to consider some recent findings on monkeys and apes reared under artificial conditions; and, finally, to place these findings within a comparative perspective.

WILLIAM A. MASON   Delta Regional Primate Research Center, Tulane University, New Orleans, Louisiana

HUMAN BEHAVIOR AND THE NONHUMAN PRIMATES

Why do we look to the monkeys and apes to shed new light on human problems? The obvious answer, of course, is that these animals are our closest kin. But how can we make the most of the research opportunities they offer? Here, we find, there are no simple answers. In general, however, there appear to be three rather different ways of looking at the nonhuman primates as a means for getting at human problems.

The Primates as Models of Human Behavior

One way is to treat the animal as a substitute for man, as a human model. To do this we must be able to assume a reasonable match between the animal model and man, at least in its response to the condition that happens to interest us. For this reason, using the monkey or ape as a model for man works best when the process being studied is fairly well defined, when the research has a limited, specifiable objective. These conditions are most often met in medical investigations in which the focus is on a particular disease category, but they are also found in certain kinds of behavioral research. For example, if we are going to study the effects of a new drug on memory, all we really require is a model that is capable of remembering; the question of how closely the performance of the model matches human behavior in other ways is of small importance. Its sex life, its child-rearing practices, or, for that matter, even its general intelligence, need not concern us.

But not all primate behavioral research is concerned with such carefully circumscribed goals. I suspect, in fact, that most of it is not. Today we are using monkeys and apes to investigate such complex matters as the nature of intelligence, the sources of neurotic behavior, and the origins of love. How far are we justified here in regarding monkeys and apes as useful substitutes for man? The hard fact — as we all know — is that, for most of the important psychological questions confronting man today, we search the crowded ranks of the nonhuman primates in vain for an acceptable human model. Our frailties, as well as our accomplishments, set us apart from the animal community. Murder and suicide are every bit as exclusively human achievements as are skyscrapers and transcontinental jets. The more troublesome aberrations of human behavior — the psychoses, the neuroses, the various character disorders — have no obvious counterparts in the natural communities of monkeys and apes. Having recognized the magnitude of these differences, we cannot avoid the conclusion that as models of human behavior, the nonhuman primates have serious limitations.

The Primates and Pure Research

One response to this problem is to ignore it altogether. The scientist can always claim that he has no professional interest in applying his findings or his theories to human problems. He sees his task as one of pure research; he denies that the animal is standing in as a model for man, and insists that he is interested in the animal "for its own sake," or as a means of working out theories, developing conceptual models, or framing and testing hypotheses, without regard to their implications for man. I think no one who is engaged in empirical research with animals will question the scientific value of this attitude, or hesitate to defend the scientist's right to adopt it. At the same time, it is clear that such an approach does not come to grips with the question of how we can increase the relevance of our findings in monkeys and apes to problems of human behavior; it simply sidesteps it.

But what if we don't want to evade the issue? Suppose we are genuinely concerned with maximizing the contribution of the nonhuman primates to questions of human conduct? How do we now proceed? I think it is clear that under these circumstances we have no choice but to search for a different approach to primate behavior, one that will incorporate the strongest features of the approaches we have already considered within a broader perspective in which man has a recognized place.

The Evolutionary-Comparative Perspective

I believe that such an approach is available, and I am convinced that this is the way we must travel if we are to realize fully the potential contribution of the nonhuman primates to problems of human behavior. Through such an approach we can achieve a better understanding not only of what we are, but of what we might have been; not only why we succeed or fail, but why our successes and failures are on such a spectacular scale; not only what we have gained, but at what costs the gains have been made. As you may have anticipated, the approach I refer to is evolutionary and comparative; it is an approach that takes the differences among the primates as seriously as the similarities, and as much in need of explanation. While acknowledging the great diversity of behavioral adaptations among the living primates, it offers the hope that patterns will be seen within that diversity, that trends will be found yielding a fresh perspective on primate behavior and illuminating the special psychological attributes of man.

We will consider some of these trends later. For the present, however, having adopted the view that the nonhuman primates are part of a comparative series in which man is included, let us turn to questions of primate development. We will look first for those elements in primate ontogeny that are most primitive or basic — in the sense of being most widely distributed — deferring for the moment a consideration of those characteristics that serve to distinguish different species.

PRIMATE BEHAVIORAL DEVELOPMENT

I will take the view here that behavioral development, like all forms of organismic growth, is based on programs that are a part of every normal individual's native endowment. They are, in short, hereditary. To be sure, their specific locus within the genotype is largely unknown, but we may leave this problem to the specialist in behavioral genetics, in whose hands it properly belongs. Our concern is with the general patterns and special features of primate infancy and childhood and with the effects of individual experience on psychological growth. For us, then, the central task is to discover the phenotypic expression of these developmental programs. How do they manifest themselves under ordinary conditions? How are they modified by the environment, and how do they act selectively upon it?

Let us consider first the general programs, the ones that seem to apply to most primates. And let us look to the infant, for we find that in behavioral, as in morphological, comparisons, the younger the individuals, the greater the similarity between members of different species.

Infancy

Probably the most widely recognized characteristic of the infant primate is that it is helpless. Indeed, it is sometimes suggested that this is a distinctive primate characteristic. But this is not true; many newborn mammals are helpless. Infant primates do differ from most other mammals, however, in that they are helpless for a long time — the chimpanzee is unable to walk with any facility until it is about six months old — and this, combined with another feature of primate life, means that infancy presents a special set of problems to primate mother and child, problems with which most other mammals are not required to deal. This second feature of primate life can be summarized by stating that, for the vast majority of primates, "mother" and "nest" are synonymous. Somehow, in spite of the helplessness of the primate infant, nature has contrived to eliminate "a place to leave the young" from the primate life plan, and this has required some fundamental changes in the relationship between mother and infant. For the mother, it means that there is no respite from the burdens of maternal care until the infant has moved some distance toward independence. Where mother goes, baby goes — a continuous, tangible presence through the daily round of finding food, of staying out of harm's way, and of keeping up with and getting along with the rest of the group. We can only guess at the practical problems that a new infant creates for the nonhuman primate mother, but there must be many of them. The circumstances would seem to require a large capacity for tolerance — a maternal bond strong enough to override the daily measure of irritation, frustration, and fatigue. And we know that primate mothers are not lacking in this capacity. There are numerous examples of the strength of maternal ties in the more advanced primates, one of the most dramatic being the persistent carrying of dead infants, to the point at which the bodies have become withered, decomposed almost beyond recognition.

But what of the infant, which, after all, is our main concern? As we have seen, in the beginning the infant primate is in virtually continual contact with the mother. Its survival depends upon this. The infant is equipped at birth with three main avenues through which contact and communication with the mother are established and maintained: clinging, sucking, and vocalizing. Naturally, species vary in the strength or efficiency of these responses — a question we will return to in a moment — and some species show, quite early in postnatal life, additional responses having a social function, a notable example being the smile of the human infant. The important point here, however, is that in the vast majority of primates whose infancy is known to us, vocalizing, sucking, and clinging appear as adaptive, organized patterns, present at birth or shortly thereafter.

I propose to discuss the adaptive and organized aspects of these responses in some detail, because a proper understanding of their biological function and organization provides an important key to understanding some of the effects of rearing conditions on behavioral development.

The adaptive properties of clinging and sucking are self-evident, at least in the nonhuman primates. Vocalizations have a less obvious function, but it is easy to demonstrate how they, too, must have definite survival value. I can find no better illustration of the functions of early vocalization than an example from my own experience. A chimpanzee had just given birth. As the infant was required for research, the mother was given a drug so that the baby could be removed safely. At the time this episode occurred, the mother was already showing clear signs that the drug was taking effect. She was woozy, her posture and movements were awkward, and the infant was having trouble clinging to her. Each time the baby slipped a little it would whimper and scream; immediately, the mother would reach down, grasp it, and pull it up higher on her belly, whereupon the crying ceased and the mother released her grasp. I suspect that the most primitive function of the baby's cry is seen in this simple example: it serves as an irritant, if you will, as something to alert and arouse the parent, causing it to do something that will turn off that distressing sound.

I also have described these infantile responses as organized, and by that I mean not only that they are integrated motor patterns, but also that they show regular relations to stimulus conditions and to motivational factors. Again, an example will serve to make this point clearer, and it would be hard to find a more illustrious figure to provide one than Alfred Russel Wallace. He recorded the following observations of a captive baby orangutan, and in doing so not only gave us an excellent description but, at the same time, established himself as the historical father of the artificial mother:

For the first few days it clung desperately with all four hands to whatever it could lay hold of, and I had to be careful to keep my beard out of its way, as its fingers clutched hold of hair more tenaciously than anything else, and it was impossible to free myself without assistance. When restless, it would struggle about with its hands up in the air trying to find something to take hold of, and, when it had got a bit of stick or rag in two or three of its hands, seemed quite happy. For want of something else, it would often seize its own feet, and after a time it would constantly cross its arms and grasp with each hand the long hair that grew just below the opposite shoulder. . . . Finding it so fond of hair, I endeavoured to make an artificial mother, by wrapping up a piece of buffalo-skin into a bundle, and suspending it about a foot from the floor. At first this seemed to suit it admirably, as it could sprawl its legs about and always find some hair, which it grasped with the greatest tenacity. I was now in hopes that I had made the little orphan quite happy; and so it seemed for some time, till it began to remember its lost parent and try to suck. It would pull itself up close to the skin, and try about everywhere for a likely place; but, as it only succeeded in getting mouthfuls of hair and wool, it would be greatly disgusted, and scream violently, and after two or three attempts, let go altogether.[28]

It is easy to see from Wallace's account why "contact-seeking" has been considered one of the principal "drives" of the newborn primate. A major contribution of Harlow's classic studies of the rhesus monkey's responses to artificial mothers was the demonstration that contact was a primary basis for the formation of the filial attachment.[6] Owing largely to this work we can, with reasonable certainty, trace the well-known properties of the primate mother as a source of emotional security to contact variables. Elsewhere, I have tried to show that, apart from their specific functions, sucking, clinging, and other infantile contact behaviors seem to share a more general property — the ability to reduce emotional arousal.[14,16] From infancy, and potentially throughout life, such responses are a means of mitigating intense emotional reactions and of keeping these disruptive states under some measure of control.

In treating the behavioral programs of early infancy, we find little need to go beyond the relatively simple behaviors we have already considered. The picture is incomplete, of course, since even the newborn primate is a sentient creature, capable of responding to visual patterns, to sounds, to temperature changes, and to other events impinging on it from the physical environment. Nonetheless, when considering the neonate I think we are justified in relegating these intrusions from the nonsocial realm to a minor position, because the principal focus of the infant primate's behavior is the mother. His contacts with the environment are mediated by her, and she stands as a buffer between him and the outside world.

Onset of Play and Exploration

We cannot say with any certainty just when the growing primate begins to shift from its psychological preoccupation with the mother to the world at large. In most species, it probably starts at birth. It is certain, however, that a shift does occur, and it is obvious that the change is gradual and progressive. It represents the emergence of a basic orientation toward the world that differs radically from the mother-directed, arousal-reducing orientation that characterizes early infancy. Although the shift never wholly supplants this earlier orientation, it overshadows it increasingly as a factor in the day-to-day activities of the developing individual.

The evidence for such a trend is abundant, although on many points it can scarcely be considered systematic. Specific indications are, first, the increasing tendency to approach and interact with objects in the physical environment — the development of exploratory or investigatory activities; second, a progressive increase in the amount, vigor, and variety of motor play — the jumping, bouncing, climbing, and swinging, for which the primates are justly famous; and finally, of course, the increase in all forms of social interaction, but particularly in romping, roughhousing, and other varieties of social play.

Developmental Trends

In summary, our grossly schematic overview has emphasized two major foci in primate behavioral development. The first of these is the filial response, the so-called contact-seeking behaviors. These are not only the basis for the initial adjustment to the mother, but, in addition, because of their general motivational properties — characterized here as the ability to reduce arousal — they are the primary basis for the development of emotional dependence, for the formation of filial attachment. Infantile contact patterns, such as clinging, become progressively less frequent during ontogeny, but they never disappear entirely, and they retain throughout life their primitive ability to reduce arousal.

The second major developmental focus can perhaps be described most simply as exploitation of the physical and social environment, as seen in investigatory behavior and in social and motor play. These behaviors, in sharp contrast to the filial or contact-seeking behaviors most prominent during the first stages of development, seem to have the general characteristic of increasing stimulation, excitement, or arousal.

Progressive changes in the relative frequency of contact-seeking and in exploitative behaviors during ontogeny describe contrasting developmental trends. As a specific illustration of these trends, I present some findings on rhesus monkeys reared individually from birth in wire cages.[13] The only opportunities these animals had for physical contact with other monkeys occurred during brief (three-minute) tests starting when they were about 25 days old. They were tested daily for 60 days, then given a 120-day break, during which they had no opportunity for contact with other monkeys, and, finally, they were given another 30 days of testing. The relative frequency of clasping, a typical filial response, and of social play, an equally typical exploitative pattern, are shown in Figure 1. It is evident that the general trend for clasping is downward, whereas play shows an upward course. You

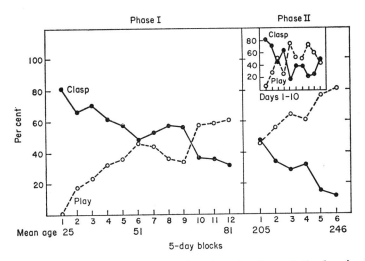

FIGURE 1 Trends in clasping and social play in socially deprived rhesus monkeys. (After Mason[13])

will note that when placed in the test situation after an absence of 120 days, the monkeys revert briefly to a high level of clasping, probably a response to the high excitement induced by return to the test situation; then, after the first few days, the trends established for play and clasping are resumed.

I am suggesting that these trends are the outcome of basic developmental programs that are present in all primates. The hypothetical condition is shown in Figure 2. I do not claim, of course, that we are dealing here with a rigidly fixed pattern, but rather with developmental tendencies or predispositions, which, given a minimum of experiential support, proceed in the manner described by these curves.

Effects of Experience on Behavioral Development

With this simple conceptual framework in mind, let us now turn to the question of how experience affects behavioral development. Although I will make some use of specific findings, my aim is still to provide a broad view that is valid for the primates in general.

In approaching the question of how experience affects behavioral development, the deprivation study is a powerful methodological resource; so powerful, in fact, that its effects can sometimes be likened

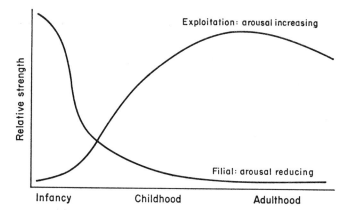

FIGURE 2 Hypothetical developmental trends in filial (arousal-reducing) responses and in exploitative (arousal-increasing) responses.

to the blow of a sledge hammer, when a few gentle taps might have been more instructive. Our knowledge of the consequences of social deprivation comes chiefly from studies in which the infant is separated from its mother at birth and raised individually, either in an open cage that exposes it to the general laboratory environment and permits it to see and hear other animals, or in an enclosed cage that provides very little social or general environmental stimulation of any kind.[4,5,11,19]

What happens to the monkey or ape reared under such conditions? The general outcome is sufficiently well established at this point for us probably to be justified in referring to it as a deprivation syndrome. One of the most striking features of this syndrome is the development of repetitive stereotyped movements, usually rocking or swaying. The close similarity in the form of these behaviors in monkeys and apes to the repetitive patterns of blind and autistic children and of the severely retarded has suggested to many investigators that repetitive stereotyped movements are a primitive primate reaction to adverse conditions, a question I will return to in a moment. Some form of self-clasping — clutching a leg, an arm, or the head — and digit-sucking frequently accompany the performance of repetitive movements. As might be expected, socially-deprived primates are also deviant in their social relations: when placed with other animals they often seem unduly fearful, or extremely aggressive; sexual inadequacies are common, particularly in males, and the female's ability to care for her first-born infant may be seriously impaired.

What can these deficiencies tell us about normal development? Can we use these findings to come closer to discovering the programs of primate behavioral development and their relations to experience? As a first step toward answering this question, let us consider a more general classification of the deprivation syndrome (Table I). Four

TABLE I

The Primate Deprivation Syndrome

1 Abnormal postures and movements. Example: rocking.

2 Motivational disturbance. Example: excessive fearfulness.

3 Poor integration of motor patterns. Example: sexual behavior.

4 Deficiencies in social communication. Example: threat by aggressive animal *A* does not produce withdrawal by subordinate animal *B*.

distinct elements can be discerned. First, the socially-deprived animal shows postures or movements that are rare or absent in normal animals, the most dramatic of these being repetitive stereotyped movements.[2,17] Second, there is usually strong evidence in the socially-deprived animal of gross motivational deviations. For example, chimpanzees reared in isolation avoid even simple and entirely innocuous objects, such as a small block of wood or scrap of cloth, on first encounter. Indeed, an animal might require daily exposures extending over several weeks before it makes its first hesitant contact with such an object.[22] Third, socially deprived animals often show an absence of certain postures or movements or a failure to form certain specific movements into larger integrated patterns. This is illustrated in Figure 3, which compares the sexual performance of socially deprived

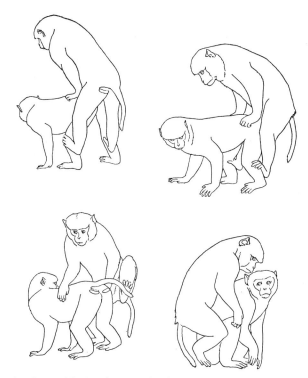

FIGURE 3 Sexual behavior of wild-born and socially-deprived rhesus monkeys with wild-born female partners. Top left: Rear view of wild-born male in typical copulatory position. Top right: Side view of wild-born male in typical copulatory position. Bottom left: Socially-deprived male attempting to mount from the side. Bottom right: Sexual behavior of socially-deprived male. (From Mason[15])

and wild-born male rhesus monkeys. Finally, there is evidence of a disturbance in interindividual stimulus-response relationships; in other words, there are deficiencies in social communication.[12,18,23] For example, if a sophisticated and receptive female solicits the sexual attentions of a socially deprived male, he does not respond to this highly distinctive pattern as though it were a signal — which it certainly is for the wild-born male — but instead may initiate play, or begin to groom the female, or ignore her altogether.

There is reason to believe that each of these elements in the deprivation syndrome can be manipulated independently, and that they differ from each other in their relations to developmental status and in the way they are affected by specific factors in the rearing environment. Let us consider the evidence that has led to this conclusion, beginning with the first element in the deprivation syndrome — the presence of atypical postures and movements.

As we have seen, the behavior and motivations of the infant primate, particularly during the neonatal period, are clearly adapted to maintaining contact with the mother. These contact-seeking behaviors constitute the salient developmental program of the neonatal primate, and it can be argued that working out this program under conditions in which the natural outlets for contact-seeking behaviors are withheld gives rise to atypical postures and movements. This interpretation applies readily to digit-sucking and to self-clasping, since both of these patterns have obvious counterparts in the normal relation to the mother; it does not seem at first glance, however, to fit repetitive stereotyped movements, such as rocking or swaying. What is the normal counterpart of these behaviors? If we recall that under natural conditions the mother ordinarily provides a great deal of passive movement stimulation to her infant in the course of her routine activities, and consider further how widespread is the practice among human parents of rocking babies to calm and to comfort them, we might conjecture that the infant monkey or ape that is deprived of such passive movement stimulation may supply it for himself through self-rocking or similar repetitive activities, just as it substitutes self-stimulation for social stimulation in the development of thumb-sucking and self-clasping. Recently, Dr. Gershon Berkson and I have obtained evidence that supports this hypothesis — at least to the extent that it establishes a presumptive link between self-rocking and the quality of maternal stimulation. We are comparing two groups of rhesus monkeys, both separated from their mothers at birth. One group is reared with a cloth-covered social substitute that moves freely about the cage on an irregular schedule, and the other with a device identical to the moving dummy, except that it is stationary (Figure 4). Thus far, three monkeys have been reared with robot devices and three with stationary dummies. All of the last group have developed stereotyped rocking as a persistent pattern, whereas none

FIGURE 4 Dummy used in investigation of effects of movement stimulation on the development of repetitive stereotyped movements.

of the monkeys reared with robot dummies has shown any evidence of this behavior (Figure 5).

The second element of the primate deprivation syndrome is some form of motivational disturbance, most often seen as fearfulness or hyperexcitability. This factor is so pervasive that it can become a definite nuisance when one is attempting to test a socially-deprived animal in a situation in which a high level of emotionality is incompatible with the aims of the test. In spite of its obtrusiveness, however, the origin of hyperexcitability is imperfectly understood. What we

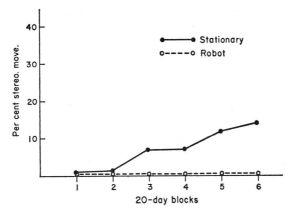

FIGURE 5 Development of stereotyped rocking in infant rhesus monkeys reared with robot and stationary dummies.

can state with reasonable confidence is this: there is a loose correlation between the general level of environmental stimulation during rearing and later emotionality. The less stimulating, the more restricted and "impoverished" the rearing environment, the greater the likelihood of panic, freezing, or other symptoms of excessive arousal when the animal is confronted with a situation that is in any way novel.[19]

Can we relate the abnormally high levels of emotionality in experimentally deprived primates to our developmental schema? It seems likely that these motivational disturbances represent a kind of environmental arrest of the exploitative trend in development. We know from normative studies that, under natural conditions, exploitation of the environment increases gradually and progressively. Descriptively, it would seem that the developing individual adapts to one set of conditions, or one level of complexity, and is thereby prepared to move on to higher levels. In the typical rearing study, however, the amount and variety of sensory input is sharply restricted. We narrow the arena in which contact with the environment is possible and, in so doing, drastically curtail opportunities to encounter novel forms of stimulation — to respond to, and to be acted upon by the stimulus complexities that the normal environment provides in abundance.

Characteristically, after several months, or a year or more, in its restricted environment, the subject is removed and suddenly confronted with something quite outside its previous experience. The impact of the new situation can be overwhelming, particularly if the animal has spent its life previously in a small enclosed cage. It thus seems clear that a reduction in general environmental stimulation during rearing is one of the major causes of the excessive arousal effects seen in socially-deprived primates. That this is the whole story is doubtful, but we have little systematic information on other relevant factors.

In particular, the effects of maternal deprivation are difficult to assess. It is clear, of course, that once an attachment to the mother is established, separation is extremely disturbing.[8,9,25] But what of the infant monkey or ape that is removed from the mother at birth and raised as a social isolate? How does such early separation affect the course of its emotional development? Present evidence offers no satisfactory answer to this question, but it is possible to discern at least two different ways in which the presence or absence of the mother might influence emotional development.

The first way is through the effects of maternal variables on the contact-seeking behaviors of early infancy. We have seen that these behaviors are strong and tenacious in the infant monkey or ape. In so far as maternal deprivation creates a condition that is unfavorable for the performance of these highly motivated responses, we might expect immediate and obvious emotional consequences. There is some evidence that this is the case: infant rhesus monkeys reared for the first 30 days of life on cloth-covered cylinders are reported to gain weight faster, to vocalize less, and to be accelerated in their behavioral development as compared to motherless infants lacking such a social substitute.[21] Presumably, these results reflect the superiority of the cylinder in satisfying infantile contact needs. And it is through the satisfaction of such needs — I have argued — that the social substitute, and the mother, become sources of emotional security.

However, natural mothers have a second way of influencing emotional development. They are not merely passive security objects, available on demand for the performance of infantile arousal-reducing responses. They also interact with their infants in a variety of ways that increase arousal: they occasionally push their babies away from the nipple, place them on the ground, cuff them, restrain them, take food from them — and in many ways provide the kind of stimulation that comes from the world in general. No one seriously doubts that such actions by the mother also have an impact on emotional development. The problem has been to specify the source and the nature of the effects.

Our observations of monkeys raised on moving and stationary dummies may have taken us a step closer to solving this problem. We have found that the monkeys reared with moving dummies are less fearful and more active than those reared with stationary devices. Robot-reared monkeys spend less time in contact with the social surrogate (Figure 6); they more often move about the cage (Figure 7); and they are quicker to approach and to interact with people (Figure 8).

I do not wish to imply that we understand the specific sources of the contrasts between these two groups of monkeys. We can be sure that the differences were produced by adding movement to one of

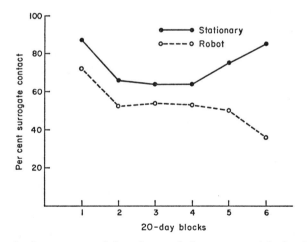

FIGURE 6   Percentage of time intervals in contact with the dummy by monkeys reared with robot and stationary dummies.

the dummies, but beyond that it is difficult to be more precise. In designing the experiment, it was our intention to compare two simulated social stimuli, one which provided passive movement stimula-

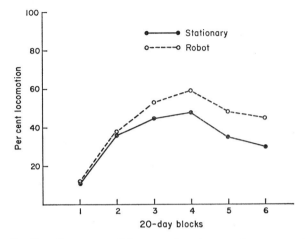

FIGURE 7 Development of locomotion in monkeys reared with robot and stationary dummies.

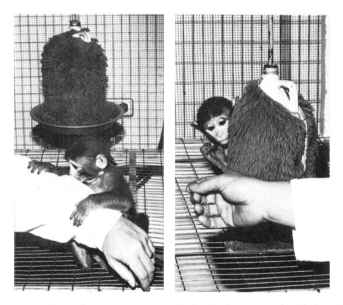

FIGURE 8 Reactions to humans. Left: Robot-reared. Right: Stationary-reared.

tion and the other which did not. We achieved our purpose during early infancy when the babies were in almost continuous contact with the dummies. As development continued, it became clear that the robot was doing a great deal more than just carrying the infant about the cage. We had unwittingly created a social substitute that was capable of a genuine, albeit limited, form of social interaction. Since the movements of the robot are essentially unpredictable, it can withdraw from the infant without warning, or sneak up behind it and deliver a gentle rap on the head; its comings and goings demand adjustments from the infant that are not required of the animals reared with stationary devices. The robot stimulates and sustains interaction: it is withdrawn from, pursued, pounced on, and wrestled with. I find it hard to believe that this interaction does not have an important impact on emotional development, similar to that which a real mother might produce.

Obviously, however, we are still a long way from understanding the mother's contribution to emotional development, or knowing how it compares with the effects of more general forms of environmental stimulation. What we can be sure about is that the deprived monkey or ape shows signs of excessive arousal, and that these disruptive emotional reactions become most prominent when the animal is placed in unfamiliar surroundings. In such circumstances he crouches, clutches himself, rocks, withdraws from contact, and, very probably, shows a lowered threshold for aggression. What this means, of course, is that the opportunities for social learning are sharply curtailed.

The two remaining elements in the primate deprivation syndrome — the absence of certain postures and movement patterns, and disturbances in social communication — relate principally, I think, to the exploitative trend in development. Under normal conditions, sensorimotor patterns and communication skills are acquired during the give-and-take of social interaction. Even here, however, emotional factors cannot be overlooked, since they set the motivational scene for the development of social skills. The animal that crouches motionless or withdraws from social contact, or responds to all social overtures with aggression, or whose social contacts are vigorous to the point at which they are painful or frightening to the social partner, is obviously in a poor position for effective social learning.

Are we to conclude, then, that the reason socially-deprived male monkeys are unable to achieve normal sexual performance in later life, and the reason socially-deprived females are poor mothers, is that they are too much aroused? Such a conclusion is probably oversimplified, but even if excessive arousal effects are not the entire explanation for the persistence of social deficiencies, they must contribute to it. It is noteworthy that the only socially-deprived female rhesus monkeys that have been reported to show adequate maternal care with first-born infants are described as "tractable," as compared with wild-born mothers.[20] It is also significant that chimpanzee males reared in isolation for the first 21 months of life and then *gradually* introduced into more complex situations, have as adults shown effective copulation with experienced females (R.K. Davenport, Jr., personal communication). These results suggest that, in any effort to establish normal social patterns in the deprived primate, it would be well-advised to aim first for control of emotional responsiveness.

I might summarize this rather sketchy survey of the general features of primate behavioral development and its relation to experience as follows: I have postulated two general programs or trends in behavioral development, one which is dominant in early infancy and then gradually recedes, and another which is relatively inconspicuous in infancy and becomes progressively more prominent. The first trend is inferred from the predominance of contact-seeking behaviors in early infancy, behaviors which we have reason to believe reduce emotional excitement or arousal. The second trend is inferred from the increasing prominence during individual development of social and motor play, and of exploratory and investigatory behaviors and the like, which increase stimulus input and thereby increase emotional excitement or arousal. Together, the two classes of behaviors — the one arousal-reducing, and the other arousal-increasing — constitute a kind of homeostatic system for the control of emotional states. They work together to pace emotional and social development, carrying the growing individual ever closer to adult norms. The relative prominence of each class changes over time, of course, but *neither* class disappears entirely, and they retain throughout life their primitive motivational properties.

The psychological consequences of the typical primate deprivation study reflect interference with both developmental trends. Rocking, self-clasping, and self-sucking represent the working out of infantile contact-seeking behaviors in the absence of the natural mother. Once established, they occur most frequently in stressful situations, where they probably function to reduce arousal. The other elements in the deprivation syndrome seem to relate primarily to the exploitative trend in development: excessive emotionality is principally a reaction to a reduction in the variety and amount of sensory input in early life. Deficiencies in the organization of motor patterns reflect the lack of opportunities for practice or rehearsal, and deficiencies in communication reflect the lack of opportunities to acquire interindividual stimulus-response relations. In other words, both of the last two deficiencies are performance deficiencies resulting from conditions inadequate for learning.

PRIMATE BEHAVIORAL DEVELOPMENT IN COMPARATIVE PERSPECTIVE

In all that has preceded, I have emphasized the general over the specific, the similarities over the differences. One might even argue that some of the generalizations suggested for the primates are broad enough to apply with equal force to other mammals. Isolation-reared dogs, for example, are also hyperexcitable, and may also show bizarre, repetitive motor patterns and deficiencies in sexual performance[27] (Beach, personal communication). Furthermore, the exceptions within the primates were not given the attention they deserve: it is patently clear that human infants are not required to cling to the mother unassisted; indeed, they are unable to do so until they are moving about under their own power and therefore no longer need to be carried continually. Also, we have good reason to suspect that rehearsal in childhood is not an essential requirement for biologically adequate sexual performance in human males, whereas it seems to be in rhesus monkeys. What basis, then, for the claim that the nonhuman primates have something special to contribute to questions of human development? How can the obvious contrasts between man and the other primates be explained in terms of the developmental schema I have proposed?

The Primates as a Graded Series

The answer is that they cannot, at least not until the schema is elaborated to take species differences into account. I now will suggest how such an elaboration might proceed. My thesis is that the living primates constitute a graded series in which the major features of behavioral development show a systematic trend. In other words, I hope to show that if we place human development within a comparative framework many of its distinctive features will be seen as evolutionary extensions of characteristics present in nonhuman forms.

The evidence that the primates do, in fact, constitute a graded series is derived chiefly from systematic comparisons of the structural and functional characteristics of the living primates and from the record of paleontology. On the basis of this information it is possible to arrange the living primates in a linear series which approximates the actual sequence of primate evolution. Figure 9 illustrates the reconstruction of primate evolution presented by Simpson.[26] It is the customary family tree, with the various branches multiplying and

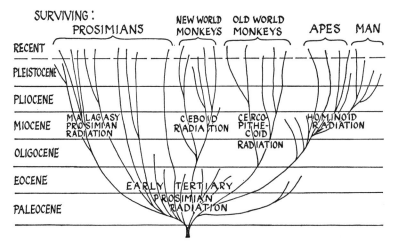

FIGURE 9   Primate phylogeny. (After Simpson[26])

diverging through time. Compare this with Figure 10, after LeGros Clark, which presents primate evolution in a linear perspective.[1]

Perhaps there is no need to emphasize that the living series only approximates the evolutionary series. We are not actually descended from the living apes, nor they from the monkeys as we know them today. The linear model of primate evolution implies, however, that the living chimpanzee is more representative of what we were in our remote past than of what we are today. It implies that we can use the living primates as a means for looking into our own behavioral past, for getting at the evolutionary trends that have culminated in human behavior. It suggests that the implications for man of our findings on the nonhuman primates will be better appreciated if they are viewed from within a comparative perspective.

You might reply that the approximation is crude, that the margin for error is too great. The rejoinder, of course, is that if we wish to discover the evolutionary antecedents of human behavior we have lit-

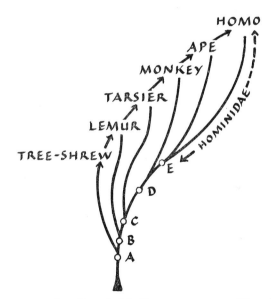

FIGURE 10 Postulated probable linear sequence of hominid ancestry. A–E: Hypothetical transitional stages at which different ramifications of the primates are presumed to have branched off. (After Clark[1])

tle else to go on. Behavior leaves no fossils to help us reconstruct the record of the past.

Trends in Primate Ontogeny

In searching for phylogenetic trends in behavioral development, it would be most helpful to have some clear and unequivocal starting point, a dimension of comparison that everyone would agree is relevant and shows systematic variation across species. Such a dimension, in fact, exists in the rate of ontogenetic development. As is well known, monkeys grow fast as compared to man, requiring only some three to five years to achieve reproductive maturity. The chimpanzee is slower than the monkey, arriving at reproductive maturity in eight or ten years. Man, of course, is slower than either monkey or ape, requiring some fifteen years to become reproductively mature. Adolph Schultz, the anthropologist, finds that rate of growth varies systematically within the primates. He states: "in regard to all parts of postnatal life one can recognize a clear trend toward prolongation, beginning in monkeys, as compared with lemurs, more pronounced in gibbons, still more in all three great apes and by far the most marked in man."[24]

What is the adaptive benefit of prolonging infancy and childhood? The explanation most often encountered is that an animal whose biological youth is extended is given a longer time to learn. Clearly, this cannot be the whole explanation, first, because the immature primate is not a very efficient learner, at least on standard measures of learned performance — were it otherwise, we would have no need for such concepts as learning readiness and mental age — and, second, because we must still explain why the granting of more time for learning would be of any special biological utility.

Neoteny

On the grounds that nature tends to display a certain economy in such matters, we might guess that the reason there is more time for learning in the advanced primates is that more learning is required. Taking this line of reasoning a step further, we might argue that the slowing down of the rate of ontogenetic development and the increasing need for learning are, in fact, different facets of the same evolutionary process, and that this is a process which was identified many years ago and given the name neoteny.

In some species it is possible for an individual to attain reproductive maturity while other systems are still immature. The classic example of this phenomenon is the axolotl, a salamander capable of reproduction while still in a larval state. This survival of juvenile traits into adult life is neoteny.

It has been pointed out that, in comparison with other primates, man can be considered neotenous. In such physical traits as brain weight, the feeble development of the brow ridges, the sparseness of hair over most of the body, the flatness of the face, and the small size of the canine teeth, the mature human resembles the young chimpanzee more than he does the adult animal. Similarly, the chimpanzee shows some indications of neoteny when compared to the monkey. Figure 11 provides an example of human neoteny. The top row compares the foot of a fetal monkey with that of a fetal human. The resemblance is obvious. The bottom row shows the foot of an adult monkey and an adult human. It is clear that the adult human foot more closely resembles the fetal form, either human or monkey, than it does the foot of the adult monkey. In this example, the human foot is neotenous.

If physical structures are subject to neoteny, might not this also be true of behavior?[3,10] From the little we know of age changes in the behavior of monkey, ape, and man, there is good reason to suspect that there is a trend toward the retention of juvenile traits into adulthood. Clinging is an infantile pattern in all the more advanced primates. In man it remains a common reaction to high emotional excitement throughout life. We see it in moments of great joy, as a response to intense grief, and, in some cultures, as a kind of formalized greeting, such as the familiar *abrazo* of the Latins. Under similar circumstances, adult chimpanzees also embrace. In monkeys, however, even though clinging may occur between adult animals, it is seen much less frequently than in apes or man. Another juvenile trait, social play, conforms to the same trend. Human parents seem to play as children with their children, and the amount and variety

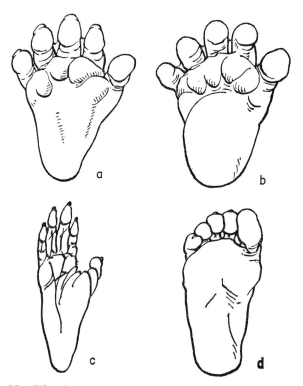

FIGURE 11   The foot in fetal and adult macaque and man. a.
macaque foetus; b. human foetus; c. macaque adult; d. human
adult. (After deBeer[3])

of playful interaction is great, as compared with chimpanzee parent
and child. The chimpanzee, however, surpasses the gibbon, which,
in turn, is probably a more playful parent than are the monkeys or
lesser primates.

If it can be shown that behavioral neoteny is a generalized human
trait, an important conceptual advance will have been made toward
understanding many of the distinctive attributes of man. The prominence of such traits as playfulness, curiosity, inventiveness in human
behavior, the persistence of infantile attachments — all these would
be seen in a somewhat different light. So, too, would the loose relationship between hormonal factors and sex and maternal behavior.
Could neoteny be one of the reasons it has been so difficult to discover
instinctual elements in human behavior, why the great students of

human nature have felt compelled to postulate broad, pervasive forces such as the libido and the death wish to explain the instinctual basis of human motivation? The possibilities here are intriguing, but to explore them would take us too far afield.

Trends in the Organization of Behavior

There is another aspect of the neoteny question, however, that we can pursue on somewhat firmer ground, and in so doing return to our main concern, which is the problem of primate behavioral development. The behavioral equipment of the newborn monkey, the newborn ape, and the newborn human are so similar that they seem to have been fashioned on the same basic plan: all show the so-called reflex grasping response; all show the rooting, oral grasping, and sucking patterns involved in the first feeding reactions; all cry when things don't go their way; and all are comforted when properly held.

If we take a closer look at these primitive responses, however, some important differences between species are at once apparent. Place a newborn rhesus monkey on its back and, unless it is given something to cling to, it immediately rights itself. Do the same thing with a newborn chimpanzee and it may perform weak and irregular sweeping movements with the arms, but it cannot right itself; and it is not able to do so with any real facility until it is several months old. The same ability is not present in the human infant until it is about eight months old. Reflex grasping displays the same trend. An infant monkey can support itself with its hands for as long as half an hour, a chimpanzee for no longer than five minutes, and a human infant for two minutes or less. In general, we can say that the strength and persistence of these primitive infantile responses are less in the human infant than in the chimpanzee, or in the chimpanzee than in the rhesus monkey.

To be sure, these differences reflect the greater developmental maturity of the newborn monkey, but, more important, they also indicate fundamental differences between these species in the way that infant behavior is organized. Viewed as a collection of responses preadapted to nursing and to maintaining contact with the mother, the behavior of the chimpanzee never displays the same reflex-like efficiency as that of the monkey. Indeed, if evolution had not brought about complementary changes in the behavior of the chimpanzee mother that permitted her to compensate for the behavioral deficiencies of her infant, its chances of survival would be slim. No human infant, of course, is able to cling, to find the nipple, and to nurse without extensive maternal assistance. The same infantile responses that make the difference between life and death for the rhesus monkey are often viewed in the human infant as mere behavioral curios, without obvious adaptive value.

In the light of these examples, I think you will agree that, even among the earliest organized behaviors to appear in primate infancy, there is evidence of a systematic trend, not only toward slowing down the rate of development, but also in the way that behavioral organization proceeds. It would not be a gross oversimplification to state that, throughout infancy, the human is a less finished product than the chimpanzee, just as the chimpanzee is a less finished product than the infant monkey.

I believe the same trend can be seen in the repetitive, stereotyped movements I discussed earlier in connection with the primate deprivation syndrome. With these responses, however, it makes no sense to talk in terms of efficiency. It is the variability of these behaviors — both within and between individuals — that provides the most striking evidence of a phylogenetic trend.

In rhesus monkeys, the vast majority of animals perform stereotyped rocking movements while crouching or sitting, often while they clasp themselves and suck their toes or thumbs. Once a monkey has adopted a particular pattern, it tends to persist in it with little variation. In chimpanzees we see a much wider range of individual differences in the way stereotyped movements are performed. A single chimpanzee may shift within the same brief period among several postures, all highly stereotyped and idiosyncratic. It may sway from side-to-side while standing erect, rock back-and-forth while seated, or roll from side to side while lying on its back. In keeping with this trend, stereotyped activities — especially the hand movements — of profoundly retarded humans are often far more complex than those displayed by any chimpanzee.

There are, of course, a host of other simple and apparently point-less motor activities that conform to the same trend. For example, consider the following behaviors, which set the chimpanzee apart from the monkey and show its affinity to man: nose-picking, pinching pimples or removing scabs, bubbling saliva, hand-clapping. Postures and modes of locomotion are similarly varied: chimpanzees may walk on all fours or on two feet; they may progress by twirling like a bal-lerina, by a series of somersaults, by using their arms as though they were crutches, or by sliding across the floor on their bellies. There are also many simple activities involving objects that are commonplace among chimpanzees and rare in monkeys: inserting twigs or straws into various body openings; placing saliva on a post and licking it off as it runs down; playing with shadows and light beams; persistent carrying in hand, mouth, or groin small objects such as peach pits, stones, bottle caps, birds, and frogs. These simpler activities with ob-jects can become integrated into more complex patterns. Sticks are used to poke, pry, push, and rake; to strike with and to throw.

All these observations suggest that the number and variety of dis-crete motor acts, and the tendency to combine such acts spontane-ously into new and more complex patterns, increases progressively from monkey to man. One of the pathways toward human behavior thus seems to be a "loosening" of motor patterns, and we can already see the process at work in the great apes. That a similar change has occurred in the internal mechanisms that govern behavior seems most likely. We might refer again to the evidence on the relation between hormones and behavior in primates, and particularly in man. In my own work with young chimpanzees I have found it necessary to speak in terms of a generalized motivational state, because more specific motives—fear, aggression, hunger, sex—do not seem to be able to provide a satisfactory account of their behavior.

Human Development in Comparative Perspective

It is not my aim, however, to convince you that the chimpanzee is more like man than is the rhesus monkey, for on that score I am sure that no one requires persuasion. Instead, I have hoped to show that human development fits within the basic primate pattern, but that because of the evolutionary trend we have considered, the human infant brings into the world a different set of behavioral potentialities and has a different set of requirements for normal psychological growth than does any monkey or ape.

With so much excellent research being done on the early behavior of human beings, it would be presumptuous of me to try to offer any concrete suggestions as to what these requirements might be. In keeping with the comparative spirit of this inquiry, however, an attempt to characterize the special features of human development will not be out of place:

1. As the result of the general neotenous trend in primate evolution, the human infant's needs for social stimulation are less specific than those of the nonhuman primates. The range of equivalent stimuli is wider, development is less dependent upon the particular features of stimulation, and the reactions to specific forms of stimulus deprivation are more variable and diffuse. Thus, it seems likely that the rhesus monkey's self-rocking is a reaction to deprivation of a specific form of stimulation ordinarily provided by the mother. We have good reason to believe that this simple explanation will not apply to the development of self-rocking in humans. Although some form of stimulus deprivation may well be a common element in the etiology of these behaviors in all primates, it is likely that at the human level a wider range of specific causes must be considered.

2. Once a developmental sequence has been set in motion, the human infant will show a greater tendency to elaborate on it than will the monkey or the chimpanzee. The progressive enrichment in stereotyped movements from monkey to man provides one illustration of this tendency, but many other examples could be given. We can see the same process at work in sound production — infant monkeys show little, if any, "spontaneous" sound production; chimpanzees "invent" lip noises, clicking sounds, and the like; but only the human infant truly babbles. And we can see it in the progressive enrichment and complication of the patterns of playful exploitation of objects. (It could be argued that this same trend leads to the progressive development of such characteristics as openness and duality of patterning,

which the linguist Charles F. Hockett has described as design features of human language.[7])

3. Because of the retardation of growth rates and the "loosening" of behavioral organization, developmental stages are less sharply delimited in humans than in other primates. Sensitive periods in development are more difficult to establish, there is less likelihood that the withholding of any specific experience will result in developmental arrest, and there is a much stronger tendency for behavior to reflect a blending or intermingling of different developmental stages, different response patterns, and different motivational systems.

4. These evolutionary changes have meant that the structure and integration of human behavior have become heavily dependent upon environmental support and, at the same time, less dependent upon specific forms of experience. Of all the primates, man has gone farthest in an evolutionary venture in which the reliability and efficiency of instinctive patterns have been sacrificed to achieve the behavioral plasticity and the liberation of psychic energies that are so much a part of the human condition.

The Crucial Nature of Early Experience

LEON J. YARROW

Studies of infrahuman primates have been concerned with a wide range of problems: with sensory and social deprivation, with interruption in mothering experiences, with adaptation to novelty and strangeness, and with various kinds of stress and trauma. All of these are parts of a larger issue, one of the central theoretical issues of developmental research — the significance of early experiences. In con-

LEON J. YARROW Social and Behavioral Sciences Branch, National Institute of Child Health and Human Development, National Institutes of Health, Bethesda, Md.

sidering the contribution of research on infrahuman primates to understanding the role of early experiences in human development and behavior, it seems essential to try to clarify the meaning and to explore some of the assumptions underlying the concept of the crucial nature of early experiences. Four major interrelated issues can be distinguished:

1   The definition and measurement of the sensitivities of the very young organism. These include problems of the changing sensitivities and vulnerabilities of the organism at different developmental points, issues essentially dealing with the critical period hypothesis.
2   The conceptualization and specification of the significant variables of the early environment.
3   The interactions between individual characteristics and sensitivities and environmental conditions, i.e., problems of direction of effects.
4   The specification and measurement of the dependent variables, with particular reference to the "end points," or the time at which the "effects" are measured.

In analyzing these issues, I would like to point up their implications for broad research strategies and designs, as well as for the selection and measurement of the independent and dependent variables. Such analysis should help clarify both the contributions and the limitations of research on infrahuman primates for problems of human development.

ORGANISMIC SENSITIVITIES

Implicit in the concept that early experiences are crucial for later development are a number of assumptions about the characteristics of the organism. A basic assumption is that the young organism is extremely sensitive during infancy and early childhood, perhaps more sensitive than at any other developmental period. This concept of a special sensitivity during the earliest period of life, which is implicit in several theoretical systems, has many ramifications. It implies that the young organism is highly receptive, is highly modifiable, and is extremely vulnerable to noxious stimuli. Receptivity refers essentially to the characteristics of the sensory system. High receptivity implies a low threshold of responsiveness to stimuli in general, or to certain classes of stimuli. Modifiability refers mainly to the characteristics of the nervous system and the receptors. High modifiability implies that the learning that occurs and the response patterns established during the earliest period of life show the greatest strength, and are least susceptible to modification. At the organic level, this concept suggests relatively irreversible changes in the nervous system.

The concept of vulnerability includes both heightened sensitivity to noxious stimuli and a high degree of modifiability, with the consequence that the young organism is easily damaged. Presumably the same mechanisms mediate high receptivity and high vulnerability. They are differentiated on the stimulus side simply in terms of the positive or negative character of the stimuli. The basic structural or physiological changes that occur will have long-term effects, to the extent that these changes directly limit or monitor simple responses or complex patterns of behavior that occur later.

The concept of a generalized sensitivity of the immature organism has been modified and refined, to some extent, by the critical-period hypothesis, which postulates differential sensitivities at different developmental periods. Although the concept of developmental differences in capacities or response capabilities has always been a central one in developmental research, only recently have the full implications of the corollary concept of changing developmental sensitivities begun to be recognized. One important implication of this concept is that the crucial variables of maternal care may change significantly from one developmental period to another during infancy, and that the time intervals during which specific variables are prepotent may be very short.[4,5,11,16] Similarly, with regard to inanimate stimulation, very simple visual stimuli may be adequate energizers of the visual system during the first weeks of life, whereas stimuli of the same level of complexity may be wholly inadequate just a few weeks later. In effect, patterns of maternal care or simple visual stimuli that are appropriate for the immature three-week-old organism may constitute maternal or visual deprivation at three months.

To be able to define precisely the levels of intensity and the degrees of complexity of stimuli that are appropriate at different developmental periods, we need much more differentiated norms of human and animal infant capacities during the earliest weeks and months of life than are now available. We know that some of the old norms, such as those on capacities for visual discrimination, have proved to be essentially incorrect,[3] probably because our techniques of measurement have not been sufficiently sensitive. With new methodology, particularly techniques of measuring fairly subtle autonomic changes, we should be able to map, with a high degree of precision, the infant's capacity for responding to and discriminating stimuli of different modalities and of varying degrees of complexity. Human and animal infants probably differ in specific sensitivities and vulnerabilities at given developmental points. There may, however, be a basic similarity in the sequential progression of dominant sensitivities. For example, the tactile mode may pre-empt the visual during the earliest period of development.

CONCEPTUALIZING AND ANALYZING THE ENVIRONMENT

One of the most significant problems in studying the effects of early experiences is that of conceptualizing and measuring the dimensions of the early environment. A great deal of our knowledge about early environmental influences on development has come from studies of gross deprivation or severe trauma. Much less frequently has the research dealt with experiential variations within the normal range. Only rarely, and most recently, have we given any attention to enriching or facilitating experiences. We have reached a level of theoretical and methodological sophistication at which we can begin to differentiate more finely a wider range of environmental influences.

As a result of the long period of the human infant's dependency, early experience has almost been equated with early maternal care. Until very recently, much of the research on maternal care has focused on complex affectional interactions, on intervening variables, such as the personal characteristics and attitudes of the mother, or on a special class of maternal behaviors, e.g., those centering around the gratification and channeling of the basic physiological needs of the infant as expressed in the interactions associated with feeding, weaning, and toilet training.

This preoccupation with complex variables, which have been difficult to identify and define with any degree of precision, has deflected attention from some of the more basic variables of stimulation and the conditions under which various kinds of stimulation are provided. These variables may, in different combinations and patterns, be the fundamental elements of more complex affective and affectional behavior patterns.

It seems more meaningful to conceptualize maternal personality characteristics and attitudes as determinants of maternal *behavior* than as primary antecedent variables. It is psychologically more meaningful, as well as methodologically cleaner, to study the impact on the child of the actual behavior of the mother rather than to study the effects of intervening variables, such as attitudes. The research on animals, and particularly on nonhuman primates, has alerted us to some of these more fundamental parameters of early experience, and has given ample demonstration of the fruitfulness of this approach.[7,8]

In our studies of early maternal care,[13,15,16] we have attempted to order maternal behavior from a conceptual framework in terms of several kinds of categories that can be linked to observable behavior: 1) amount and varieties of stimulation; 2) activities of the mother concerned with tension reduction; 3) the learning conditions under which these kinds of stimuli are provided. Within each of these broad categories, the functional properties of the environment can be systematically organized for study. In regard to stimulation, several classes of stimuli can be distinguished: stimuli that elicit or evoke responses; stimuli that facilitate the expression of developmentally emergent behaviors; stimuli that support or maintain ongoing behavior patterns. With regard to learning conditions, the environment can be analyzed in terms of schedules of gratification and frustration, and the contingencies under which various kinds of stimulation are provided. This type of conceptualization appears to be useful for studying many kinds of environmental conditions, dyadic interactions—such as early mother-infant relationships—as well as more complex environments, such as group settings for preschool children.

INTERACTIONS BETWEEN ENVIRONMENTAL
STIMULI AND ORGANISMIC CHARACTERISTICS

The study of environmental influences has grown out of the tradition of objective definition of stimuli independent of the organism. In the simple antecedent-consequent framework, stimuli whose properties are defined independently of the organism are seen as acting *upon* an organism. From this orientation, the infant or child is essentially a passive recipient of stimuli; his behavior is controlled and molded by the environment. This unidirectional model should be replaced by an interactional one that posits a reciprocal interplay between the environment, particularly the human environment, and the child. This model proposes that the effective environment be defined in relation to the organism's characteristics, capacities, and sensitivities. Not only does the child *respond* selectively to stimuli in terms of his idiosyncratic and developmental characteristics; he *elicits* responses from other people. In effect, the infant or young child determines his own environment to some extent.[1,16] This model has significant implications for research on early experiences. It emphasizes that the measurement of a given experience at any point in time must be related to the characteristics of the organism. It also emphasizes the dynamic changing character of the environment throughout the developmental cycle.

THE DEPENDENT VARIABLES:
IMMEDIATE AND LONG-TERM EFFECTS

In regard to the dependent variables, the concept that early experiences are crucial implies that changes in the organism occur not only immediately after an event, but also that there are effects on behavior which become evident at later points in development. The immediate effects of severe trauma or deprivation are usually quite evident. It is much more difficult to establish direct relationships between a given set of experiences and later behavior patterns. Behavior patterns and response predispositions found at later developmental periods are rarely so similar to the early patterns that they can be unequivocally related to early experience. A basic and difficult problem is to determine the extent to which earlier behavior patterns are precursors of later ones. The establishment of such relationships is especially complex because later behavior patterns, although they may be genotypically related, are likely to be phenotypically dissimilar in organisms at different levels of maturity.[6,9,10,14,17]

RESEARCH STRATEGIES: EXPERIMENTAL AND NATURALISTIC APPROACHES

One of the presumed advantages of research with nonhuman primates is that much greater experimental manipulation is possible than with humans. Such manipulation can be extremely valuable in identifying significant variables. However, for many reasons, experimental investigation of a limited number of variables under controlled conditions cannot be a satisfactory substitute for studies under natural conditions. Moreover, there are many life settings that, in effect, are natural experiments. With regard to research strategy, my own predilection is to utilize such natural situations to investigate some of the basic issues of early influences on human development. Among the kinds of natural experimental situations that highlight important variables of early experience are the following:

1　Child-care institutions which differ in basic child-rearing philosophies. There are great variations among these institutions in caretaker ratios and in various characteristics of the physical-sensory environment, such as amount, variety, and complexity of visual and auditory stimulation. Even though past studies of these settings[2,12] have been theoretically unsophisticated and have had serious methodological shortcomings, they have produced some significant findings. With sharper conceptualizations and more refined observational techniques, more precise data on the effects of very early sensory and social deprivation in human infants can be obtained. Moreover, such settings also lend themselves to simple enrichment studies involving experimental intervention, e.g., programing specific kinds of sensory input, training caretakers to give measured degrees of language or social stimulation, or to respond contingently to specific aspects of the infant's behavior.

2　Several kinds of separation situations that occur with moderately great frequency in the life of young children allow exploration of important aspects of early experiences. Among the many kinds of situations in which variables such as loss of a significant relationship figure, broad environmental changes, or novelty, can be teased out and studied independently or in interaction are the following. A) Situations in which the mother leaves the infant temporarily in familiar surroundings, as distinguished from temporary separation associated with gross environmental change. B) Situations in which the infant is temporarily moved to another home with an attentive caretaker, as distinguished from separation followed by gross deprivation of maternal care, as in institutionalization. C) Separation experiences associated with adoptive placement involving a change in mother figure.

3   Foster-home placement offers unique opportunities for studying child effects on maternal behavior. In this situation, in which there are usually several infants being cared for simultaneously by one mother, there are many possibilities for studying the extent to which maternal behavior is influenced by such characteristics of the child as activity level, social responsiveness, frustration tolerance.[16]

The use of natural situations in research has inherent difficulties because of the many variables in complex and uncontrolled interactions, only some of which we are aware of and can specify. To use natural situations effectively, it is necessary that we conceptualize as clearly as possible the theoretical issues, and identify clearly the variables in the situation relevant to the theoretical issues being studied.

Our longitudinal studies of adopted children illustrate the kinds of natural variations in a complex life situation that can be used to examine some important issues in early experiences. This investigation focused on separation with a change in mother figure, in which there was no gross antecedent or subsequent deprivation. The core of the concept of separation involves a disruption in a relationship, but in much theoretical writing and research the effects of separation have not been distinguished from concomitant trauma and subsequent deprivation. In our studies, the primary independent variables were the age of separation and the character of the relationship with the mother prior and subsequent to separation. A major question formulated within the framework of the critical period hypothesis was: Do the effects of a break in relationship with a mother figure differ, depending on the developmental point at which it occurs?

Adoptive placement offered a natural experimental situation. Infants were obtained from several social agencies that differed in their policies regarding age of placement. In this way, we secured a sample of children, separated at different developmental points during the first year, that was free from systematic biases related to age of placement. That is, the time of placement for adoption was unrelated to any characteristics of the children. The comparison group consisted of infants who left their natural mothers at five to ten days of age and went into adoptive homes directly from the hospital. The infants were studied immediately after the break with the first mother figure, and at several later points throughout the first five years. In the study of the immediate reactions to separation, the design was comparable to a pre-post experimental design. Data were obtained on infants in the foster homes immediately preceding separation, and comparable data to measure change and adaptation were obtained two, four, and six weeks later. This design offered some measure of control over the known variability of infant behavior by providing a baseline for evaluation of behavioral changes following separation. In a sense, each infant functioned as his own control.

The effects of the separation experience were analyzed in terms of the following kinds of behavioral changes: disturbances in social behavior; affective disturbances; loss in developmental functions; disturbances in adjustment to routines; and disturbances in physiological functions.

The findings point up some of the limitations of a simple critical-period hypothesis. With regard to statistically significant differences in intensity of disturbance and number of children affected, there appear to be two critical age points: three months and six months. In regard to immediate effects there are significant differences between the infants separated before three months of age and infants placed between three and twelve months. After three months a greater number of children show a significantly greater degree of disturbance. With increasing age, there is increasing severity of disturbance, and an increasing number of areas of functioning are involved. However, comparisons of adjacent age groups between three and six months show no statistically significant differences.

The kinds of immediate temporary disturbances shown by the three- to six-month-old infants might most parsimoniously be interpreted as reactions to environmental change — changes in specific qualities of tactile, kinesthetic, visual and auditory stimulation, as well as changes in response contingencies in the new environment. The types of behavior disturbances found after six months of age might be interpreted as reactions to the loss of a significant person.

With regard to the long-term effects of separation, an interpretation of these data in terms of the critical-period concept is even more complicated. By five years of age, there are no significant differences in adaptation between the children who had been separated before three months and those separated between three and six months. Six months is the critical point in terms of statistically significant differences.

If one traces the longitudinal course of development of these children in detail, it is even more difficult to make any simple generalizations about the effects of a single traumatic experience during infancy. The five-year-old children who are functioning least well tend to have histories characterized by recurrent traumatic experiences. In some cases, one could interpret these later environmental traumas as being at least partly determined by the child. For example, the infants who were initially most disturbed by separation precipitated tensions in the mother-child relationship that set up a circular process of disturbed interaction that continued throughout early childhood. Certainly this is one way in which early disruptive experiences may be associated with long-term effects.

These data emphasize the extent to which conclusions about the effects of early experiences are dependent on the behavioral criteria used to define the outcome variables, as well as the point in time at which outcomes are measured. There appears to be some support for the notion of a critical period for separation, if one amends the concept somewhat. That is, there is a critical developmental point, after which a break in relationship may have significant long-term consequences. That there are significant differences between infants separated before three months and those separated after three months might have been interpreted, in a cross-sectional study, as evidence that three months is a critical point. From a longitudinal perspective, there is much less clarity about outcomes.

The need for refinement and elaboration of the general thesis regarding the crucial nature of early experiences for later development is evident. Any given experience cannot simply be considered traumatic or beneficent. The same kinds of experiences or traumatic events may have differing behavioral outcomes for different developmental periods. A specific kind of experience may be associated with the development of behavior patterns and behavioral predispositions that are adequate for the adaptive requirements of one developmental stage, but maladaptive for the demands of another. Not only may the timing of the experience significantly modify its effects; conclusions about effects may differ, depending on the developmental point at which they are measured.

From a longitudinal orientation, another clear implication of these data is that we cannot simply isolate a single experience at one point in time. We must consider subsequent events, and the extent to which they reinforce the kinds of response patterns elicited by the earlier experiences. Moreover, from an interactional or transactional viewpoint we might hypothesize that intervening experiences are determined, at least partly, by the organism; that there can be self-perpetuating response patterns.

The question of whether early experiences are significant is clearly too simple a formulation. Rather, we must ask more complex and differentiated questions. For example, what are the effects of specific kinds of experiences occurring at given developmental periods on specific aspects of behavior at other developmental points?

THE RELEVANCE OF INFRAHUMAN INVESTIGA-
TIONS TO THE STUDY OF HUMAN DEVELOPMENT

It is clear that the studies of infrahuman organisms have made many significant contributions to understanding human development. They have pointed up specific hypotheses about the important dimensions of early experience, such as the role of tactile or oral stimulation. They have suggested larger integrative concepts, such as the critical-period hypothesis. It is important to distinguish the heuristic contributions of this body of research for human investigations, that is, its value in stimulating hypotheses and theories, and in highlighting certain variables of early experience from the substantive findings. It is obvious that there are difficulties in simple extrapolation of findings to organisms of widely differing levels of complexity, as evidenced by attempts at a simple transfer of the imprinting notion across species and levels.

The studies of social isolation in primates have shown that discrete, measurable aspects of sensory deprivation can be identified as antecedents of behavior patterns which in humans have been labeled "emotional" disturbances. Clinical studies have usually attributed these kinds of disturbances to gross affective or affectional deviations in the mother or caretaker. The findings that deprivation of tactile or kinesthetic stimulation during early infancy is associated with the development of similar aberrant behavior patterns in nonhuman as well as human primates suggest that the basic mechanisms underlying these developments may be similar across species.

There are many pitfalls in cross-species generalizations. There may be important interspecies differences in factors that influence the reversibility of behavior disturbances. We do not know whether the environmental or physiological-organic factors that sustain given behavior patterns are similar across species.

Basic differences in levels of organization of various primate organisms may be important. As Dr. Mason has suggested, the human infant differs from the nonhuman primate in the repertoire of responses available during the early months of life and in basic behavioral flexibility. Thus, there may be significant differences in fixity of response patterns associated with early experiences, with differing implications for long-term effects.

The values and limitations of experimental studies with animals under closely controlled conditions should be weighed against the values and limitations of investigations with humans in naturalistic settings. Some kinds of problems clearly lend themselves to experimental manipulation of a limited number of variables; for other kinds of problems, such an approach can yield only suggestive hypotheses that must be tested in more complex settings. There are obvious limitations in the extent to which relationships established in a controlled "pure situation" can be generalized to the complex naturalistic setting. The action of a single variable in a hypothetical vacuum may be very different from the action of this same variable in a network of other variables. In environments in which there are many variables in complex interaction, as in most human environments, the significance of any given variable or limited set of variables may be radically altered by the larger context. Such considerations emphasize the need for a high level of theoretical sophistication in the selection of variables and research designs. As the behavioral sciences become more mature, I think we will have to give up the inordinate value placed on experimental manipulation of a few simple variables, and give increasing attention to the development of research designs for controlled analyses of complex environments.

The Social Environment of Infant Macaques

PETER MARLER
and
ANDREW GORDON

It is important that the views of field-oriented biologists should be represented among the several approaches to behavioral development in nonhuman primates. Dr. Mason presents an unusual combination of psychological and biological attitudes, and zoologists have much to gain from attending to the new developments in primate biology that he has summarized. It is, then, from a zoological viewpoint that

PETER MARLER The Rockefeller University and The New York Zoological Society, New York, N.Y.
ANDREW GORDON Department of Social Psychology, Columbia University, New York, N.Y. Present address: Department of Sociology, Northwestern University, Evanston, Illinois

we respond, and there are three issues on which we would like to comment: one is a central theme in his paper, the other two he touches on only obliquely.

That one can explain much of the developing series of behavioral interactions between infant chimpanzee or macaque and its mother by postulating a relatively simple motivational system is attractive and thought-provoking. Actions such as clinging, suckling, and grooming are regarded as arousal-reducing. Another set, which becomes predominant later in infant life, serves to increase arousal. Such activities as play and the whole gamut of outgoing, exploratory activities are viewed in these terms. At least two zoologists are convinced of the value of this kind of approach. T. C. Schneirla[31,41,42] has been pressing for some years for support of a biphasic model of motivation, as he calls it, which seeks to explain many interactions between organisms and their environment, physical or social, in terms of approach or withdrawal contingencies. The central idea is that weak external stimulation tends to elicit approach, while strong external stimulation elicits withdrawal. Here, as in Mason's model, there is an assumption that the norm to which the animal tends to gravitate is an intermediate level of arousal. In another series of papers concerned with the behavior of both birds and monkeys, R. J. Andrew[1,2] has advanced a somewhat similar notion, embodied in his concept of stimulus contrast.

The idea of an optimal intermediate level of intermediate arousal is one which others have felt the need to postulate. D. E. Berlyne[3] developed such a notion to explain the varying stimulus effects on exploratory behavior and play. In his book *Conflict, Arousal, and Curiosity* he was even able to find support for the animal's "quest for intermediate arousal potential," as he puts it, in the work of Wundt,[50] from whom he reproduces a curve relating the pleasantness of a stimulus as a function of its intensity, which is also maximal at intermediate values (see Berlyne's Figure 1, page 186. Sensory physiologists have found parallels in the relationship between the concentration of solutions of various substances and the readiness of animals to drink them.[43] There are so many unrelated examples of such nonmonotonic relationships,[24,34] even with rather limited ranges of the independent variable (e.g., stimulus intensity), that one wonders if the far more commonly reported linear relationship would persist if a wider range of stimuli were used.

It seems clear, then, that the idea of an unspecific arousal system as a basic force for molding development of behavior in primates and other animals is a significant and valuable one. One of its attractions is that it counters the tendency among ethologists and even some comparative psychologists to postulate a plethora of separate drives, each motivating a separate class of activities. Until simpler interpretations are found wanting, such complex models should, perhaps, be kept in abeyance. At the same time — and now we come to the point of this comment — we wonder whether a model such as this can really explain effectively all of the behavior patterns that are observed in a chimpanzee or macaque infant. Suppose that it were possible to raise a chimpanzee in a situation that permitted its general level of arousal to be kept at the optimum, while at the same time avoiding presentation of any stimulus situations for, say, clinging behavior. The arousal hypothesis, in its simplest form, would seem to predict that such an animal should be content never to cling. Care would be taken never to allow it to become aroused, so the arousal-reducing properties of clinging behavior would not be called for. If this experiment could be done, we suspect that such an animal would still be motivated to cling.

Similarly, with the other major classes of activity, one may suspect that a complete explanation requires not only the postulation of the consequences of these activities for general arousal, but also that of some more-or-less specific pre-disposing states or appetites. This was one of the central ideas in Konrad Lorenz's hypothesis about behavior motivation. He felt that the endogenous springs for certain types of behavior were so fundamental that it was necessary to invoke what he called some "action-specific potential" that contributed to the waxing and waning of the animal's tendencies to perform certain classes of activity.[30] Is a complete account of behavioral development possible without the postulation of some mechanism such as this?

There are many forms such action-specific potential could take. A periodic compulsion might arise to engage in certain types of motor activity. Another possibility is change in some sensory mechanism, periodically sensitizing the animal to certain types of external stimuli. In the cases that Dr. Mason has been discussing, the second possibility seems more likely. He has emphasized the great importance, to the primate infant, of physical contact. Some of the behavioral stereotypes of an infant reared in isolation are plausibly explained as consequences of deprivation from such contact stimulation and efforts to substitute for it in other ways.

But does the explanation of clinging behavior in terms of arousal help in understanding the genesis of the initial appetite for the class of stimuli of which the animal has been deprived? To be sure, the requirements in this case are not very specific, but at least it is a deficit of tactile stimulation, rather than, say, auditory or visual stimulation, which generates the appetite. In nature there are many alternative motor patterns used in contact between mother and infant, and although occurrence of some of these alternatives can no doubt be understood as a function of modulation by different, current, external, stimulus situations such as those which the mother presents to the infant, we may question whether this could explain all of the behavioral patterning that we see. One wonders whether, in the growing infant, there may not be some more specific requirements. The many different patterns of activity obviously do not appear randomly. While some order is surely imposed by stimulus situations confronting the animal, it seems likely that some endogenous constraints are also involved. Of course, Dr. Mason acknowledges the possibility that the arousal hypothesis may not be a complete one. Our question, then, is as follows. If he were pressed to make the explanation still more complete, would he feel any necessity to postulate more specific, endogenously generated appetites for certain kinds of activity or stimulation, or can the arousal hypothesis be modified to explain the nature of the initial predispositions or appetites as well?

This leads to another comment about the special kind of environment that confronts an infant primate, a subject on which it may be appropriate to expand a little further. As Dr. Mason mentioned, primates are unusual mammals in that virtually none provides a nest for the young.[7] Thus, from the moment of birth there is necessarily a very intimate physical relationship between infant and mother, further exaggerated by the early developmental stage at which primates are born and their slow maturation. In a number of species the infant is a focus of attention not only for the mother but for all other members of the troop, males as well as females. The growing infant has many social privileges, permitting free contact with other members of the troop. This occurs even in societies which are strongly dominance-oriented, such as those of macaques and baboons. Furthermore, there is good evidence that the growing infant of several species is buffered from more violent social interactions by direct intervention of the mother, and that it gains a great variety of social experiences long before it is called upon to engage in aggressive encounters, to participate in generating peaceful sequences of grooming and other activities, and in reproduction. The sharing of infant care among members of the troop must surely contribute to the success and subtlety of the adjustments that the growing primate can reach with its social environment.[6,9,16-19,36]

We should like to review two lines of evidence hinting at the sort of consequences that such social interplay can have, one concerned with dominance behavior, the other with the development of feeding habits. In particular, they reflect the durability of the bond between the mother and her offspring, which continues into reproductive age, and involves both male and female young. This bond seems to affect the maturing infants in many different ways.

DOMINANCE BEHAVIOR

It is well known from the work of Koford[25] and Sade[37,39] on the rhesus monkeys on Cayo Santiago, and from studies of the Japanese macaques,[44,51] that kinship has a strong influence on the dominance status that young animals achieve as they become adults. Even in troops which have been studied in artificial feeding situations, dominance bouts consume but a fraction of the animals' time. One plausible reason that dominance relationships need not be continually ratified is that the hierarchy, which for males is linear and fairly stable,[21] is firmly established in early aggressive encounters. Over the years, observers of many macaque troops have seen that, although there is a great deal of playful and not-so-playful aggression between young monkeys, the stability of the relationships and the age levels at which they arise cannot easily be explained by these juvenile bouts. Clearly, monkeys know where they stand relative to all others in the troop, without actively challenging each individual. Juvenile behavior is always circumspect around dominant animals. A youngster seizing food in the presence of an unnoticed superior is soundly punished, but such a *faux pas* is rare indeed.

For 15 years Japanese scientists have been studying such behavior in several troops of *Macaca fuscata* at feeding stations in the animals' own habitat. Fully aware of the limitations of such field studies, and hesitant to leap to hasty conclusions about the interpretation of some of this work, we remain intrigued and excited by much of the data. Many of the findings concerning the social influences impinging on growing macaques, some of them obtainable only after reliable individual identification, are pertinent to any discussion of behavioral development in primates.

When traveling, macaque troops have a concentric organization. Females of all ages, infants, and the most dominant males are in the center; subdominant males are outside this group; four- and five-year-old juvenile males are around the periphery.[49] Subdominant males sometimes enter the troop center; juvenile males rarely do. The subgroups formed when the troop stops to rest or eat are nearly always matrilineal family groups, usually consisting of adult females who are sisters, and their children — infants, and subadult males and females.[37] Macaques are promiscuous, and although some consort pairs last more than a week, it is almost impossible to determine paternity.

Grooming, too, is primarily a family activity. In careful investigations of rhesus macaques on Cayo Santiago,[37] Donald Sade found that 62 per cent of all observed grooming behavior was intrafamily during the nonbreeding season, compared to a 15 per cent chance expectancy. (That is, assuming an equal probability that any monkey will groom any other, 15 per cent of such pairs would be intrafamily.) During the breeding season, 64 per cent of all observed grooming was still intrafamily, despite the formation of many interfamilial consort pairs.

Even sexual behavior does not seem to intrude strikingly on these family bonds.

The clear interaction patterns based on blood-relation are not uniquely between the mother and her fragile, dependent infant. The mother not only grooms her infant and yearling offspring, but also actively grooms her other children. If a mother has died, juvenile and subadult grooming normally shifts within the family, to an older or younger sibling or to an aunt. These new grooming partners do not merely assume token responsibility for the young ones. Females have been known to devote as much time and energy to an orphaned niece or nephew as they do to their own infant, and to become the major grooming choices of older nephews and nieces.

The family relationship appears to be a source of support and comfort from which the monkeys emerge into other relationships, extending into adulthood.[13] The sibling relation is a nuclear one; the less a macaque interacts with its mother, the more it interacts with those who most frequently interact with its mother — its relatives. We want to stress that these kinship effects are long-lasting.

Yamada[51] fed one troop of *Macaca fuscata* (called the Minoo-B troop) for several months by placing several piles of wheat around their feeding ground. The macaques seldom ate alone. Some piles remained untouched while the monkeys crowded around the others. Feeding groups were nearly always family units. Most frequently mother and child ate together. (The older the child, the less true this becomes; the older children co-feed with their brothers, sisters, aunts, and grandmothers.) It was revealing to see the ratio of frequencies of eating with one's own family versus eating with members of other families. For every animal this quotient exceeded 1.00, and, in general, the more dominant the animal the more exclusively he fed with his family. Age is a confounding variable here, for the older macaques are more exclusive; infants sometimes eat with other families. A relationship between exclusivity and dominance held for nearly every pair of animals: if A is dominant to B he also eats with his family more than does B. By contrast, the exclusivity of grooming behavior is reversed with respect to age, primarily because infants seldom groom outside the family, whereas consorting estrous females often do.

It is possible to rank animals by improvising one-to-one confrontations over some palatable food, such as a sweet potato, and recording which animal picks it up.[48] The outcome of aggressive encounters is often also used as a criterion for dominance status. Even though this usually ranks animals in the same order as priority at food sites (e.g., Sade,[39] Lindburg,[29]) there are sometimes discrepancies, and it is probably desirable to distinguish between the two hierarchies. Sade points out that in the feeding situation the "dominant" monkey is often interrupted by other activity and leaves before seizing the food, whereupon the subordinate monkey will grab it. He prefers to restrict the term "dominance" to relationships based on aggressive encounters and that is his usage when quoted in this review. When derived in this way, the dominance relationships of Japanese macaques are stable and clear-cut early in the life of an individual.

However, Kawai[20] pointed out that several important social variables are being ignored when macaques are tested in isolated pairs. Food is normally available to several animals at once. By tossing sweet potatoes into clusters of macaques, he found consistent reversals of many of the paired dominance patterns. Food tossed between any two macaques while the mother of the generally subordinate monkey was present, even if at some distance, was often seized by the subordinate. This would only occur when the mother was dominant to the monkey vying with her offspring for the tidbit. Sometimes the mere presence of the mother was sufficiently intimidating, and sometimes there was more direct intervention. In the latter cases, for instance, one monkey might snatch and begin to eat the food, only to throw it down and retreat as the mother of the subordinate monkey threatened. The offspring of the threatening mother would then pick up the food and eat it. The influence of one animal in enabling another to take food in the presence of a third does not affect only infants. Grown males, five and six years old, benefit from such parental intervention.

Macaques do not gain dominance status only from their mothers, although the hierarchy is more subject to maternal influences than any other, as Hinde and Spencer-Booth[10] found with captive rhesus. Some sisters often raise the dominance position of their younger siblings, but brothers were seldom observed to intervene in this way.[21]

In another variant of the feeding test, Kawai[21] placed loose wheat on a box in the middle of the feeding ground, in full view of the whole troop, and tabulated the feeding order at the box. Whenever the troop came in to feed, the alpha male always climbed on the box and ate first. No other macaques came near the box while he ate, except the most dominant female. Any other approaching monkey was threatened or attacked. The dominant female was equally intolerant of any other animal when she was feeding. The second- and third-ranking males would often approach the box when she was eating, but would scurry away if her screaming and gesticulating brought the alpha male running. If the alpha male wasn't nearby, or if the female's contortions didn't arouse him, the next two ranking males could chase her away. When the dominant males and the female had finished, the other troop members would come to feed, in a stable order. The infants freely approached the box and, in the presence of any macaques except the alpha male and female, ate the wheat strewn on the ground.

In general, the older a macaque the higher his rank. Juvenile males rank lower than would be expected; this seems to occur because these males enter the central section of the troop only rarely and with great trepidation, which deprives them of much opportunity to exploit the presence of their mothers and other kin in dominance encounters. When one examines macaques of the same age, a fascinating further finding emerges. Sade[38] and Kawai,[20] observing troops of *M. mulatta* and *M. fuscata*, respectively, found that age mates occupy a linear arrangement that parallels that of their mothers.

Koford[25] noted some exceptions to the general rule that four- or five-year-old rhesus macaques leave the central region of the tribe for the periphery. In three of six bands he observed in detail on Cayo Santiago, at least one subadult male remained in the troop center throughout his juvenile and subadult life. Each of these privileged exceptions was the child of a very dominant female.

Kawamura[23] also studied the Minoo-B group of Japanese macaques.

The only adults were females. Two adult males from a neighboring troop occasionally wandered in and out, but the only permanent males were juveniles and infants. (Male macaques of all ranks commonly wander from troop to troop, mostly during the mating season.[29] Koford[26] notes that this must greatly increase genetic cross-fertilization between troops.) The troop has a clearly superior alpha female. Further, the adult females arrange themselves into a stable hierarchy, and, without exception, the children of each adult female succeed her directly in the dominance pattern. That is, the alpha female's children all feed before the second-ranked adult female, who is followed directly by her children, and so on. These ranks are retained in the absence of any older relatives on whom the younger animals can depend. Within each family there is predictable shuffling of the hierarchy at broadly specifiable times: the youngest daughter *over four years old* ranks next to her mother; she is followed by the next youngest daughter over four; and so on. All the young males who remain in the troop are ranked on the lowest rungs of the intra-family pattern, although they, too, precede all members of the next family. The high rank of the youngest adult daughter is believed by some[23] to follow from the fact that she was most recently dependent on the mother, gaining her superior position from the after-effects of this dependence. Kawamura thinks that this would be the predominant troop pattern if it were not for the overriding influence of the dominant males.

Sade[38] also observed that, among rhesus macaques at Cayo Santiago, females have been elevated above their older sisters within the family unit by the time they are four years old. He finds Kawamura's "most-recently-dependent" explanation untenable, because in one of three genealogies recorded in detail, while a mother had died and left two young females, the elder nevertheless shifted predictably upwards when she turned four, and one year later her younger sister was elevated above her. The sisters, then, were deprived of their mother's grooming attention at precisely the same time and yet their rank had shifted as expected. Sade speculates that physiological changes at puberty, rather than dependent dominance, may be responsible.

The family organization may have direct implications for reproductive behavior in adulthood. Sade made a longitudinal study[38] of seven rhesus macaques on Cayo Santiago from infancy to maturity, and his data showed that the relative ranking of pre-adult age-mates parallels the ranking of their mothers among the adults at every age level, as we noted earlier. At maturity, all males and females rank just below their mothers in the dominance hierarchy. Sade finds a positive correlation between rank and copulatory activity, which has been reported by others in macaques and baboons. The higher the rank of the female the more frequently she copulates with the dominant males. While some have assumed that dominance rank is determined by the frequency of copulation, Sade's work seems to imply that the ranking of females is genealogically determined, and has an effect on many activities, including reproduction.

The Japanese observers have seen no male copulating with his mother.[12] Sade observed only one case of mother-son incest, and that was between a mother and her son after he had surpassed her in the dominance hierarchy, in the middle of the breeding season. Sade[40] carefully distinguishes single mountings, with or without anal or vaginal penetration, which seem clearly to be indexes of general agitation, from mountings in series, which almost surely have one primary motivation (see also Bernstein and Mason[5]). In an earlier paper,[38] Sade inferred that sons are prohibited from mother-son incest by the higher rank of their mother. Later observations by Koford,[25] Sade himself, and others show that some females freely copulate with subordinates, leading to a model that postulates subordination, and "reverberance of the mother-offspring relationship" as variables that cooperatively suppress mother-son incest.

That macaques can acquire status in the dominance hierarchy without frequent disruptive, aggressive encounters has advantages for the continuity of the troop. Imanishi[11] believes that the young monkeys learn from their mother's actions in the presence of others when it is propitious for them to take precedence at food and when the priority belongs to another. This learning must eliminate many potentially dangerous conflicts. However, even if several rhesus monkeys are brought together as strangers, the aggressive behavior involved in establishing dominance rapidly declines after the first days.

Bernstein and Mason[5] assembled a group of rhesus macaques, selected to duplicate as nearly as possible the composition of a free-ranging tribe in northern India. They were simultaneously released into a $48' \times 24' \times 8'$ cage. During the first hour, 82 per cent of the social interactions were aggressive or were responses to aggression (156/195 social acts). Adults exhibited 80 per cent of the behavior, mostly aggression towards the smaller animals. No aggressive threat was answered; that is, the threats and cuffings were from the stronger animal to the weaker, and no attacked macque hit back. (Bernstein and Draper[4] found that agonistic behavior in an experimentally assembled group of juvenile rhesus monkeys, although mostly unidirectional, was marked by some reciprocal aggression.) Aggressive acts then appeared to be manifestations of a hierarchy which could have been predicted from relative size alone. The two females presented sexually only to the larger of the adult males. The alpha male and the two adult females were by far the most aggressive. Immediate cowering by a weaker, threatened monkey ensured that no animal was physically harmed; cowering stopped even the most violent attack. Juvenile males were aggressive only toward each other or the sub-adult females. In 71 per cent of the sexual mounts, the dominant male mounted the two estrous females. In the other 29 per cent females mounted each other. The alpha male made 20 per cent of the aggressive gestures and received 60 per cent of the submissive responses. It appears, then, that in the absence of any prescribed hierarchy, size alone, or some subtle correlate of size, determines relative dominance status. After this initial period of dominance assertion, combined sexual and aggressive acts accounted for only 5 per cent of the total social interactions.

Although we have emphasized the role of mothers in molding the behavior of juveniles, females other than the mother often serve a variety of protective functions.[36] Adult males also can exert an influence. Itani[15] notes what he calls "paternal behavior" in tribes of Japanese macaques. Young of both sexes are cared for by some adult males during the birth season, when the mother is preoccupied with her newborn. This paternal behavior is more typical of leaders than of subleaders, who in turn are more "paternalistic" than peripheral males. A subordinate male can walk casually into the center of the troop only if accompanying an infant. Males may care for either a male or a female yearling. They carry or lead "their" child around, feed and cuddle it, and protect it against aggression from the other troop members. By the second year, males generally care for female young. After the second year only the smaller, weaker young are escorted. This paternal behavior is common in only a few of the observed troops of Japanese macaques.

Itani also notes that females whose infants die are likely to attempt to steal the infants of subordinate females. The mother will often fight back desperately, sometimes to no avail. (In the instances of infant-snatching Sade [personal communication] has observed, the subordinate females unhesitatingly retrieved their purloined offspring. Almost the only fights won by subordinate females, in fact, concerned the lower-ranking female's young.) Itani adds that as these adopted monkeys mature they behave as though they were blood relatives of the foster mother.

THE TRANSMISSION OF FEEDING HABITS

Care for infants is a major preoccupation of adult female macaques, who clearly play a dominant role in shaping the development of behavior in infants. There is also evidence that females play a key part in the transmission of troop norms and traditions, the final issue on which we would like to comment.

Many troops of Japanese macaques occupy comparable habitats. There are literally hundreds of species of edible plants available to each troop, but they selectively eat certain ones and avoid others.[11] The group at Takasakiyama eats about 120 plants, many in common with the neighboring troops, and many not. Although caged adults will devour anything edible offered to them, constraints seem to operate to limit the feeding of these monkeys when with their troop.

Itani[14] says that yearling macaques learn which plants are to be eaten by seizing and eating the food which their mother drops from her mouth. If they pick up something which their particular troop does not eat, the mother will snatch it away from them. By the age of two, he says, all young restrict their diet to the natural food of their troop without further prompting.

There are several other examples of local idiosyncrasies. Each troop follows a consistent trail in traveling from forest to feeding ground. The trails nearly always pass by rice paddies, but while some troops are infamous for invading and destroying rice crops, other troops ignore them. Minoo troops regularly dig up sweet potato roots with their hands, but Takasakiyama macaques never do this.

One tribe has a tradition of washing sweet potatoes.[22] Washing is thought to have originated for cleaning sand from the vegetables. The Koshima macaques have shifted from fresh-water to sea-water dunking, however, thereby seasoning as well as washing their food. It is unclear from the reports whether the observers deliberately contrived the situation or just observed its first instance. At Koshima in 1953, Imo, a female a year and a half old, was seen to wash a sweet potato in fresh water. As others picked up this behavior, its propagation through the tribe was carefully noted. Sweet-potato washing spread rapidly at first, but only to Imo's playmates, which were other one- and two-year-old males and females. Koshima macaques have a strong aversion to water, and although Imo's mother hesitated even to come near enough to watch, she attempted the procedure herself after having witnessed it repeatedly.

Until 1958, the only other adults over five years of age who ever learned to wash sweet potatoes were mothers of infants who had copied from Imo. Then came what Kawai considers a distinct stage in the propagation of the tradition. New infants learned by example from their mothers — those that had been Imo's yearling playmates or that had learned from those yearlings. As these mothers waded into the sea to wash their potatoes, with youngsters clinging tightly to their midriff, the children imitated the behavior without ever realizing, supposedly, that monkeys hadn't always washed sweet potatoes.

The wheat provided for Japanese monkeys often blows from the feeding troughs and sticks to the wet sand by the sea.[22] For several years the Koshima monkeys scoured the wet sand, laboriously combing it for single grains of wheat. This same Imo, when three years old, was the first animal seen to pick up a handful of mixed sand and wheat, toss it into the sea, and then scoop up the wheat after the sand had sunk. Four years later, only the two-, three-, and four-year-olds, and one adult, Imo's mother, were tossing and scooping. No adult Koshima male, including those of highest rank, dares pursue even his favorite food when it is thrown into the sea. The few other adults who braved the water, mostly the mothers who had learned sweet-potato washing, were often seen to huddle around those casting their wheat upon the waters, and to snatch the floating grains.

Itani[14] attempted a more rigorous study of the propagation of a new habit in the 320-member Takasakiyama troop. In tests conducted during six brief periods spread over 15 months, he tried to get these macaques to eat wrapped caramels. Again, young under four were the least hesitant to pick up the candy, unwrap, sniff, and eat it. Once one juvenile had caught on, another would often watch carefully, again and again, and then imitate. Males and females over four, of any rank, sometimes picked up the candy and scrutinized it, but refused to eat it.

The only adults who ever learned this candy-eating habit acquired it from the infants for whom they cared. Typically, a mother was at first indifferent to her offspring picking up the candy. However, after it had done so several times she would either snatch the candy from her offspring or be the first to pick it up. Then, after repeatedly throwing the candy away, she might eat it herself. The behavior was propagated in the following manner: infants to mothers; infants to subleaders or leaders who cared for them; adult females to consort males whom they saw constantly for more than a week; adult females to adult males whom they regularly groomed; young males and females to elder brothers and sisters. In each case, a close and stable relationship between participants had to precede propagation up the dominance hierarchy.

A fascinating pattern emerges from these studies. Nature seems to have endowed young macaques with a behavioral plasticity that proves extremely valuable in allowing them to adapt to a dynamic environment. As adults, macaques become rather inflexible, bound by tradition. We can easily think of a species at another, more familiar phylogenetic level whose societies boldly mingle these conservative and liberal tendencies.

It is clear, then, that the way in which a given infant develops will vary drastically with the predispositions of its own troop. We can draw many human parallels here, and one might be mentioned. The special feeding habits of the Koshima Island macaques require the use of the hands. These monkeys have also developed a begging hand gesture which they present to human observers. Presumably as a consequence of these special uses of the hands, the animals in this troop spend much more time walking bipedally than does any other group of Japanese monkeys studied.

Cultural transmission of feeding habits in wild primates probably has considerable ecological significance. However, we look in vain for evidence of parallels with language — the most striking human example of cultural transmission. No case is known where patterns of either vocal or visual signaling are thought to be culturally transmitted. The few attempts to teach nonhuman primates to utter new sounds have been dismally unsuccessful.[8,35,52,53] In this respect, monkeys and apes seem much less accomplished than certain birds. We know that the natural songs of some species of birds are transmitted by learned tradition from generation to generation.[27,32,33,45-47] It may not even be too ridiculous to suggest certain parallels with human speech development, as in the manifestation of critical periods of life for song-learning. The predispositions of some songbirds to learn certain sounds rather than others are somewhat reminiscent of the kind of constraints on language learning in human children that Lenneberg[28] thinks he can detect. At any rate, these birds are closer to man than any nonhuman primate in this regard.

This deficiency in vocal learning ability is still perhaps the greatest puzzle in trying to span the gap from apes to man. On present information, it seems that a chimpanzee is no more accomplished than a dog in this respect. However, we know too little about communicatory behavior in apes to pass judgment here. There is still no good study of the natural systems of vocal communication in wild chimpanzees. Once this is accomplished, it will be possible to make comparisons with the vocal behavior of captive chimpanzees. Subtle differences may appear, differences that we will perhaps be able to attribute to some elementary capacity for vocal imitation.

Communication of Affects in Monkeys

I. ARTHUR MIRSKY

Before discussing Dr. Mason's masterful presentation of data and inferences derived from his exciting and productive approach to the ontogenesis of behavior in primates, I cannot refrain from commenting about the title of this conference, viz., Biology and Behavior: Environmental Influences. Surely the variety of expressions — that is, the behaviors — exhibited by every living organism, from those of the ameba to those of man, are biological. To distinguish biology from behavior, or vice versa, is to imply a return to the era when an *élan vital* or some other mystical vital force was deemed responsible for behavior. Redundant as it may be to do so here, I must reiterate what Dr. Dubos has said with clarity and erudition in many publications — that the dynamic stability that characterizes the healthy organism is the result of continuous flux within and between numerous levels of organization, from the intramolecular to the social. The processes involved in the regulation of the various levels of organization are all biological, in that they are concerned with the total ecology of living matter. Thus, the processes involved in the social transactions that determine a society are just as biological as are the processes involved in the translation and transcription of the ontogeny encoded in the DNA of the chromosomes.

Just as the functioning of genes or groups of genes is subject to repression or stimulation at the intracellular level, so the functioning

I. ARTHUR MIRSKY Laboratory of Clinical Science, University of Pittsburgh, Pittsburgh, Pennsylvania

of the intact organism is subject to stimulation or repression at the behavioral level. Although such analogies may permit the application of General Systems Theory,[15] they are not homologous and do not imply similarities in organization. The study of these processes requires the application of different disciplines, each of which provides concepts and techniques relevant to some specific level of organization or some aspect thereof. To emphasize the data obtained by any single discipline or the events at any one level of organization is to ignore concomitant events at all other levels. Difficult as it may be to do so, the interacting determinants of any event can be evaluated only by the concomitant study of all levels of organization.

Every piece of behavior represents an expression of the organism in interaction with the environment. Such expressions have an evolutionary, developmental, and social history. Thus, in considering the similarities and differences in the development of various environmental adjustments of human and subhuman primates, Mason utilized this multidimensional point of view and, consequently, advanced some fascinating hypotheses which may be applicable to the study of various facets of human behavior.

Analysis of the evolutionary history of the ontogenesis of infantile behaviors in man and his phyletic predecessors led Mason to remind us of the relative prolongation of human infancy, its protracted period of helplessness, and its paucity of fixed patterns of behavior. This phenomenon has been most intriguing to all who have considered it — from the philosopher to the practical scientist. In explanation of the discrepancies between neonatal man and nonhuman primates, Mason offered the fascinating concept of neoteny, or paedomorphosis — that is to say that the characteristics of the adult human are homologous with features of the fetal or juvenile nonhuman primate. Although this concept takes origin in mythology,[5] it was John Fiske[7] who, in 1874, first advanced the theory of fetalization as a general law of evolution.

Fiske, like many who followed him, regarded the prolonged period of infancy as a "period of plasticity . . . a door through which the capacity for progress can enter . . . [to] modify . . . inherited tendencies.[8] A similar concept of fetalization was utilized by the Dutch anatomist, Bolk, who used the term "retardation" to account for many aspects of human anatomy which resemble those of fetal rather than adult, nonhuman primates.[2] Subsequently, as Mason noted, de Beer[6] and others[20,22,23,27] utilized the concept of neoteny in explanation of the phylogeny and ontogeny of behavior. The same concept has been proposed in explanation of the persistence into adult life of infantile needs, urges, and patterns of behavior.[20,23]

In contrast to Fiske and many others, Mason proposes that the adaptive or survival value of the prolongation of human infancy is related to a "greater need for learning" rather than a "greater period in which to learn." This need is attributed to the relative paucity of fixed, reflex-like patterns of behavior, to a "loosening up" of the components of such behaviors, to a decreased influence of hormonal regulation of behavioral acts, and to the development of a more pervasive, generalized, motivational state. As a result, the human neonate starts with a larger set of behavioral potentialities than his phyletic predecessors. With greater potential, however, comes greater dependence upon the mother with whom the primary social bond is established.

It is pertinent to emphasize that the principle of neoteny is a denial of the concept that ontogeny recapitulates phylogeny. Instead of regarding some biochemical, physiological, or behavioral response by man as either a vestige of a behavior which had some adaptive significance in the phyletic past but has no apparent adaptive significance in the present, or as an elaboration of some formerly less-perfected adaptation, neoteny implies the development of a new behavior from components of phylogenetically old behaviors. Thus, as Montagu stated, "Man is not born with a built-in-system of responses to the environment as are most other creatures. Man is born with a built-in-system of plastic potentialities which under environmental stimulation are capable of being caused to respond in a large variety of different ways."[19]

By "general motivational state," Mason has reference to the influence of the degree of arousal on the organization of behavior during different periods of development. His experiments on the systematic variations in the social behavior of young chimpanzees as a function of the level of arousal revealed that the type of social interaction elicited on a particular occasion reflects the attempts of the animal to maintain optimal levels of behavioral arousal.[14] In familiar situations, the young chimpanzee seeks the more active and stimulating contact afforded by play, but, in new and unfamiliar situations, the animal prefers passive interactions such as clinging and other "security-seeking" behaviors. Mason has proposed that the arousal level elicited by a stimulus is manifested by the young animal without specific differentiation, i.e., the particular stimulus characteristics, apart from their intrinsic novelty, do not alter the mode of the organism's response. The level of arousal per se modulates the behavior of the subject. This explanation of the changes in the character of the social response avoids the necessity of postulating specific drives that require fulfillment. In accord is the demonstration by Bridger that the major determinant for sucking by the human infant is the state of arousal rather than the degree of hunger.[3] The role of the state of arousal in the behaviors of human infants is now a most important consideration among investigators of child development.

The recent "explosion" of most provocative experimental data regarding the persistent and pre-eminent capability of very early experiences to shape the entire life-style of the organism has been accomplished by many scientists, working in several different disciplines, and with many diverse approaches.[1,10,24] It is Mason and his former collaborator, Harlow, however, who are responsible in large measure for the intensified interest in this field as a result of their dramatic findings on the effects of isolation and social impoverishment of infant rhesus monkeys. Their studies have yielded new insights into the nature of the social exchanges between infant and mother at various stages of development. Certainly, there could be no more convincing evidence of the tremendous significance of early social experience than that afforded by the bizarre and pervasive disturbance in the behaviors of the social isolates.

It is becoming increasingly clear that those environmental and social events that occur within the first few weeks of life are vital to the adequate development of the infant. Opportunities lost during this period may not be provided later in order to overcome the impairment, and, in this sense, the critical period concept may apply.

The reasons for such irreversibility may be debatable, but the data clearly imply that the behavioral damage incurred during infancy is immutable.

In an earlier presentation, Mason advanced the hypothesis that the marked impairment in social ability exhibited by the deprived monkey may be due, in part, to a lack of opportunity to develop the communicative skills that facilitate social interaction.[12] Subsequent studies in our laboratories provided data in support of this hypothesis.[17]

Through the courtesy of Dr. Harry Harlow, we obtained three monkeys that had been removed from their mothers within 24 hours of birth and raised in total isolation for the next twelve months. Extensive social and behavioral opportunities were provided to these animals in the Harlow laboratories during the ensuing three years, during which they were exposed to other isolates and to normal monkeys of all ages. The data from these social confrontations, as reported by Rowland,[25] Sackett,[26] and Mitchell,[18] on their studies with these monkeys at various stages, demonstrated unequivocally that the animals manifested only minimal social interactions, and those that did occur were of an increasingly aggressive nature.

The isolates were between four and five years old when they arrived at our laboratory. After a period of several weeks, during which they were permitted to recover from the possible effects of transport and their new environmental circumstances, they were placed in primate chairs. Three wild-born monkeys of equivalent age, which had never been used in any experimental program, were also placed in chairs.

Parenthetically, it is of interest to note that it has been reported that socially isolated monkeys do not develop the devastating physiological derangements that have been reported to occur in children under much milder conditions of deprivation. Yet, we have found evidences of an impairment in water regulation, suggestive of diabetes insipidus. Subsequently, Dr. Mitchell of Harlow's laboratory advised us that, on checking our reports, they found that "wire-cage-reared animals consume much more water than feral monkeys over a 24-hour period." He also advised us that a pilot study on the water intake of eight six-month total social isolates indicates that they consume approximately 50 per cent more water than do mother-peer-raised laboratory animals in their home cages. One interesting observation was that one of the isolates, when restrained in the chair, would empty its water bottle as rapidly as it was filled. This suggests that exposure to a stressful situation such as the restraint of the chair may magnify the derangement in the regulation of water intake and output of the monkeys. Accordingly, it is possible that social isolation may induce some disturbance in the hypothalamo-hypophyseal mechanisms involved in the regulation of water metabolism.

All of the monkeys were conditioned to press a lever upon exposure to a visual stimulus in order to avoid delivery of a shock that followed the onset of the stimulus by six seconds. When each of the monkeys had acquired the avoidance response, they were paired in the paradigm we called "cooperative-conditioning."[16] One animal of the pair, the "stimulus" monkey, received the conditioned stimulus but lacked the lever which would permit it to perform the required avoidance response. The second monkey, the "responder," was provided with the avoidance lever but did not receive the conditioned stimulus, which indicated when a response was appropriate. Each monkey was placed in a separate test room, which precluded direct observation, but a television camera focused on the head and face of the "stimulus" monkey was transmitted to a receiver located before the "responder." A satisfactory joint solution to the dilemma confronting the pair of monkeys depended upon (1) the evocation of emotional facial expressions in the "stimulus" monkey upon presentation of the conditioned stimulus, and (2) the recognition of such expressions by the "responder," which could then perform the essential avoidance response. Previous studies with feral monkeys have demonstrated that very precise and discriminated communications may be measured in the "cooperative-conditioning" situation. The wild-born animals of the present study likewise were found to communicate adequately both as "senders" and as "receivers" of nonverbal facial expressions when they were tested with other wild-born monkeys. The isolates, however, although they had had extensive social experiences during the preceding three years, were totally incapable of responding either physiologically or instrumentally to the nonverbal facial expressions of other monkeys. Furthermore, they were very seriously impaired with regard to the nature of the "messages" that they sent to others.

The data clearly indicated that the social isolation which had occurred during the first year of life of these now-adult monkeys did not affect their capacity to acquire both discriminated instrumental and cardiac responses to avoidance stimuli. It did impair their ability to respond to social stimuli, such as the facial expressions that communicated information regarding impending shock. Thus, they could neither express normally nor interpret accurately the social behavior of others of their species. Accordingly, it would appear that the ability to communicate effectively with other members of their species must be acquired by monkeys during early infancy, or not at all. This acquisition may be analagous to the phenomenon of "imprinting," or "primary socialization," described in other species. It is quite possible that the socially deprived monkey's inappropriate or deficient interpretation of nonverbal and other cues from other animals may account for the fact that normally reared monkeys prefer other normals and ignore or avoid social isolates. Mason[13] and, more recently, Pratt and Sackett[21] have shown that a socially normal monkey detects, discriminates, and avoids isolates, thus further isolating them from the social group.

Our data on the communication of affects are in accord with Mason's hypothesis that the social inadequacies of monkeys reared in isolation are caused, in part, by the lack of opportunity to acquire the requisite communicative skills. It is also apparent that facial and other expressions denoting various emotional states serve as communicative signals in consequence of social experiences during the first year of life. Thus, as Mason has indicated, the monkey that has not learned to interpret the intent of another animal from the latter's postures, gestures, and expressions, cannot develop social relations. For example, it will respond to sexual and other solicitations as if to a threatening gesture.

With due regard to species difference, it is nevertheless quite probable that in man, as in other species, the development of social relations is determined by the efficiency with which various motoric activities attain communicative significance through the child's inter-action with his mother. Although a variety of motor activities — such as rooting, facial grimaces, etc., exhibited by infants even during the first few days of life — have no affective significance, they attain such significance by the type of interaction that ensues between mother and child. Thus, a facial grimace, the smile, becomes a social signal only after the mother has responded to the expression as if it were indeed a signal of a positive affect. Such a transition from a purely motor ac-tivity to a cognitive representation of the activity can go astray if the mother cannot or will not recognize or respond to the expressive cues and appropriately gratify the underlying need or state. Cogent evi-dence of the clinical consequences of such disturbance in the non-verbal transactions in the dyad of mother and child has been reported by Bruch[4] and others.[9,29] Similar derangements, however, may be postulated to ensue when the innate physiologic characteristics of the infant are such that even the most perceptive, empathic mother may fail to provide the qualitatively and quantitatively appropriate grati-fications, stimulations, and inhibitions.

Such speculations become permissive in the light of the observa-tions made by Mason and by Harlow on the many similarities be-tween the bizarre behaviors of the socially isolated monkeys and those exhibited by autistic children. Like these monkeys, autistic children differ from normals in processing facial-expressive information. Hutt and Ounsted[9] recently demonstrated that such children avoid eye-to-eye contact with others and will not even inspect drawings of the human face. While the similarities may be purely coincidental, it is quite possible that the autistic child, like the deprived monkey, is suffering from some innate or acquired flaw in the utilization of the myriad nonverbal expressive cues in the social milieu that surrounds him.

In accord with the possibility that a learning defect is involved in the etiology of schizophrenia are the conclusions which Lidz, et al.,[11] derived from their intensive and extensive studies of the families of patients with this disorder. They find that the distortions of meanings and the faulty reasoning of such patients are reflections of the parents' faulty meaning systems, aberrant ways of conceptualizing, disturbed ways of communicating, and a failure to inculcate consistent or instrumentally valid meanings. Likewise, Singer and Wynne[28] find that the parents of schizophrenics "convey their ideas and reasoning in piecemeal, blurred and deviant ways that reveal their own attentional defects and induce and reinforce difficulties in listeners."

Speculations are meaningless unless they lead to hypotheses that can be stated in operational terms. Such operations will become evident when the concepts and tools of classical ethology, clinical psychology, psychoanalysis, sociology, and other behavioral sciences are merged with those of biochemistry, physiology, and other physical sciences. The resultant convergence promises the development of a truly scientific approach to the behavioral aspects of both animal and human biology.

Environmental Determinants
of Human Life

RENE DUBOS

In *Genetics,* the second volume of this series, Professor Dobzhansky forcefully asserted that the genetic endowment does not determine the traits of a person; rather, the genes govern the responses of the body and the mind to environmental forces. My theme will be that the physical and mental personality is built out of these responses.

Because of the nature of his assignment and of his professional activities, Professor Dobzhansky emphasized in his essay the genetic determinants of personality and behavior. For the same reasons, I shall emphasize here the environmental determinants. This difference of approach is only for convenience, and does not originate from a difference in scientific convictions. Professor Dobzhansky and I represent the two complementary aspects of the nature-nurture interplay. I shall try to promote my own interests, however, by quoting a statement by Ralph Waldo Emerson that gives a slight edge to environment over heredity in the determinism of behavior.

In his essay on "The Uses of Great Men," Emerson stated one century ago: "There are vices and follies incident to whole populations and ages. Men resemble their contemporaries *even more* than their progenitors." (Italics are mine.)

As a moralist, Emerson was primarily concerned with the intellectual and moral attributes of human beings, but his aphorism is just as valid for physical and physiological attributes. Men resemble their progenitors because they derive from them their genetic endowment. They resemble their contemporaries because, within a given country

---

RENÉ DUBOS   The Rockefeller University, New York, N.Y.

and social group, the members of a given generation develop under the influence of the same environmental factors. Since the human genetic pool remains essentially the same from one generation to the next, its phenotypic expression represents the responses to the total environment and the ways of life, which are continuously changing. In the following pages, I shall consider the consequences for human behavior of some of the environmental forces that are most characteristic of the modern world.

My presentation will be focused on three different aspects of man's response to the environment:

1 The effects of environmental factors are most profound and lasting — indeed often irreversible — when they take place early in life, during the developmental periods, prenatal as well as postnatal.
2 Although man is highly adaptable and can therefore achieve adjustments to extremely undesirable conditions, such adjustments often have long-range, indirect effects that are deleterious.
3 Because man is shaped by environmental forces, it is desirable that a wide range of experiences be made available to him so as to favor the phenotypic expression of various types of genetic potentialities. Diversity is an essential aspect of functionalism.

Barring nuclear warfare or some other global cataclysm, the world population will continue to increase for several decades, in affluent as well as in underdeveloped countries. With the low mortality rates that now prevail wherever modern policies of public health have been introduced, the population can be stabilized only if the number of children per couple is from 2.2 to 2.5. Even assuming a much more widespread and drastic family control than is practiced at present, it can be taken for granted that the world population will increase greatly in the immediate future and probably double within much less than a century. As a consequence, it can be assumed that the largest percentage of human beings will be born, will develop, and that their children will be born and develop within the confines of large urban agglomerations. Whatever individual tastes may be, mankind will thus be shaped by the urban environment.

Before considering the biological consequences of this fact, however, it must be pointed out that the phrase "urban environment" has a meaning somewhat different from the one conveyed by the word "city." The classical city of the European tradition was compact and its inhabitants were apartment dwellers. Such is still the case in Rome, Florence, Paris, Hamburg, and other continental cities (although less so in English cities). In contrast, the typical American city is sprawling. Its inhabitants live in individual detached houses with a lawn that often exceeds in size the land available to the Chinese farmer. Its loose structure is influenced by the agrarian and nomadic tradition of American life. This is true even of huge Eastern cities like New York or Philadelphia, because a very large percentage of their inhabitants live in one-family houses that they own.

In many respects, life in the suburbias of megalopolis differs from life in the historical European city. By moving to suburbia, the modern urbanite tries to escape the constraints of city life and to recapture the pastoral and village atmosphere of the traditional past. The detached house with its garage and front lawn can be regarded as the equivalent of the farm, its dependencies, and its pastures. The huge urban area is divided into a multiplicity of water, sewage, and fire districts, zoning boards, and school systems, each subunit appearing to perpetuate the town-hall tradition of administrative autonomy.

The apartment house and the suburban house thus represent different formulas of life, and the differences have important consequences for the social and emotional aspects of behavior. But many other aspects of life are essentially the same in all Westernized areas of the world, whether the urban environment is of the compact European type or of the spreading American type.

The suburbanite may have a lawn in front of his house; but the air he breathes, the water he drinks, and the food he eats are as polluted chemically as that of the apartment dweller. He may have a tool shop in his basement; but he is increasingly dissociated from the rhythms of nature that have governed human life in the past and that have shaped its physiological functions. He may consider his home an inviolable castle, but, as much as the apartment dweller, he experiences crowding, traffic jams, aggressive competition, and social regimentation wherever he goes for work or for leisure. The very design and decoration of his living quarters is governed by the need to accommodate equipment that he does not understand, and his ways of life expose him to stimuli very different from those under which human evolution took place. To discuss the effects of the city or suburban environment is, in practice, tantamount to a discussion of the consequences of modern technology on human life.

The science of the effects that environmental factors exert on human characteristics has a long tradition, and reached a highly sophisticated level 2500 years ago in the Hippocratic writings. The treatise on "Airs, Waters, and Places," in particular, boldly suggested that climate, topography, soil, food, and water affect not only physical stature and health, but also behavioral patterns, military prowess, and political structures.

The evidence for environmental effects is even more striking in contemporary life than it was in Hippocratic times. Suffice it to mention the acceleration of physical and sexual maturation among all people who have adopted the ways of Western civilization; the change in the patterns of disease all over the world; the progressive disappearance of some of the neuroses, such as those based on sexual repression, that were most prevalent in Europe at the end of the nineteenth century.

The directive effects of environmental factors on phenotypic expression are particularly striking during the formative stages of prenatal and early postnatal development. Moreover, the effects of such early influences are long-lasting, often irreversible, and thus condition what the adult will become. (The word irreversible is used here to denote that no technique is, at the present time, available for reversing certain effects of early influences. Although such techniques may eventually be discovered, it is probable that many effects of early influences will be found to be truly irreversible, because, as stated on page 152, organization inhibits reorganization.) It seems justified, therefore, to deal first with the fact that practically all aspects of physiological and mental life reflect the biological remembrance of responses made by the organism to early environmental stimuli.

The profound and lasting effects of early environmental influences have been richly documented in a great variety of animal species. The following are but a few among the many environmental factors that have been manipulated experimentally: nutrition, infection, temperature, humidity, type of caging, extent and variety of stimuli, degree of crowding and of association with other animals of the same species. The effects observed have included initial rate of growth, ultimate size of the adult, resistance to various forms of stress, learning ability, behavioral patterns, emotional responses, and, indeed, most physiological as well as mental attributes.

The experiences of early life are of special importance in man because the human body, and especially the brain, are incompletely differentiated at the time of birth and develop as the infant responds to environmental stimuli. Anatomical structures, physiological attributes, and behavioral patterns can thus be shaped by the surroundings and the conditions of life during childhood.

Although information concerning the effects of early influences is, of course, difficult to document in human beings, it is nevertheless convincing. For example: Japanese teenagers are now much taller than their parents and differ in behavior from prewar teenagers, not as a result of genetic changes, but because the post-war environment in Japan is very different from that of the past. A similar phenomenon is observed in the settlements of Israeli kibbutzim. The kibbutz children are given a nutritious diet and live under sanitary conditions. Early in their teens, as a result, they tower over their parents, who originated in crowded and unsanitary ghettos in Central and Eastern Europe.

As mentioned earlier, the acceleration of growth in Japan and in the Israeli kibbutz constitutes but a particular case of a constant trend toward earlier maturation of children in Westernized countries. This is evidenced by greater weights and heights of children at each year of life, and by the earlier age of the first menstrual period. In Norway, for example, the mean age of menarche has fallen from 17 years in 1850 to 13 in 1960; similar findings have been reported from Sweden, Great Britain, the United States, and other affluent countries.

Growth is not only being accelerated; the final adult heights and weights are greater and are attained earlier. Some fifty years ago, maximum stature was not reached in general until the age of 29; now it is commonly reached at about 19 in boys and 17 in girls. Change in the age of puberty seems to consist of the restoration of the developmental timing that had prevailed in the past and that for some unknown reason became greatly retarded at the beginning of the nineteenth century.

The factors responsible for these dramatic changes in the rate of physical and sexual maturation are not completely understood. But there are good reasons to believe that improvements in nutrition and in the control of infections have played a large part in the acceleration of development during early childhood and that such changes, in turn, have been responsible for the larger size achieved by adults.

Although no systematic study has been made of the long-range consequences of the maturation rate, it can be assumed that being early or late in development exerts an influence upon self-confidence, social success, and, more generally, on the ease of finding one's place in the social order of things. In this regard, it is rather disturbing that our society increasingly tends to treat young men and women as children and to deny them the chance of engaging in responsible activities, even though all aspects of their development are accelerated.

As far as can be judged at present, early development does not mean a shorter adult life; in fact, menopause seems to be delayed as puberty is advanced. Whether the acceleration in physiological development increases the incidence of behavioral difficulties under the present social conditions is an important, but moot, question.

There is no doubt, on the other hand, that development is handicapped both quantitatively and qualitatively by certain toxic conditions, nutritional deficiencies, infectious processes, or sensory and emotional deprivations experienced during the prenatal and early postnatal phases of life. This well-established fact poses a number of grave social dilemmas, especially in the formulation of medical programs for the underprivileged countries.

Man is endowed with an extremely high level of adaptability to many different forms of stress, an attribute that enables him to survive, function, and multiply under a very wide range of conditions. Paradoxically, however, man's very adaptability may be his undoing in the long run. Tolerance to stressful conditions is achieved through histological, physiological, and mental responses that are usually homeostatic and therefore serve a useful purpose at the time they occur; but they may eventually become deleterious, especially if they are called into play early in life. The wisdom of the body is all too often a short-sighted wisdom. In practice, many types of chronic and degenerative disorders, both physical and mental, are the delayed and indirect effects of responses that first served a useful homeostatic purpose. Such chronic degenerative disorders are often referred to as "diseases of civilization," because they are most common in highly urbanized and technologized countries. But, in fact, a more accurate phrase would be "diseases of incomplete civilization," because they reflect mismanagement of our societies and ways of life. The factors involved in the genesis of chronic and degenerative disorders will not be discussed here. However, a few examples will be quoted to illustrate that in behavior, too, the development of tolerance can have consequences that are dangerous in the long run.

Studies with experimental animals have revealed that nutritional deprivations or imbalances occurring early in life (prenatal or postnatal) will interfere with the normal development of the brain and of learning ability. Furthermore, bad dietary habits acquired early in life tend to persist throughout the whole life span. For instance, rats that become used to low-protein diets tend to continue eating them even though a better diet is made available to them later. Such habituation is not only behavioral in origin; it has metabolic determinants. Epidemiological evidence indicates that similar phenomena occur in human beings.

Adjustment to malnutrition can have remote and indirect consequences of far-reaching importance. Recent physiological and behavioral studies have revealed that people born and raised in an environment where food intake is quantitatively or qualitatively inadequate achieve a certain form of physiological and behavioral adaptation to low food intake. They tend to restrict their physical and mental activity and thereby to reduce their nutritional needs; in other words, they become adjusted to undernutrition by living less intensely. Furthermore, throughout their whole life span they retain the physiological and mental imprinting caused by early nutritional deprivation. Physical and mental apathy and other forms of indolence have long been assumed to have a racial or climatic origin. In reality, these behavioral traits often constitute a form of physiological adjustment to malnutrition, especially when nutritional scarcity has occurred during very early life.

Adaptation to an inadequate food intake has obvious merits for survival under conditions of scarcity; indolence may even have some romantic appeal for the harried and tense observer from a competitive society. However, the dismal aspect of metabolic and mental adjustment to malnutrition is that it creates a vicious circle. It is responsible for much of the difficulty experienced in several parts of the world by those who attempt to stimulate national economies. Populations that have been deprived during early life remain healthy as long as little effort is required of them, but they commonly exhibit little resistance to stress. For this reason, probably, they find it difficult to make the efforts required to improve their economic status.

Undernutrition is now rare in affluent countries. However, malnutrition can take many other forms, including, perhaps, excessive artificial feeding of the infant. Unfortunately, little is known of the physical and mental effects that result from a nutritional regimen which differs qualitatively from that of the mother's milk and exceeds it quantitatively. Infants fed a rich and abundant diet tend to become large eaters as adults. There is much evidence that such acquired dietary habits are objectionable from the physiological point of view, and it would be surprising if they did not have behavioral manifestations. Rapid growth and large size may not be unmixed blessings, for, as already mentioned, earlier maturation may add to the behavioral problems of the teenagers in affluent societies.

Because many of the effects exerted by early influences persist throughout the entire life span, they affect the social and economic performance of adults and, therefore, of the whole society. Control of disease during childhood and guidance of early physical and mental development thus constitute a far-reaching aspect of medical action. Indeed, it can be unequivocally stated that the beneficial effects derived from building ultramodern hospitals with up-to-date equipment are trivial when compared with the results that could be achieved at much lower cost by providing infants and children with well-balanced food, sanitary conditions, and a stimulating environment. The aged obviously need help and sympathy; the adults naturally constitute the resources of the present; but the young represent the future. Much social wisdom will be needed to formulate medicosocial policies and research programs for a more rational appraisal of the comparative degrees of emphasis to be placed on the different age groups.

Many experiments with various animal species have revealed that crowding commonly results in disturbances of endocrine function and of behavior, but the precise effects differ profoundly, depending upon the conditions under which high population density is achieved. If adult animals (young or old), obtained from different sources, are brought together in the same area, they exhibit extremely aggressive behavior and a large percentage of them die. In contrast, if animals are born and allowed to multiply within a given enclosure, they can reach very high population densities without displaying destructive aggressiveness, because they commonly achieve a social organization that minimizes violent conflict. As the population pressure increases, however, more and more animals exhibit varieties of abnormal behavior. These deviants are not sick organically, but they act as if they were unaware of the presence of their cage-mates. Their behavior is asocial rather than antisocial.

The most unpleasant aspect of behavior among crowded rats is that it resembles so much the behavior in some crowded human communities. Man has developed a variety of social mechanisms that enable him to live in high population densities; Hong Kong and Holland, for example, prove that such densities are compatible with physical health and low crime rates. In other communities, however, extreme crowding leads to types of asocial behavior very similar to the social unawareness recognized in overcrowded animal populations.

The humanness of man is not innate; it is a product of socialization. Some of the peculiarly "human" traits disappear under conditions of extreme crowding, probably because man achieves his humanness only through contact with human beings under the proper conditions. Man needs the socializing effect of a truly human group in order to become and remain human.

History shows that sudden increases in population density can be as dangerous for man as they are for animals. The biological disturbances created during the Industrial Revolution by crowding in tenements and factories were probably most severe in groups that had immigrated from rural areas and were therefore unadapted to urban life. In contrast, the world is now becoming more and more urbanized. Constant and intimate contact with hordes of human beings has come to constitute the "normal" way of life, and men have adjusted to it. This change has certainly brought about all kinds of phenotypic adaptations that are making it easier for urban man to overcome biological and emotional threats. As already mentioned, the effects of progressive increase in population are less dramatic than those of sudden crowding, especially if the new members of the population are born and develop in the environment which is becoming crowded.

The readiness with which man adapts to potentially dangerous situations makes it unwise to apply directly to human life the results of experiments designed to test the acute effects of crowding on animals. Under normal circumstances, the consequences of human crowding are mollified by a multiplicity of social adaptations. In fact, crowding per se, i.e., population density, is probably far less important than the intensity of the social conflicts or the relative peace achieved after social adjustments have been made. Little is known concerning the density of population or the intensity of stimulation that is optimum in the long run for the body and the mind of man. Crowding is a relative term. The biological significance of population density must be evaluated in the light of the past experience of the group concerned, because this experience conditions the manner in which each of its members responds to the others as well as to environmental stimuli and trauma.

During its evolution, the human species probably became adapted to social life in small groups, where each member knew each of the others personally. Perhaps there was a need for larger social gatherings from time to time, but certainly not often. Now and then, furthermore, man needs to be by himself, or, at most, with a few intimate associates. Buddha, Lao Tzu, Moses, Christ, and all the great creators after them have searched in solitude to discover themselves and their mission. Man reacts to continued oversocialization with all sorts of frustrations, repressions, aggressions, and fears that soon develop into genuine neuroses.

Admittedly, it is possible to rear and train children in such a manner that they become habituated to oversocialized conditions — to such an extent, indeed, that they do not feel safe and happy outside a crowd of their own kind. This does not invalidate the view that there is danger even in our present level of overcrowding. For instance, children and even adults can be trained or habituated to avoid everything good and healthy, to search for happiness in overeating all sorts of unbalanced food, in perversions, of simply unsuitable amusements. Once habituated to these ways of life, the deprived individual feels dejected and miserable. Yet such habituations, as well as "adjustment" to crowded life, may in the long run do more harm than drug addiction or alcoholism.

The design of human settlements and homes may compensate to some extent for insufficient space, but there are limits to such compensation. Beyond these limits, overcrowding is likely to produce irreversible damage. It may even, eventually, change the prospect of nuclear warfare from a threat to a temptation — the salvage from an evil life. In the absence of a world holocaust, crowding will probably lead to the evolutionary selective survival of persons best adapted to regimented life. The two alternatives to population control are thus nuclear destruction and the social regimentation of the ant-hill.

Man, having evolved under the influence of cosmic forces, has been "imprinted" by the rhythms of nature — from those of the mother's heart beat to those associated with the daily and seasonal cycles. A process of adaptation is, of course, continuously going on between man and the new world he is creating. However, the traits that are built into the human fabric are not likely to be eliminated or significantly modified by social or technological changes in ways of life. Even when a man becomes an automated and urbane city dweller, his physiological processes remain geared to the daily rotation of the earth around the sun; the paleolithic bull that survives in his inner self still paws the earth whenever a threatening gesture is made on the social scene.

It is also questionable that man can really change his concepts of reality and accommodate them to those developed by theoretical and technological sciences. In many cases, the manifestations of nature revealed by complex instruments appear unrelated to what the untutored mind perceives. The reason is, of course, that much scientific research now depends on a complex technology, which converts natural phenomena into signs registered by instruments but meaningless to the senses. There is no convincing evidence that the phenomenology thus revealed is any more objective than the kind of reality perceived by direct experience. As repeatedly emphasized by Niels Bohr and other theoretical physicists, the aim of science is to order various fields of human experience rather than to provide an actual description of reality.

In any case, it is probable that man's ability to comprehend the world has limitations inherent in his mind. These limitations are determined by the genetic make-up of *Homo sapiens* that seems to have been almost stabilized some 100,000 years ago, when the human mind was being shaped by the sensual responses to the external world.

Admittedly, civilized man could survive and multiply in underground shelters, even though his regimented subterranean existence left him unaware of the robin's song in the spring, the whirl of dead leaves in the fall, and the moods of the wind. In the United States, schools are being built underground, with the justification that the rooms are easier to clean and the children's attention is not distracted by the outdoors!

Millions upon millions of human beings who have developed in the urban and industrial environment are no longer aware of the stench of automobile exhausts or of the ugliness generated by the urban sprawl; they hardly mind being trapped in automobile traffic, or spending much of a sunny afternoon on concrete highways among streams of motor cars. Life in the technologized environment seems to prove that man can become adapted to starless skies, treeless ave-

nues, shapeless buildings, tasteless bread, joyless celebrations, spirit-
less pleasures — to a life without reverence for the past, love for the
present, or poetical anticipations of the future.

While there is no doubt that man can function and reproduce in a
completely artificial environment, it is probable that alienation from
nature will eventually rob him of some of his important biological
attributes and most desirable ethical and esthetic values. Until the
present era, the population of all large cities has been constantly re-
newed by immigration from rural areas or from underdeveloped
countries, but this biological transfusion will soon come to an end as
the whole world becomes urbanized. Throughout history, furthermore, city dwellers had easy access to nature; but farmland, meadows,
and woods are now progressively eliminated by the urban sprawl.
Yet, the pathetic weekend exodus from urban areas and the wood-
burning fireplaces in overheated city apartments bear witness that
soil, water, sky, and even fire still represent values meaningful for
human life. In fact, it is questionable that man can retain his physical and mental health if he loses contact with the natural forces that
have shaped his biological and mental nature. Man is still of the
earth, earthy, and like Anteus of the Greek legend, he loses his
strength when both his feet are off the ground.

The most interesting effects of the environment for man's future
are the ones that enable him to convert genetic potentialities into
phenotypic realities. In this regard, it must be emphasized that mere
exposure to a stimulus is not sufficient to affect the phenotype. Environmental information becomes formative only when it evokes a
creative response from the organism.

The social importance of the formative effects exerted by the environment was expressed in a picturesque way by Winston Churchill
in 1943 while discussing the architecture best suited for the new
Chambers of the House of Commons. The old building, which had
been badly damaged by German bombardment, was uncomfortable
and impractical. Yet Mr. Churchill urged that it be rebuilt exactly
as it was before the war, instead of being replaced by one equipped
for greater comfort and with better means of communication. He
argued that the style of parliamentary debates in England had been

conditioned by the physical characteristics of the old House, and that changing its architecture would affect not only the manner of debates but also, as a result, the structure of English democracy. In his words, "We shape our buildings, and afterwards our buildings shape us."

Just as the physical environment can condition behavior, so does the social environment condition the way people perceive space in interpersonal encounters. Suffice it to quote here a few statements by Edward T. Hall, a social anthropologist who has repeatedly emphasized that people brought up in different cultures live in different perceptual worlds.

"Consider for a moment the difference between a Greek who garners information from the way people use their eyes and look at him, and the Navajo Indian whose eyes must never meet those of another person. Or consider the disparity between a German who must screen both sight and sound in order to have privacy, and the Italian who is involved with people visually or auditorially almost 24 hours a day. Compare the sensory world of the New England American, who must stay out of other people's olfactory range and who avoids breathing on anyone, and the Arab who has great difficulty interacting with others in any situation in which he is not warmly wrapped in the olfactory cloud of his companion. All the senses are involved in the perception of space; there is auditory, tactile, kinesthetic, and even thermal space. . . . The kind of private and public spaces that should be created for people in towns and cities depends upon their position on the involvement scale." Needless to say, the national differences in perception of space during interpersonal encounters are not genetically determined; they are expressions of social influences rooted in history.

The preceding remarks give substance to the famous epigram by the Spanish philosopher Ortega y Gasset: "Man has no nature, what he has is history." But this does not deny that human history has biological determinants. Some of these determinants involve the early experiences of the individual person; others are the consequences of man's evolutionary past.

As mentioned earlier, the formative effects of the environment are especially pronounced and lasting when they occur during the early phases of life. The organism's structure — physical and mental — can be strongly affected only while the processes of organization are actively going on. Furthermore, as the biological system achieves its organization, it becomes increasingly resistant to change. Organization inhibits reorganization. These statements are valid not only for anatomical and physiological differentiation, but also for behavior patterns. A recent study of Boston slum children, for example, found that they continued to conform to the ways of life of their destitute parents despite intensive efforts by skilled nursery school workers to change their habits and tastes. As early as three or four years of age, the children were already victims of environmentally and culturally determined patterns; and there was much reason to fear that they would, in turn, imprint their own children with these patterns. They were not culturally deprived; they had a slum culture from which they could not escape.

The most crucial phases of physical and mental development occur very early in life. By age six, the brain is three times larger than it was at birth; its cytoarchitectonic structure has been essentially completed through an elaborate sprouting of dendrites and immense proliferation of synapses; language, thought, imagination, and the sense of self-identity have reached a high level of development. It is legitimate to assume, therefore, that the very structure of the brain and the fundamental patterns of behavior are conditioned by the early experiences of extrauterine existence, because their development occurs during the period when the infant is first subjected to the stimuli of the total environment.

The immense plasticity revealed by the development of the brain and of behavior patterns accounts for the fact that nurture affects so profoundly the phenotypic expression of human nature. Granted the genetic diversity of human beings, each individual genotype allows a very wide range within which experience can shape the phenotype.

Man's evolutionary past naturally imposes constraints on his life in the modern world. In fact, the frontiers of technology and sociology are determined by biological limitations built into man's fundamental genetic make-up, which has remained much the same since the late paleolithic times, and which will not change significantly in the foreseeable future.

There certainly exist in the human genetic pool, on the other hand, rich potentialities that have not yet been fully expressed and that will permit man to continue evolving socially. The diversity of civilizations originates from the multifarious responses made by human groups to environmental stimuli. This versatility of response, in turn, is a consequence of the wide range of potentialities in human beings. Of course, persons differ by reason of their genetic constitution. Except for identical twins, no two individuals are genetically alike. Equally important is that physical and mental traits are profoundly influenced by the accidents of experience, which are never exactly the same for two different persons. As a result, each person is unique, unprecedented, and unrepeatable.

Contrary to popular belief, genes do not determine the traits of a person; they merely govern his responses to the life experiences out of which the personality is built (as was pointed out by Dobzhansky in the second volume of this series). Through complex mechanisms that are only now being recognized, environmental stimuli determine which parts of the genetic endowment are repressed and which parts are activated. In other words, the life experiences determine the extent to which the genetic endowment is converted into functional attributes. From nutrition to education, from the topography of the land to religious background, countless are the influences that contribute to shaping the body and the mind of man. Each one of us lives, as it were, in a private world of our own.

Whether physical or mental, human potentialities can become expressed only to the extent that circumstances are favorable to their actualization. Society thus plays a large role in the unfolding and development of man's nature.

In practice, the latent potentialities of human beings have a better chance to become actualized when the social environment is sufficiently diversified to provide a variety of stimulating experiences, especially for the young. As more persons find the opportunity to express their biological endowment under diversified conditions, society becomes richer and civilizations continue to unfold. In contrast, if the surroundings and ways of life are highly stereotyped, the only components of man's nature that flourish are those adapted to the narrow range of prevailing conditions. Hence the dangers of many modern housing developments, which, although sanitary, are inimical to the development of human potentialities and are designed as if their only function was to provide disposable cubicles for dispensable people.

In his recent book, *The Myth of the Machine,* Lewis Mumford states that "If man had originally inhabited a world as blankly uniform as a 'high-rise' housing development, as featureless as a parking lot, as destitute of life as an automated factory, it is doubtful that he would have had a sufficiently varied experience to retain images, mold language, or acquire ideas." To this statement, Mr. Mumford would probably be willing to add that, irrespective of genetic constitution, most young people raised in a featureless environment and limited to a narrow range of life experiences will be crippled intellectually and emotionally.

We must shun uniformity of surroundings as much as absolute conformity to behavior, and make instead a deliberate effort to create as many diversified environments as possible. This may result in some loss of efficiency, but the more important goal is to provide the many kinds of soil that will permit the germination of the seeds now dormant in man's nature. In so far as possible, the duplication of uniformity must yield to the organization of diversity. Richness and variety of the physical and social environment constitute crucial aspects of functionalism, whether in the planning of cities, the design of dwellings, or the management of life.

The Effects of Social Isolation and Social Interaction on Learning and Performance in Social Situations

RICHARD H. WALTERS

DISCUSSION

Indifferent Exteroceptive Stimulation and Reinforcement
D. E. BERLYNE   185

The Construction and Selection of Environments
WILLIAM KESSEN   197

Social Conditions, Physiology, and Role Performance
P. HERBERT LEIDERMAN   202

To present an adequate coverage of research related to the topic of this paper would require a book of considerable length rather than an essay of very limited scope. Necessarily, therefore, the research that is discussed represents a biased sample of data that support my current theoretical position concerning the influence of the presence and absence of others on learning and performance. First, I shall attempt to deal with some general conceptual and theoretical problems that relate closely to the studies whose outcomes I later discuss. Second, I shall describe in some detail representative studies of the effects of social isolation and social interaction that have been conducted in my laboratories and try to relate the outcomes of these studies to findings that have been guided by somewhat different theoretical considerations and sometimes directed toward solving prob-

---

RICHARD H. WALTERS University of Waterloo, Waterloo, Canada

lems with which I have myself not been directly concerned. Finally, I shall propose some general, although perhaps not particularly well-substantiated, hypotheses that may, I hope, prove a fruitful impetus to further investigations in the area of social development.

Permit me, however, to state at the outset: *Caveat emptor.* The concepts "social learning," "social motivation," and "social reinforcement" are probably snares for the unwary rabbit who thinks that there are distinctively *social* learning processes, *social* motives, and *social* reinforcers, as opposed to distinctively *nonsocial* learning processes, *nonsocial* motives, and *nonsocial* reinforcers. All human learning and performance occurs in a social context; in fact, if responsibility for a behavioral outcome cannot be assigned, we are inclined to attribute it to an act of Chance, Fate, or God, abstractions that tend to elicit responses similar to those that are elicited by blood-and-flesh organisms.

GENERAL CONCEPTUAL AND THEORETICAL PROBLEMS

The Quasi-Objective Nature of the Categories Customarily Utilized in Social-Psychological Research

Social and developmental psychologists who have been influenced by learning-theory viewpoints have frequently interpreted the effects of social interaction and social isolation (the presence and absence of others) in terms of the previous occurrence, reinforcement, or frustration of responses that are manifestations of an acquired dependency habit or drive. The concept of dependency provides an excellent example of the manner in which the adoption by scientific psychology of motivational concepts utilized in commonsense explanations of behavior[21] may hinder the progress of psychological investigation.

In a footnote to a paper published three years ago, I wrote:

Social and developmental psychologists sometimes state that they are interested only in "socially significant variables"; and it is precisely because dependent, aggressive, achievement-oriented, and sex behavior are socially significant that they have received so much attention in the literature on socialization. However, the cultural-value systems that direct attention to these kinds of behavior also influence the identification of the response patterns that are regarded as falling within one or other of these categories. Thus, attaching the label (for example) of dependency to a specific response pattern is a very different process from selecting a variable such as the tensile strength of steel to which numerical values may be unambiguously attached. Strictly speaking, aggression, dependency, and other socially significant behavior patterns are not variables in the sense in which the term "variable" is used in the natural sciences. Perhaps it is time that social scientists stop pretending that they are. The status of concepts like aggression and dependency does not, in fact, greatly differ from that of the more general evaluative labels — such as emotional disturbance and mental illness — that pervade the vocabulary of clinical psychologists.[53]

Let me elaborate this statement. When we label a person as dependent, we are making a statement of the same logical type as when we label a material substance as having a physical property such as hard, soft, or brittle. In both cases we are using what philosophers (e.g., Ryle[34]) have called "dispositional adjectives" to summarize a large number of possible predictions that may be expressed in the form of if-then statements. For example, when we say that "X is brittle," we are covertly making a nonfinite number of predictions, such as, "If you drop X on a hard surface, there is a high probability that it will break." In a similar manner, when we say "X is dependent," we are covertly making a prediction concerning how X is likely to behave in a variety of social situations.

In spite of this general similarity, the dispositional adjectives utilized by social scientists are, for the most part, much more imprecise than those utilized by natural scientists, mainly because they represent generalizations based on norms or standards of behavior, as well as on empirical observations concerning what changes are likely to occur in respect to the behavior of the referent "X" when stimulus conditions change. For example, whether responses of an individual, "X", are categorized as dependent is a function of the age, sex, social status, social role, and other characteristics of the agent and also of the social standards of the judge. For this reason, concepts such as dependency may ultimately prove to be deleterious, rather than helpful, for organizing data assembled in social and developmental research.

I have proposed, therefore, to substitute the term "attachment" for that of "dependency," as this term has been used within the context of most developmental theories, in the belief that the former concept is less contaminated by evaluative overtones.[54] To be dependent on someone is not equivalent to being attached to someone, as Bowlby[8] has pointed out; in fact, the concept of dependency, as this has been most frequently employed in the child-training literature, is appropriate only if one accepts the position that attachment behavior is necessarily a product of an infant's *physical* dependence on caretakers.

The Concept of an Acquired Dependency Drive in Developmental Theory

According to some influential stimulus-response interpretations of the development of attachment behavior,[40–42,57] the primary socialization agent, normally a mother, comes to function as a secondary reinforcer for a child because of her association with the reduction of physical (biologically-based) pain or discomfort arising from internal stimulation during an infant's first few months of life. As a result, the socialization agent's activities and presence and the withdrawal of her interest, affection, and approval can serve to energize and direct behavior that is a manifestation of a specific dependency drive. Conditions under which such a drive is developed have been suggested (e.g., Sears, et al.[42]) but never convincingly substantiated.[53–55] The shift from the concept of an acquired dependency *habit* to that of an acquired dependency *drive* may, in fact, reflect a switch from an attempt to explain the genesis of attachment behavior in scientific terms to an explanation in terms of commonsense psychology. The evidence that is ordinarily produced for the assumption of a dependency drive is that when the primary socialization agent is not present, is not attending to the child, or is not demonstrating affection, the child *seeks* the mother's presence or *strives* to obtain her attention and affection. The developmental psychologist who answers the question, "Why does the child behave in this way?" by postulating the existence of a dependency drive is using a level of explanation similar to that of the man in the street who answers the question, "Why does Smith beat his wife?" with the comment "Because he is aggressive."

Moreover, the available evidence suggests that human attachment behavior is not primarily related to the relief of discomfort, pain, or distress that is occasioned by biologically-based internal stimulation. In fact, the primary object of a human infant's attachment is likely to be a person who produces a great deal of exteroceptive stimulation, even if he or she is not much, or not at all, involved in routine caretaking activities.[37,54] In addition, there is good evidence to support the view that infants' distress (emotional-arousal) reactions are frequently occasioned by exteroceptive stimuli that are unrelated to biological deficit states such as hunger, and that these reactions can be counteracted by stimuli originating from external sources — for example, rocking, and rhythmical auditory stimulation[25,54,55] — that do not serve to repair such deficits. In fact, the production of stimulation may, under some circumstances, serve more effectively than its reduction to eliminate distress reactions of human infants.

Nevertheless, psychologists who have postulated a more-or-less unitary dependency habit or drive have some evidence to support their position. Positive, although usually relatively small, correlations have been reported among classes of responses customarily categorized as dependent in the child-training literature.[6,39,41] The classes of responses that have been examined are, in many respects, highly diverse; it is possible, however, that they have in common two related response components — orienting toward, and attending to, another person. Consequently, I have proposed[53] that evidence presented in favor of the assumption of a unitary dependency habit could be attributed to the relative strength and weakness of orienting and attending responses that are modifiable in accordance with well-established principles of learning.

The persistent analogy between primary (biologically-based) and secondary (acquired) drives as specific deficit states has led to at least three classes of studies of "dependency" behavior. It has been assumed that just as the withholding or restriction of food arouses hunger in the deprived organism, so the withholding or restriction of social contact arouses a specific "dependency," "affiliative," or "social" drive. Experiments related to this point of view have involved the experimental isolation of subjects, the withdrawal of attention or approval by the experimenter, and comparisons of institutionalized and noninstitutionalized children on the assumption that the former have restricted social contacts. These studies have been reviewed in some detail by Walters and Parke[53]; consequently, only a selected sample of social-isolation studies will be referred to in this paper.

A Problem in Learning Theory

Learning theory has been developed, to a large extent, without reference to specifically social phenomena. Therefore, I wish to suggest a terminology that, I believe, may be more useful than the vocabulary customarily utilized by social and developmental psychologists who have adopted learning-theory principles. I suggest that we use the term "incentive" to refer to the production of rewards and punishments, and to their withholding and withdrawal, by the members of a social group in the anticipation that these maneuvers will facilitate socially desirable behavior or inhibit socially undesirable behavior. Since incentives do not always have their expected effects, we need also the concepts of positive reinforcement, negative reinforcement, and nonreinforcement to refer to the actual effects of incentives on behavior. For example, by not equating the concept of reward with that of positive reinforcer, one can meaningfully speak of a reward being nonreinforcing or even negatively reinforcing for a particular individual under given circumstances. In such a case, the anticipation of the rewarding agent is not confirmed.

While incentives may play a relatively important part in the acquisition of behavior patterns by infrahuman organisms and very young children, it is evident that much of the learning of older children and human adults occurs in the absence of immediate rewards and punishment, as these are conventionally defined. Observational learning occurring in the absence of rewards to the demonstrator or to the observer has been reported in a number of studies of complex motor-skill tasks[30] and of social behavior patterns.[2,3,5] In such cases, learning can be most adequately regarded as a stimulus-stimulus (S-S) associational process based on contiguity principles. In fact, incentive learning — as this term is used, for example, by Logan and Wagner[29] — can readily be conceptualized as a special case of contiguity learning, whereby an individual observes on a number of occasions the *consequences of his own actions* (the conventional response [R]) in the form of rewards and punishments dispensed to him by others, and acquires an anticipation that certain actions are likely to be followed by a stimulus situation that has an affective impact on himself.[45] From this point of view, all learning is observational learning, requiring only that stimuli be presented in conjunction and that their association is, in some sense, "registered" within the memory "storage" of the organism. Presumably, neurophysiological and biochemical events are ultimately involved in the registration process, although too little may be known about these at present to aid much in the prediction of behavior. There is, however, sufficient evidence to support the view that, as a result of contiguous presentation, sensory experiences may be "chained" in such a way that the re-presentation of a stimulus can elicit an imaginal re-presentation of an associated stimulus, and that the perceptual-cognitive structures that are evoked may serve to guide behavior.

Obviously, the presentation of two sets of stimulus complexes in conjunction does not inevitably lead to anticipation that whenever stimulus complex A occurs, stimulus complex B will follow. The observer must at least attend to the stimuli that are present (in other words, respond in a nonspecific way), and there are many other facilitating conditions, some of which have been discussed by Bandura and myself.[3,5,45]

For human adults, incentives seem to be important primarily for maintaining behavior that has already been acquired and for changing the direction of behavior in ways that permit the occurrence of novel conjunctions of stimuli. These properties of incentives, through learning, come to be shared by many other cues — for example, observations of the consequences of actions of others that may have little or no emotional impact on the observer.[45]

This rough outline of a general theoretical approach, which has been elaborated elsewhere,[44] may at first seem irrelevant to the topic under discussion. The approach is, however, closely related to my current view that the concept of an acquired dependency motive or drive and the account of its development by neo-Hullian theorists have had unfortunate effects on the thinking of psychologists concerning early social development.

At present, my thoughts about the problems of social development and social behavior are in a transitional stage, and I must therefore ask you to bear with me if there are some inconsistencies among my statements. I believe that at least these inconsistencies are no more numerous than those that may be found among the empirical data that relevant experiments have yielded. I have organized the highly selective sets of data to which I make reference under three headings: arousal induction through brief social isolation, arousal-reduction effects of affiliation, and arousal and imitation.

AROUSAL-INDUCTION THROUGH BRIEF SOCIAL ISOLATION

Gewirtz[11,12] utilized Skinner's concepts in a learning-theory analysis of the effects of maternal deprivation on dependency behavior. In this analysis, social drive was defined in terms of the experimental operations of social deprivation, nondeprivation, and social satiation, which were presumed to modify the effectiveness of social reinforcers. Gewirtz's hypotheses were tested in two experiments carried out in collaboration with Baer.[14,15] In the initial study,[14] 32 children (16 boys and 16 girls) were each tested twice — once after a 20-minute period of social isolation, and again after being brought directly from the classroom. On each occasion the children were required to learn a simple two-choice discrimination task, during which the experimenter dispensed reinforcers in the form of verbal approval for "correct" responses. In general, the children modified their responses more readily after isolation.

The second study[15] employed three experimental conditions: (1) isolation, again of 20 minutes' duration; (2) no deprivation; and (3) interaction consisting of 20 minutes of free-play activity in the presence of a responsive adult, which was conceptualized as a satiation procedure. Children under the nondeprivation condition were tested immediately upon arrival at the experimental room and presumably had been exposed to a heterogeneous set of conditions involving varying degrees of social contact. Both boys and girls again served as subjects, but only one experimenter, a woman, participated. Learning was most rapid following isolation, intermediate after nonisolation, and slowest following social interaction.

About the same time, Hartup[17] tested the hypothesis that withdrawal of nurturance increases children's dependency behavior and thus facilitates the acquisition of responses that elicit adult approval. Girls and high-dependent boys from whom nurturance had been withdrawn learned simple cognitive tasks more rapidly than did children who experienced consistent nurturance. On the basis of these findings and the outcome of a study of imitation by Rosenblith,[33] Hartup and Himeno[18] predicted that social isolation would have frustrative, i.e., emotionally arousing, effects and would therefore lead to an increase in aggression. In their study, children participated in two doll-play sessions, one of which was preceded by a 10-minute isolation period, the other by 10 minutes of interaction with the experimenter. The results were in accordance with prediction and led the authors to conclude that isolation had effects, other than the arousal of a social drive, that motivate behavior "for" a social reinforcer.

The findings of Hartup and Himeno provide strong evidence against the social-drive hypothesis advanced by Gewirtz and Baer. Aggression, even in doll-play, can hardly be regarded as behavior aimed at eliciting positive social reinforcement. However, it is not necessary to conclude that isolation leads to two different kinds of effects — approval-seeking responses and aggression.[18] With increased arousal, more frequent and intense behavior should ordinarily be expected. The kind of behavior that is exhibited should, however, depend on the nature of the stimulus conditions and the relative strength of the component responses in the habit hierarchies associated with these conditions. Given a learning situation in which verbal approval is dispensed by an adult experimenter, one would expect attending responses to be relatively dominant. In contrast, a doll-play situation is not conducive to eliciting identifiably dependent behavior, but is likely to evoke a variety of acts that are classifiable as aggressive.[28]

This conclusion may be restated as follows: an increase in arousal level facilitates the occurrence of all classes of responses in an organism's response hierarchies. Assume a relationship between arousal and habit strength similar to that postulated by Spence.[43] Then responses that are already well established within a respondent's habit hierarchies will become more prepotent as arousal increases. The class of responses that is dominant will, of course, be a function of the total stimulus situation.

Dr. Ray and I[56] investigated a hypothesis first proposed by Walters and Karal[50] that social isolation has a general arousal effect for young children and that the data reported by Gewirtz and Baer[14,15] could be explained more parsimoniously in terms of this effect than in terms of eliciting a specific social drive. Since its outcome was crucial for further interpretations of "social-motivation" phenomena by my collaborators and myself, this study will be described in some detail.

The subjects were 40 boys in the first and second grades who were assigned to one of four experimental conditions within a 2×2 factorial design: social isolation with anxiety; social isolation without anxiety; social satiation with anxiety; social satiation without anxiety. The isolation manipulation involved leaving a child alone for twenty minutes in a room, adjacent to that in which testing was conducted, immediately before testing occurred; children who were not isolated were tested immediately after a mid-morning or noon-hour break during which they had been interacting with peers for at least twenty minutes. The anxiety manipulation was more complex. A subject under the anxiety condition was brought from his classroom by the experimenter's assistant—a man who was unfamiliar to the child—led without explanation to an adjacent experimental room, and abruptly told that he was to stay with the experimenter, who would show him what to do. If the subject was under the isolated-anxiety condition, he was told that waiting was necessary because "the machine had broken down and had to be fixed." Subjects under the nonanxiety condition were, in contrast, taken to the experimental rooms by the school secretary, a familiar adult woman, who talked to them in a friendly manner, introduced the experimenter as a friend of hers, and generally behaved in a manner that was designed to make the children feel relaxed about the proceedings.

The testing procedure was essentially the same as that used by Gewirtz and Baer. The children were set the task of dropping a marble into one of two holes in the top of a box. During the first four minutes of testing, the experimenter simply noted which hole, left or right, the child preferred. During a further ten minutes the experimenter verbally approved the child for dropping the marble in the hole for which he had shown less preference during the baseline period. The approval was administered on variable fixed-ratio schedules.

Figure 1 indicates the mean frequency of responses to the originally less-preferred hole over five successive two-minute intervals during which verbal approval was given. The data seemed to indicate that the arousal level was the primary factor in increasing the sub-

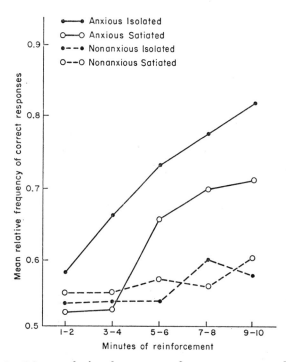

FIGURE 1 Mean relative frequency of responses on each of five pairs of trials for each of the four experimental groups. (From Walters and Ray[56])

jects' susceptibility to the social influence exerted by the experimenter.

The greatest change, as Figure 1 indicates, occurred among the group that was both isolated and subjected to the anxiety manipulation. We interpreted this finding in terms of the additional degree of arousal induced by the assistant's remark that a "machine" had to be fixed and by the possible arousal effect of isolation per se. Further reflection, however, led to the suggestion that isolation induces arousal only if the isolated individual perceives being alone as a source of danger or if some threat has already been created; in the latter case, the absence of distracting or counteracting social stimuli when alone may permit anxiety to mount.

Evidence confirming the arousal hypothesis was secured in several subsequent experiments.[49,51,52] Dr. Parke and I[52] introduced a physiological index of arousal in a study that partly replicated the previous procedures, including the orthogonal manipulation of threat and isolation. Since the original interpretation of social-isolation effects offered by Gewirtz and Baer seemed to imply that the dispensing of rewards by a warm, nurturant adult was an essential ingredient of their experiment, we also varied the procedure whereby rewards were dispensed. Half the subjects in the study received verbal approval from a woman experimenter who interacted with them in a warm, friendly manner whenever they gave "correct" responses; the remaining subjects received rewards in the form of tokens dispensed through a screen that shielded the experimenter from the subject. Both boys and girls were used in the study, so the design involved four independent variables.

Table I presents the mean numbers of trials to criterion (eight successive correct discriminations) for subjects under each condition. Children who had experienced the high-arousal manipulation took significantly fewer trials, on the average, to acquire the discrimination than those under the low-arousal condition ($F=7.20$; $p<.01$ for 1 and 64 degrees of freedom [df]). The effects of isolation, sex of subject, type of reward, and interactions were all nonsignificant. According to the social-drive hypothesis, it is the nature of the experimenter's approval or attentiveness that accounts for the heightened suscepti-

TABLE I

Means and Standard Deviations (SD) of trials to criterion for all subgroups[a] of subjects

	BOYS					
	High arousal, isolation			Low arousal, isolation		
	Trials			*Trials*		
Reward	*Mean*		*SD*	*Mean*		*SD*
Verbal	20.8		17.82	50.4		28.76
Material	17.0		13.02	47.2		27.11
	High arousal, no isolation			Low arousal, no isolation		
	Trials			*Trials*		
	Mean		*SD*	*Mean*		*SD*
Verbal	36.4		24.22	34.8		31.51
Material	24.2		12.07	25.4		27.43
	GIRLS					
	High arousal, isolation			Low arousal, isolation		
	Trials			*Trials*		
	Mean		*SD*	*Mean*		*SD*
Verbal	20.2		10.81	19.6		16.31
Material	30.2		26.73	47.4		27.16
	High arousal, no isolation			Low arousal, no isolation		
	Trials			*Trials*		
	Mean		*SD*	*Mean*		*SD*
Verbal	28.2		24.83	53.6		25.29
Material	20.8		12.62	43.0		27.25

[a] $n = 5$ in each subgroup.
(Adapted from Walters and Parke[52])

bility of previously isolated children, so the absence of an interaction between the isolation and reward variables favors the arousal hypothesis. A crude index of physiological arousal (change in finger temperature) that was utilized in the study indicated that the "arousal" manipulation had been successful. This index was completely unrelated to any other independent variable.

Dr. Ray and I[56] interpreted the findings as indicating that increased arousal increased reinforcer effectiveness. Obviously, this relationship must be mediated by changes *within* the subject, because arousal cannot directly influence the characteristics of stimuli *external* to the subject. One possible explanation is that increases in arousal, at least of a moderate extent, facilitate perceptual organization and cue utilization.[9,24] Another possible explanation is that changes in arousal differentially influence the probability of occurrence of dominant and nondominant responses. These explanations are, of course, not mutually exclusive. However, as Zajonc[58,59] has pointed out, the habit-times-drive hypothesis leads to the prediction that in early stages of learning, when correct responses are nondominant, arousal should hinder, rather than facilitate, learning. This was certainly not the case in the isolation experiments I have reported. Nevertheless, the tasks confronting the subjects were in every case rather simple discrimination tasks in which the responses of the experimenter could very readily serve as cues indicating the manner in which the subjects were expected to respond.

AROUSAL-REDUCTION EFFECTS OF AFFILIATION

Most of the studies to which reference has so far been made have, according to the interpretations I have offered, examined the effects of rewards dispensed by another person to children who vary in arousal level; in most cases, the dependent variable has been an index of performance on a relatively simple motor task. Another group of studies has been concerned with the effects of the reduction of anxiety or arousal, resulting from associating with others, on verbal-learning tasks. These studies have been inspired by both Schachter's work on affiliative behavior[35] and Spence's theories concerning the differential effects of emotionally-based drive on the learning of simple and complex paired-associate items.[43]

Schachter investigated affiliative responses in anxiety-arousing circumstances on the assumption that avoidance of isolation is a function of anxiety about, or fear of, being alone when pain or danger threatens. In his initial experiments, undergraduates who were led to believe that they were about to participate in a study that involved their receiving painful electric shock were given the choice of waiting alone or in the company of others. First-born subjects showed a marked preference for waiting with others, even when communication was restricted, providing that the group members were presented as being in the same predicament; this preference was not exhibited by later-born subjects.

Schachter hypothesized, partly on the basis of data presented by Sears, et al.,[42] that first-born children tend to receive more inconsistent nurturance from their parents than later-born children and, as a result, exhibit a higher degree of "dependency" behavior; therefore, under conditions of stress the former are more likely to seek the company of others in order to reduce their anxiety.

In a study recently conducted in my laboratory, Amoroso[1] investigated the effects of anxiety arousal induced by experience of shock and of anxiety reduction induced by affiliation on the performance of first-born subjects given a paired-associate verbal-learning task. Half the subjects received instructions designed to elicit anxiety, and were subsequently shocked four times during the learning of a twelve-item, simple (high-association), paired-associate list; the remainder received neutral instructions and learned the list without receiving shock. Half the subjects under each of the above conditions then waited together with three confederates of the experimenter (the three had been trained to appear calm and relaxed), before taking part in a second learning session; the other half of the subjects waited alone. Following the waiting period, all subjects were again tested on a paired-associate list consisting of six high-association and six low-association pairs. Throughout the experiment the subjects' heart rates were recorded by telemetry.

Figure 2 indicates the mean percentage of correct responses on Trials 2, 3, and 4 of the pre-waiting and post-waiting tests. No differences among groups were found for high-association items, in either the pre-waiting or the post-waiting test, possibly because of the extreme ease with which they could be learned. In contrast, analysis of the data for the low-association items presented in the post-waiting period yielded a significant main effect involving the shock–no-shock manipulation and a significant interaction between the two independent variables. A Duncan Multiple-Range Test indicated that the performance of the shock–nonaffiliation subjects was significantly poorer

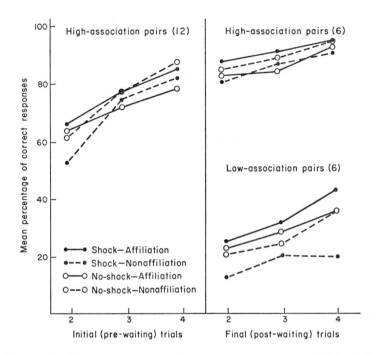

FIGURE 2 Mean percentage of correct responses on Trials 2, 3, and 4 of pre-waiting and post-waiting tests. The initial paired-associate list was made up of 12 high-association pairs of items. The final list was composed of six pairs of items left unchanged from the initial list (high-association pairs) and six pairs which were made by re-pairing the remaining stimuli and responses from the initial list (low-association pairs). (From Amoroso[1])

than that of the other three groups. Although the second-order interaction effect involving trials, in addition to the two independent variables, was not significant, Figure 2 suggests that learning, as well as performance, was impaired under the shock–nonaffiliation condition.

Let us now turn to the physiological data, which are presented in Figure 3. The graphs represent group differences in changes in heart-rate, corrected for baseline for each individual, over seven critical periods of the experiment. During the final phases of the experiment, the shock–nonaffiliation subjects differed considerably from the other groups in arousal level. The Duncan Multiple-Range test of group

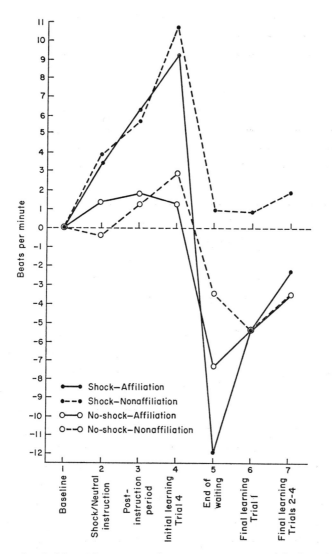

FIGURE 3 Subjects' heart-rate changes over seven critical periods. (From Amoroso[1])

differences indicated that on the first trial of the post-waiting learning task (period 6), the difference between these subjects and those in each of the other three groups met at least the .10 criterion of significance. Thus, the study yielded evidence that being alone under conditions of threat may be an arousal-maintaining, if not an arousal-inducing, condition and that high arousal may impair performance (and possibly acquisition) of a complex learning task.

The effects of affiliation are probably a function of the behavior of confederates; if the confederates appear aroused, affiliation is unlikely to have an arousal-reducing effect. Consequently, as a supplementary exercise, Amoroso and I ran an additional group of subjects who affiliated with confederates who were trained to behave as if they were extremely fearful of forthcoming events. The results were as expected; these subjects performed the complex learning task about as poorly as the shock–nonaffiliation subjects of the original experiment. Additional data from ongoing studies by Amoroso and myself suggest that the emotional-arousal cues provided by confederates are crucial variables in determining whether arousal is increased or decreased in affiliation situations.

The findings of recent experiments by Kiesler[26] are consonant with those reported by Amoroso. Kiesler proposed that whereas the presence of others serves to *increase* drive in a low-stress situation, their presence serves to *decrease* drive in a high-stress condition. Consequently, she argued, the presence of others should facilitate performance of *simple* tasks and hinder performance of *complex* tasks when they are presented under low-stress conditions, but should have the reverse effects when tasks are presented under high-stress conditions. Her results were largely supportive of her hypotheses.

Clearly, social facilitation, one of the earliest areas of interest in experimental social psychology, and social isolation, an area of more recent interest, may represent two different facets of a single more general problem: "In what manner does the presence or absence of others modify the motivational level of an individual and thus influence his behavior under specific stimulus conditions?"

The literature on audience and coaction effects has been reviewed by Zajonc[58,59] and has led him to propose the hypothesis that the presence of others, as spectators or coactors, increases an individual's general arousal level and thus facilitates the emission of dominant responses and hinders the emission of nondominant responses; Zajonc suggests that the presence of others facilitates *performance* but hinders *learning*. At first, this point of view may seem diametrically opposed to the one I advanced earlier — that is, that isolation from others is emotionally arousing and therefore facilitates learning. However, the discrepancy may be more apparent than real. In the first place, a sharp distinction between learning and performance in terms of emission of dominant and nondominant responses is probably untenable. *Any* changes in the relative probabilities of responses, whether these affect initially dominant or initially nondominant responses, would appear to constitute learning as this term is ordinarily used, if these changes can be demonstrated to be a function of specifiable stimulus changes. (The qualification is, I think, necessary to allow for changes that occur primarily as a result of maturational processes.) Moreover, the emission of nondominant, as well as of dominant, responses is ordinarily regarded as performance. Thus, the discrepancy largely reflects a semantic issue, although not entirely, if Zajonc is implying that arousal will facilitate response emission *only* when a response class is *the* dominant one. The available evidence suggests rather that high arousal facilitates changes in the relative dominance of responses that are high in an agent's response repertory, but not in the relative dominance of responses that are low. Probably, this is all that Zajonc intends to say; if so, however, the distinction he makes between the influence of drive *on* learning and its influence *on* performance obscures his meaning.

AROUSAL AND IMITATION

There has been a tendency to regard observational learning as a very different process from incentive learning.[5] In fact, Bandura[3] has suggested that vicarious learning processes represent cases of no-trial (or one-trial) learning. I doubt that observational learning ordinarily occurs as a result of a single presentation of stimuli in conjunction. Some years ago, Jakubczak and I[23] secured trial-by-trial data in an autokinetic situation in which a series of judgments contrary to those made by child subjects were delivered by confederates of the experimenter. A nonparametric approach to trend analysis was employed. Figure 4 depicts mean changes in subjects' responses over two training trials, based on a within-subject rank-ordering of individual responses. These data definitely suggest that observational learning can be a gradual process. In fact, the group curves conform to the modal pattern found in the majority of learning studies. Since the

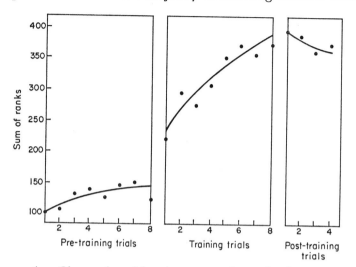

FIGURE 4A   Change in subjects' responses from the first pretraining to the last posttraining trial (first session). (From Jakubczak and Walters[23])

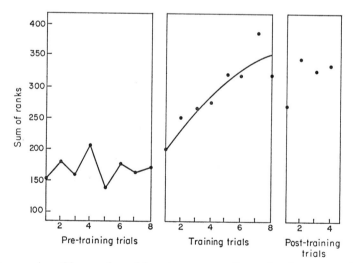

FIGURE 4B   Change in subjects' responses from the first pretraining to the last posttraining trial (second session). (From Jakubczak and Walters[23])

subjects in this study were not presented with a number of individual items, the curves favor an associative-strength, rather than an all-or-none, model of the acquisition process. In fact, I suspect that experimental studies of learning designed to assess the influence of a model on the behavior of an observer could lend considerable support to Spence's model of acquisition,[43] as opposed to that advanced by Estes.[10] At the time our study was run, the Estes-Spence controversy had not crystallized, and the data for individuals are no longer available. As I remember them, however, these data indicated a gradual movement of the responses of subjects towards those of the model.

One might ask: What, precisely, are the first and second stimuli (S_1 and S_2), presented in conjunction, that become gradually associated in an experiment of this kind? S_1, I believe, was not simply a spot of light, but an apparently *unstable* spot of light; S_2 was not simply the response of the confederate, but his response to an apparently *unstable* spot of light. The point of this remark will, I believe, be clearer after I have reported some of our more recent data.

I shall now turn my attention to the possible effects of variations in arousal level within the kinds of learning situations that have customarily been utilized in imitation studies. The data are not plentiful, but I believe they are suggestive. On the basis of a review of relevant literature, Parke and I[53] suggested that an observer who is uncertain how he should behave in a social situation and is consequently in an aroused state is very likely to seek out cues that could enable him to behave in a socially appropriate manner.

The major source of this hypothesis was a study[47] originally designed to demonstrate the possibility of changing an observer's sexual responses through exposure to social models. A female experimenter showed unmarried male undergraduates a movie film consisting of "shots" of nude or semi-nude male and female figures, photographed in poses that were evidently designed to arouse erotic responses, and also pictures of fully clothed males and females selected from advertisements in conventional fashion magazines. Before the film was shown the subjects were informed that a moving spot of light on the film indicated the eye movements of a previous subject. For approximately half the subjects, the light stayed in the vicinity of the breasts and genital areas of the nude figures and on the clothing of the "neutral" figures. For the remaining subjects, in the case of both the nude and clothed figures, the spot of light moved around the background of the pictures, in order to give the impression that the previous observer had not been looking at the human bodies. Following their exposure to the film, the subjects' own eye movements were recorded as they watched a series of slides of figures that paralleled the stimuli depicted in the film. The subjects' galvanic skin responses were obtained throughout the experimental procedures. Very marked modeling effects were secured with the sexual stimuli, but were almost completely absent with the neutral stimuli.

The galvanic-skin-response records suggested that the sexually significant stimuli had had a considerable emotional impact on subjects; thus, there were some grounds for concluding that the differential affective impact of the two groups of stimuli was related in some way to the presence of modeling effects in the case of the sexual stimuli and their absence in the case of the neutral stimuli. However, it seemed possible that it was not the arousal factor, in and of itself, that was crucial, but rather the differential cognitive contexts that the stimuli created. Given the presence of the female experimenter, the subjects may have been uncertain how to respond to the sexual stimuli and may therefore have taken the standard subject's behavior as a directional cue. Presumably, exposure to the neutral stimuli created no uncertainty among the observers; consequently, their looking responses were probably guided more by the intrinsic interest of various characteristics of the pictures than by the standard subject's "looking behavior."

Amoroso and I[46] explored this possibility in a recent modeling study in which physiological arousal and the subjects' degree of certainty concerning the appropriateness of their behavior were independently manipulated. Eighty male undergraduate students were assigned to one of eight conditions in a $2 \times 2 \times 2$ factorial design. The eye-movements of the subjects were recorded by an eye-marker camera as they looked at two series of slides divided into quadrants. Two quadrants of each slide depicted nude female figures, while the remaining two depicted clothed figures. After the first series of slides had been presented, half the subjects were shown the eye movements of a model who freely looked at the nude figures; the remainder were shown the eye movements of a model who avoided looking at these figures. The subjects' eye movements were subsequently recorded as they looked at the second series of slides. Before exposure to the model, half the subjects under each model condition were given the impression that their behavior while looking at the first set of slides was atypical, while the remainder were given the impression that their behavior was conforming. The groups were again subdivided to permit a nonsocial manipulation of physiological arousal, which was accomplished by continuously stimulating half the subjects with a 95-decibel pulsed white noise, piped through earphones, while the rest of the subjects were stimulated with a relatively low-intensity 60-decibel noise. Subjects' heart-rate records were secured throughout the experiment.

The influence of the standard subjects was assessed by subtracting the percentage of frames on which a subject's point of regard fell within a quadrant depicting a nude figure while watching the first set of slides, from the corresponding percentage for the second set of slides. Table II indicates the mean percentage changes for subjects under the various experimental conditions. There was a significant main effect ($F=5.03$; $p<.04$) involving type of model and a significant interaction effect ($F=6.01$; $p<.03$) involving type of model and the conformity–nonconformity manipulation.

On the average, all but one of the subgroups looked less at the nude figures during the second session than during the first. This finding can be attributed reasonably to a decrease in the influence of "collative variables,"[7] such as surprise and novelty, that might tend to attract subjects' attention to the nude figures on the first presentation; thus, the data probably reflect strong modeling effects under the nonconformity condition but virtually none under the conformity condition.

The heart-rate data, depicted in Figure 5 (p. 179), are illuminating. The noise manipulation produced only transient and somewhat weak effects, except that subjects who received the nonconformity information and also were stimulated by the high-intensity noise exhibited a

TABLE II

Group means and standard deviations of percentage-change scores[a]

| | Nonconformity | | | | Conformity | | | | |
| | High Arousal | | Low Arousal | | High Arousal | | Low Arousal | | |
	Mean	SD	Mean	SD	Mean	SD	Mean	SD	
Model looks	5.8	7.54	—0.1	11.26	—4.2	11.77	—4.6	10.33	—0.8[b]
		2.85[c]				—4.4[c]			
Model avoids	—9.9	15.15	—11.3	17.89	—1.0	12.90	—6.6	12.95	—7.2[b]
		—10.6[c]				—3.8[c]			

[a] n=10 in each cell.
[b] Means of scores for all subjects under the model-looks and model-avoids conditions, respectively.
[c] Mean of combined scores of subjects in the two subgroups above.
From Walters and Amoroso[48]

marked increase in heart rate from the first to the second exposure to the slides. On the other hand, differences between subjects under the nonconformity condition and those under the conformity condition were highly significant with respect to average heart-rate change from the first to the second series of slides; the mean heart-rate of the non-conformity subjects increased by 2.2 beats, while that of the conformity subjects decreased by 2.5 beats (F=9.03; p<.005).

These findings again suggest that, under some circumstances, there may be a correlation between observers' emotional-arousal levels and the extent to which they imitate a model. However, the subjects under the high-arousal–nonconformity condition, although they became relatively highly aroused, did not display more imitative behavior

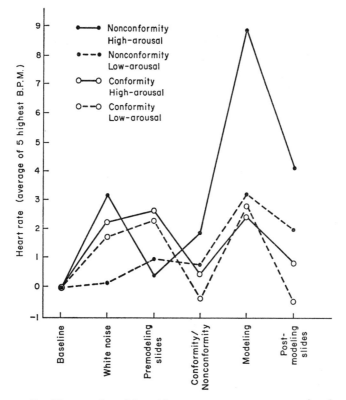

FIGURE 5   Changes in subjects' heart-rate responses over six phases of the experimental procedure. (From Walters and Amoroso[46])

than the far less aroused low-arousal–nonconformity subjects. Thus, physiological arousal per se did not appear to have a direct influence on the occurrence of imitative behavior. However, an indirect relationship may be postulated. When a person thinks that his behavior is nonconforming and is placed in a situation in which he believes that he is required to conform, he may become emotionally aroused and, as a result, may actively search out cues that are capable of guiding his behavior. In more general terms, it seems likely that emotional arousal occasioned by stimulus conditions (for example, the suggestion of nonconformity) that elicit imitative behavior may facilitate the occurrence of imitative behavior; in contrast, emotional arousal occasioned by stimulus conditions that did not themselves elicit imitative behavior (for example, stressful nonsocial stimuli) may have no facilitating effect and may even hinder its occurrence.

This suggestion is perhaps supported by the finding of Bandura and Rosenthal[4] that vicarious conditioning of avoidance responses to shock was facilitated by emotional arousal generated by threat of shock but was hindered by physiological arousal produced by epinephrine injections. It seems reasonable to suppose that threat of shock created a perceptual-cognitive set that facilitated vicarious acquisition of emotional responses and, at the same time, induced an emotional-arousal state that promoted effective utilization of task-relevant cues.[9,24] On the other hand, the epinephrine-induced arousal may have interfered with, rather than facilitated, the conditioning procedure because of its lack of relationship to a relevant perceptual-cognitive set.

The interplay of emotional and cognitive determinants of imitative behavior has, up to the present, been examined in but few studies. The results reported in this section are not entirely in accord with those reported by Schachter and Singer,[36] who found that imitative behavior was greatly facilitated by arousal resulting from epinephrine injections if the subjects were unfamiliar with, or deceived about, the physiological symptoms induced by the drug. Unfortunately, the available studies differ so greatly in respect to design, experimental manipulations, and dependent variables that, at the present time, reconciliation of the divergent findings appear to be impossible.

The suggestion that emotional arousal occasioned by stimulus conditions that elicit imitative behavior facilitates the occurrence of such behavior *may* be equivalent to saying that emotional arousal (or emotionally-based drive) facilitates the occurrence of relatively dominant responses. At least, the proposition appears to be compatible with Zajonc's interpretation[58,59] of social-facilitation phenomena, provided that we overlook his apparently sharp distinction between learning and performance.

CONCLUDING REMARKS

In this paper, I have attempted to present some data that bear on the relationship of the presence and absence of others to learning and performance, and I have suggested that this relationship is a function of the arousal level of an observer. This, in turn, bears a functional relationship to perceptual and cognitive factors that themselves have significant influences on learning and performance.

One crucial question is: "Precisely how do the presence and absence of others influence arousal?" Under some circumstances, social isolation appears to increase arousal, but under other circumstances social interaction appears to have a similar effect. A great deal of research[19,20,31] suggests that there is an optimal level of stimulation that may be both idiosyncratic and species-specific. While individual differences within species probably reflect largely the influence of experiential factors, differences among species may reflect primarily the influence of constitutional factors.

Let me suggest a hypothesis, for the development of which I am indebted to some comments recently made by John Paul Scott.[38] If the behavior of a species tends to be highly uniform or stereotyped, the members may have a high toleration for social interaction; if species behavior is highly diverse, the toleration level of members may be lower. In other words, the more diverse or complex the typical behavior of the species, the greater the "sensory bombardment" that is induced by interaction with other members. For example, the behavior of most herd animals tends to be highly uniform; therefore such animals can tolerate a great deal of interaction. In contrast, humans, who emit a great deal of diverse and complex behavior, tend to isolate themselves from further stimulation from fellow members after a high degree of interaction.

This phenomenon was rather dramatically drawn to my attention by the responses of the subjects of a study I organized a few years ago.[48] In this study, we arranged to place volunteer penitentiary subjects in isolation cells for a four-day period, assuming that isolation would be a stressful experience. Volunteers were not hard to find. Being alone, as some prisoners explicitly stated, was a relief from the continual stimulus bombardment that characterized ward living.

Essentially the same type of reaction is observed among human beings who are not living under the same constraints as prisoners. People who seem to enjoy the constant and intense stimulation of city life may experience a sense of relief upon escaping to the serenity of the country and the summer cottage. After a while in the country, however, they tend again to seek the stimulation provided by social interaction in a city setting.

However, species-specific responses to social isolation and social interaction are undoubtedly modified by experiential factors that result in within-species variations. The research of the Harlows and their associates[16] into the effects of early social isolation of varying duration provides convincing evidence that this is the case.

Within species, the effect of isolation is probably a function of age as well as of prior experience. Even a brief period of isolation may be an emotionally arousing experience for a young child, whereas most older children or adults are relatively unaffected by brief isolation experiences. The self-stimulation that older organisms produce may compensate for the relative scarcity, under isolation conditions, of stimulus input from external sources.

Gewirtz[13] has recently challenged the necessity of utilizing the concept of arousal for explaining the effects of social isolation and social interaction on the grounds that this concept is superfluous. Instead of defining "social drive" in terms of the deprivation and satiation of social reinforcers, as he formerly did,[14,15] Gewirtz now prefers to explain observed stimulus-response changes without reference to motivational changes occurring within an organism. Let us consider, however, his description of the series of experiments conducted in support of his position. He writes: "The design, experimental manipulations, and response indices are formally similar to those used in 'prefeeding' studies of appetitive drives. In such studies, limiting the availability of a stimulus class relative to its usual availability pattern constitutes deprivation *when* it is followed by an increase in its reinforcing efficacy, and provision of a relative abundance of a stimulus class constitutes satiation *when* it leads to a decline in its reinforcing efficacy." (Italics are mine.) This statement appears to rob the terms "deprivation" and "satiation" of any usefulness they may have for referring to manipulations of independent variables, since they are not to be applied unless the manipulations result in previously specified changes in dependent variables. What are we to say, for example, if "limiting the availability of a stimulus class relative to its usual availability" is not followed by "an increase in its reinforcing efficacy?" Do we say that the organism was not deprived? I do not believe that such a conclusion could in any way assist the discovery of functional relationships between prior stimulus conditions and the behavior of organisms. It seems to me that defining deprivation and satiation in terms of both stimulus and response conditions can lead us nowhere and largely reflects unwillingness to accept the necessity of attempting to discover and measure mediating processes within the organism. "Arousal," "activation," "perceptual-cognitive set," "memory storage," and similar concepts are imprecise terms referring to hypothetical processes for which we have not, as yet, devised precise measures. However, with continuing advances in neurophysiology and biochemistry, we may progress from hypothetical variables to a much greater understanding of the biological basis of behavior. The more adequately we understand, the more precisely we are likely to predict.

I shall conclude with a comment on the Hull-Spence theory of behavior, but only in respect to its use of intervening variables. I believe that this theory[22,43] has greater heuristic value than any other that psychology has produced. It may suffer, however, from the assumption that the overt S–R relationship, central to the theory, is an adequate model for s_g-r_g relationships that provide the intervening links between the overt S and the overt R. The constructs, s_gs and r_gs, have been heuristically helpful substitutes for our lack of knowledge of brain functioning, but should not stand as obstacles to the assimilation into psychology of the discoveries of neurophysiologists and biochemists concerning central-nervous-system and autonomic-nervous-system functioning. The s_g-r_g model is undoubtedly inadequate to deal with the complexities of the "internal" functioning of living organisms. In fact, this model assumes an isomorphism of external-stimulus–external-response and internal-stimulus–internal-response processes that may not exist. Gestalt psychology floundered partly because of its assumption that external events and internal processes are isomorphic. Indeed, Köhler's most ambitious book, *The Place of Value in a World of Facts*,[27] has had little impact on subsequent psychological thinking, mainly, I believe, because of the clarity with which it set out the implications of the assumption of isomorphism for theorizing about social behavior. Behavior theory has stimulated so many more important empirical investigations than Gestalt theory that it would be extremely unfortunate if the assumption of isomorphism were to hinder its progress in the future. Nevertheless, the adoption of an "isomorphic" model could be no more disadvantageous to the future development of psychology than the "empty-box" approach, the implications of which are presented in an undiluted fashion in Reichenbach's[32] *Experience and Prediction*.

Indifferent Exteroceptive Stimulation and Reinforcement

D. E. BERLYNE

I should like to endorse and elaborate on four points made by Dr. Walters (page 155ff).

1 We urgently need more research into the factors that determine if an event will reinforce a learned response and, if so, how effectively. I am here using the term "reinforcement" in a broad sense to cover any variable that affects learning other than the length of time intervening between the associated stimulus and response and the number of occasions on which they have been paired. Like Dr. Walters, I shall concentrate particularly on "reward," the kind of reinforcing event that pertains to instrumental or operant conditioning. In the laboratory, several convenient rewarding agents of proved effectiveness are in common use. However, we must discover the kinds of reinforcement, at work in everyday life, that promote the learning of naturally occurring responses and those that are most likely to, say, facilitate education and eliminate neurotic, delinquent, and other socially undesirable forms of behavior.

2 Social reinforcement must, in principle, be no different from other kinds of reinforcement. Responses that are associated with social stimuli and contribute to social interaction presumably follow the principles that govern the acquisition of learned behavior in general. In recent years, neurophysiologists have made some remarkable discoveries, but, as far as I know, nobody has yet detected more than one central nervous system in the same individual (split-brain preparations notwithstanding!). It seems that we must use the same old brain for all forms of learning, from the most primitive to the most intricate, and it is hard to believe that this brain changes over from one set of laws of operation to a completely different set when it moves from one kind of task to another.

3 Many of the rewards that are most important in child development, as in adult learning, seem to come from indifferent exteroceptive stimulation. By this I mean stimulation that possesses no manifest correlations with biologically necessary processes in tissues other than the sense organs and the nervous system.

D. E. BERLYNE   University of Toronto, Toronto, Canada

4   There is reason to believe that reward and other forms of reinforcement depend on changes in arousal, and that the effectiveness of a particular reward varies with an organism's arousal level.

Although knowledge on this topic is lamentably deficient, clues to the nature of reward can be gathered from a surprising variety of research areas, including neurophysiology, animal learning, human verbal learning, psychopharmacology, and preference-scale studies. If one examines the evidence, as I have recently had occasion to do,[4] one is, I think, forced to the tentative conclusion that an event can be rewarding either if it causes a drop from an uncomfortably high level of arousal or if it causes a moderate increment of arousal, regardless of whether that increment is promptly reversed. The facts as we have them today can be summarized with reasonable fidelity by a curve that was introduced by Wundt[19] (Figure 1), but we need to reinterpret its coordinates. Now we must regard it as a curve represent-

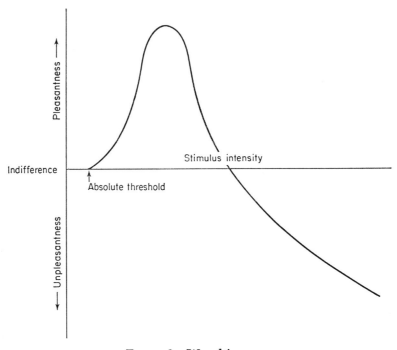

FIGURE 1   Wundt's curve.

ing reward value (which should, strictly speaking, be deduced from behavioral data but which seems to be highly correlated with verbal expressions of preference) as a function of "arousal potential." "Arousal potential" is a term I have proposed[1] to cover the various stimulus properties that tend to raise arousal or to intensify the magnitude of the transient rise in arousal that we call the "orientation reaction." These properties include intensity, biological significance, novelty, complexity, surprise, ambiguity, and variability.

The work of several contemporary researchers[9,10,15–18] suggests that the brain contains two systems, which we may call a "reward" system and an "aversion" system. It seems likely that the aversion system has a higher threshold, so that the degrees of activation of the two systems, resulting from differing amounts of arousal potential, might very well be as depicted in Figure 2. If we sum the two curves in Figure 2, Wundt's curve (Figure 1) is obtained.

In accordance with what has just been said, there seem to be two ways in which exteroceptive indifferent stimulation can be rewarding. First, if its arousal value is inordinately high — as it will be, for ex-

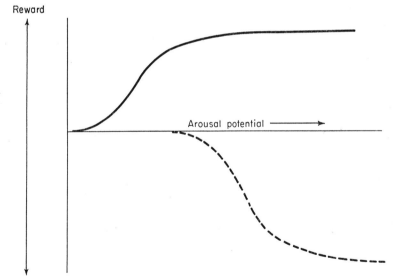

FIGURE 2 Curves representing activity of hypothesized reward and aversion systems.

ample, if it is markedly novel, complex, or puzzling — it will generate disturbing subjective uncertainty and conflict.[1,2,3] Further stimulation, containing information that can alleviate the uncertainty and conflict, can be rewarding. To afford access to such stimulation is the function of the kinds of stimulus-seeking responses that form "specific exploratory behavior."[1] They are apparently reinforced by the removal of an aversive condition of heightened arousal that might appropriately be termed "perceptual curiosity."

At the University of Toronto, Nicki[14] has performed a series of experiments whose results are in keeping with this view. In one of his experiments, undergraduate subjects went through 20 trials, in each of which they were exposed to a blurred picture of a common object projected on a screen for 10 seconds. At the end of that period, they had to choose between pressing a key that replaced the blurred picture with a clear version of the same picture and pressing another key that replaced the blurred image with a different clear picture. On the average, they pressed the former key on 13.6 trials out of 20. This finding confirms the expectation that the reward value of a clear picture is intensified if a subject has just been exposed to the same picture in a blurred form.

The hypothesis that this intensification of reward value is the result of elimination of perceptual curiosity, resulting from subjective uncertainty and inter-response conflict, is supported by two other findings reported by Nicki. First, he measured subjective uncertainty (or degree of conflict) by presenting the pictures in four different versions, representing clarity and three degrees of blur, for 30 seconds each to another group of subjects and requiring them to make as many guesses as they could about the identity of the depicted object, together with a rating of confidence in each guess. The number of guesses and the subjective uncertainty reached a peak with an intermediate degree of blurredness. Nicki found that the superior reward value of the clear picture corresponding to the blurred picture appeared only when this same intermediate degree of blurredness was used.

In another experiment, subjects were presented at each trial with a clear picture followed by a blurred version of the same picture and then were given a choice between the two responses. These subjects, in whom the blurred picture cannot have induced any subjective uncertainty or perceptual curiosity, were more likely to press the key displaying the picture that did not depict the same object as the preceding blurred picture. Other subjects, who saw a completely different clear picture before the blurred picture appeared, still learned to press predominantly the key displaying the clear picture that corresponded to the blurred picture.

Another series of experiments in which we have been engaged, this time with rats as subjects, has more to do with situations in which exteroceptive indifferent stimulation rewards by generating a mild rise in arousal. Responses through which such stimulation is sought are classed as "diversive exploratory responses." They have nothing to do with curiosity and are apparently more closely related to activities customarily labeled "play," "entertainment," and "art."

In these experiments, the reinforcing agent has mostly been light increment—the one-second replacement of a lower level of illumination by a slightly higher level when a bar is pressed in a Skinner box. We have always taken the precaution of having test sessions during which the reinforcing stimulus is not produced when the bar is pressed, and training sessions, when the reinforcing stimulus is used, on different days. This is the only conclusive way[4,5] to distinguish learning effects—which mean long-lasting changes in behavior—from transient performance effects, which do not outlast the presentation of the reinforcing stimuli by more than a few minutes. Experimenters working in this area and, in fact, investigators of animal learning in general have not always taken such a precaution. They have often drawn inferences about reward value from differences in response rate. Consequently, all too often it is impossible to tell whether certain experimental findings reflect differences in reward value or represent phenomena of quite a different nature, such as short-lasting effects on motivational condition (emotional state, level of arousal, activity level, etc.) or cue effects, through which what is unjustifiably called the "reinforcing stimulus" evokes a repetition of the response.

One of the main outcomes of our experiments has been evidence that the reward value of light increments and other indifferent stimuli depends jointly on their arousal value and the arousal level of the subject.

One discovery was actually made by accident.[6] In the experiment in question, light increment was used as the reinforcing stimulus for half of the rats and a one-second buzzer sound for the other half. It made little difference which was used. The experiment went on for eight days, of which the odd-numbered days were training days and the even-numbered were testing days. Each animal was put into a Skinner box daily for a 15-minute session. The rats received the appropriate reinforcing stimulus every time the bar was pressed on training days, but not on test days. On training days, the animals were kept in the box for a 30-minute pretraining period, during which time the bars were absent. Half of the animals received what was to be the reinforcing stimulus once a minute during the pretraining period, so that for them the stimulus was *familiar* when it resulted from a bar press during the training session. The other animals did not receive the reinforcing stimulus during the pretraining period, so that for them it was *novel* when it appeared.

The mean numbers of responses on test days show how much learning resulted from training sessions on previous days, and thus provide information permitting comparisons of reward value. As Figure 3 shows, novel reinforcing stimuli seem to have been less effective for the noisy-maintenance rate but more effective for the quiet-maintenance animals.

The data appeared contradictory, but then it occurred to us that the animals maintained in noisy and in quiet conditions very probably differed in prevailing arousal level. There is no lack of evidence that novel stimuli produce more intense orientation reactions than do familiar stimuli and are therefore more effective at raising arousal. So it seemed that we might have stumbled upon an interaction between the arousal value of a reinforcing stimulus and the arousal level of the subject.

To test this speculation, we resorted to methamphetamine, which could be relied on to heighten arousal. In the next experiment, half the animals were injected on training days, 15 to 20 minutes before

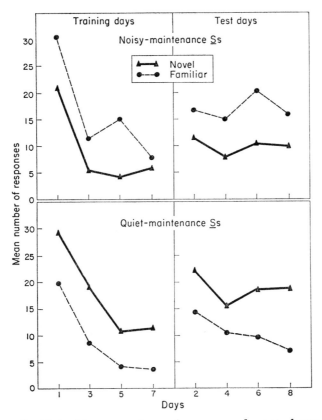

FIGURE 3   *Top*: Mean numbers of responses by rats housed in room next to noisy print-out counters. Familiar reinforcing stimuli were more effective than novel ones. *Bottom*: Rats housed in quiet quarters showed opposite effect.

the pretraining period, with 2.5 mg/kg of methamphetamine; the others had a control injection of saline solution. Half of the animals in each group received a novel light increment as the reinforcing stimulus and the other half a familiar light increment. This experiment lasted for eight days; once again, training days and test days alternated. As Table I shows, the predicted interaction was obtained, with familiar reinforcing stimuli producing more learning in the drugged animals and the novel reinforcing stimuli producing more learning in the control animals.

The next experiment was designed to show the effects of high

TABLE I

Mean numbers of responses on test days

	Familiar stimuli	Novel stimuli
Methamphetamine	13.9	6.5
Saline	4.8	10.7

(From Berlyne, Koenig and Hirota[6])

arousal induced by methamphetamine injections on relative reward values of light increment and absence of light increment. Because we should expect the stimulation (tactual, kinesthetic, and possibly auditory) of a bar press not followed by light increment to have a lesser arousal value than such stimulation combined with light increment, we predicted that a similar interaction with arousal level would appear. This experiment lasted for 12 days, with a break of one day in the middle. Once again, training days and test days alternated. On training days, light increment served as the reinforcing stimulus and, before each training session, equal numbers of rats received injections of methamphetamine in doses ranging from 0 to 3 mg/kg.

The results differed significantly from the first week to the second week, so the mean scores for the two weeks are presented separately in Figure 4. In week one, the findings conformed remarkably well to predictions. With saline injections, light increment was more rewarding than absence of light increment, as found repeatedly in previous experiments. Under methamphetamine, however, absence of light increment surpassed light increment in reward value, and its superiority became more pronounced as the dose increased. In week two, light increment had become relatively less rewarding in the groups receiving the two lower doses and relatively more rewarding in the groups with the higher doses. This corresponded to what had been found in the two previous experiments — that novelty enhances the reward value of an indifferent stimulus at a normal arousal level but depresses it at a high arousal level. The contrast is that, in those experiments, it was a matter of short-term novelty — whether or not the

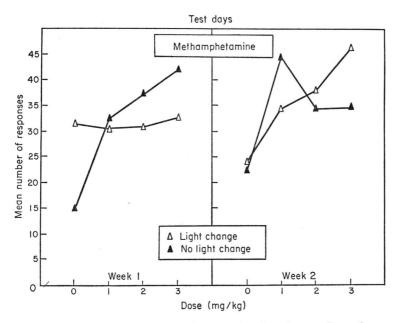

FIGURE 4   Test-day responses of rats trained under methampheta-mine with and without light change.

stimulus had been experienced during the last few minutes; here it was a matter of long-term novelty — how many times the stimulus had been experienced on previous days.

In order to complete the picture, we have been studying the effects of lowered arousal, using injections of pentobarbital. Various views represented in the literature would lead one to expect different outcomes of such an experiment. One particularly influential view, put forward by Hebb,[11] by Fiske and Maddi,[8] and echoed by many other investigators, holds that animals seek to approximate an intermediate, optimal level of arousal, so that conditions that bring arousal down from an excessive level and conditions that raise arousal from a deficient level will both be rewarding. Proponents of this view might expect relatively more arousing stimuli to be more rewarding than usual when arousal is subnormal.

The procedure of this experiment was identical with that of the preceding one, except that injections of pentobarbital ranging from 0 to 20 mg/kg were given before training sessions. What actually hap-

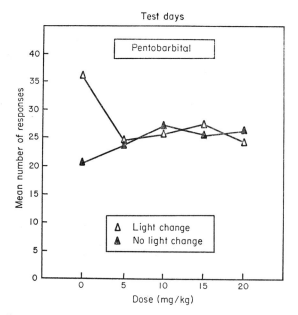

FIGURE 5　Test-day responses of rats trained under pentobarbital with and without light change.

pened on test days is shown in Figure 5. Again, light increment was more rewarding than absence of light increment when there was no pentobarbital, but the drug evidently caused the reward values to converge.

These findings, then, are not in accord with the view that animals are especially inclined to welcome arousing stimuli when arousal level is unusually low. Of various possibilities that might be entertained,[5] the one that may tentatively be held most consistent with the data is that the most rewarding degree of arousal potential is higher at intermediate levels of arousal than at supranormal and subnormal levels. Intermediate levels of arousal are likely to be those that best permit the central nervous system to handle the challenges offered by arousing stimuli.

It might be thought that these findings are relevant only to rats that press bars in Skinner boxes or are subjected to light increments. But let us consider human verbal learning. White noise can be expected to be more arousing than absence of white noise, just as a novel light increment is presumably more arousing than a familiar light increment, and the presence of light increment more arousing than its absence. Also, we can suppose that human subjects with high scores on the Taylor Manifest Anxiety Scale (MAS) have a higher arousal level than subjects with low scores, just as rats under methamphetamine have a higher arousal level than rats with saline injections. So the analogy with the rat experiments would lead us to think that white noise might improve verbal retention in low-anxiety subjects and impair it in high-anxiety. Table II shows the mean retention

TABLE II

Mean numbers of items recalled (out of 10)

	No white noise	White noise
High-anxiety Ss	7.6	6.7
Low-anxiety Ss	5.4	5.9

(From Copperman[7])

scores in an experiment[7] on paired-associate learning with subjects taken from the extremes of the MAS-score distribution and a retention test held 24 hours after the training trials. The interaction appears as expected. Unfortunately, data for this experiment were collected by two people, and there was an unanticipated experimenter effect; the interaction appeared with only one of the experimenters. Nevertheless, the results are suggestive. Actually, a number of experiments (see Berlyne[5]) show that both animals and human beings are usually reluctant to seek novelty and complexity when arousal is unusually high.

So we are left with several phenomena that call out for further investigation and, apart from their basic theoretical interest, have a strong bearing on social, educational, and other practical problems. Indifferent exteroceptive stimuli can, it seems, have rewarding or aversive and punishing effects at different times. When they have rewarding effects, we can expect them to be sought out, thus facilitating the learning of any instrumental response that produces them. Even if they are disturbing, two opposite kinds of behavior could be used to relieve the disturbance. One is withdrawal (whether bodily withdrawal or withdrawal of attention) or avoidance. The other comprises approach, exploration, and directed thinking, which can relieve the disturbance either through habituation or through the acquisition of information that mitigates puzzlement, complexity, uncertainty, and conflict. Whether a particular stimulus is going to be rewarding or aversive, and whether, if aversive, it will be approached or shunned, apparently depend on the magnitude of the arousal increment resulting from it; on the arousal level of the subject; on the subject's temperament; on the level of stimulation (arousal potential) to which he has been exposed during his past life (and especially in the recent past); and on how much gratification or frustration he has previously derived from approaching or attempting to understand and master unfamiliar stimuli.

We are just beginning to see how far-reaching the effects of these factors must be and how unevenly they must be distributed among sectors of the population. For example, McMahon[13] studied children living in three areas of Greater Boston. She compared the extent of differing reactions to complex, unconventional, and dangerous "behavior settings." Children from the more complex of these environments tended to rate more complex photographs more "interesting," to exhibit more curiosity when exposed to photographs, and to answer affirmatively when asked if they ever "go exploring." Lore,[12] in a doctoral dissertation presented at the University of Tennessee, has shown that culturally deprived children look at visual patterns for a shorter time than do culturally enriched children and attend to the patterns less intensely, as shown by a smaller reduction of restless activity. Particularly striking is the lesser tendency of the former to spend more time looking at incongruous pictures than at others.

With the present-day emphasis on creativity and independent thinking, there is great interest in fostering what is often called an "outgoing" attitude to the external world, which means a predisposition to widen one's experience, to approach and explore things beyond one's ken, to seek out and attack problems. Above all, however, we need to develop the skills that enable the child, and later the adult, to distinguish those problems whose solutions are within his capacity from those that are best left alone and to choose among alternative forms of exploratory and epistemic activity. Whether or not we are partial to terms like "reinforcement" and to the kinds of theoretical approach and language associated with them, we cannot afford to shirk the task of identifying the conditions under which exteroceptive stimuli promote or impede learning.

The Construction and Selection of Environments

WILLIAM KESSEN

Professor Walters' paper is specific enough to be examined in detail, is an instructive example of how linked empirical studies can be brought to bear on a problem of practical and theoretical consequence, and illustrates well the difficulty of conceptual analysis that is inherent even in so clearly circumscribed a domain of psychological research. Professor Walters went beyond these virtues by going beyond his data, by raising questions about research methods, questions about the definition of psychology, and questions about the nature of the child. I will speak to these larger issues because they are relevant not only to an appreciation of Professor Walters' contribution but also to the emerging general themes of the conference. Altogether too elliptically, I will comment on methodological and metaphysical behaviorism, the nature of the response in psychology, the child as solver of problems, and, finally, the construction and selection of environments.

WILLIAM KESSEN   Yale University, New Haven, Connecticut

BEHAVIORISM, METHODOLOGICAL AND METAPHYSICAL

The behavioristic revolution grew from the distaste of the Chicago school for introspective analysis and from the desire of Knight Dunlap and John Watson to provide the natural science of psychology with some simplifying assumptions. Their liberating and enlarging proposal on method — that psychologists can *measure* only what can be observed objectively in the world and in behavior — was, in the alchemy of history, transmuted into the stupid and confining proposal on metaphysics that psychologists could *talk about* only what can be observed objectively. Professor Walters is right to be concerned about behavioral isomorphism, the confusion of the methodological reform of behaviorism with its metaphysical analog. The notions of s_g and r_g, among others, can claim no special privilege because they appear to be in the language of objective observation. They are theoretical equations, formally equivalent to *image* and *dream* and *schema* and *thought*. Psychology has fully assimilated methodological behaviorism; it is time to discard, once and for all, metaphysical behaviorism.

THE NATURE OF THE RESPONSE

There are so many ways to ask "what is learned?" that it has become a somewhat tainted question. Nonetheless, Professor Walters' experiments, as he meant them to, force attention to the old distinction between performance and learning. What is learned, for example, when children put marbles in one or the other of two holes? They are not learning a new manual skill. They are not learning anything new about inanimate nature. They may, in fact, only be engaged in the social game of figuring out the experimenter's intention. Think of what children would do if the experimenter said, "I think you will do better if you put the marbles over in this hole," or "Okay, stop dropping marbles." As Professor Walters pointed out, the "learning" of marble-dropping is selective rather than innovative, transient rather than permanent, probably indicating no structural change in knowledge but only the selection of an effective tactic for solving social problems.

Analogously, and perhaps more dramatically, the subjects who diverted their glances from pictures of nudes did not learn thereby never to look at pictures of nudes. On the contrary, we may be confident that, after the experiment and without any special intervention that would produce extinction, Professor Walters' students returned to nude-picture-looking. As in the case of marble dropping, the "response hierarchy" most appropriate to the experiment—for example, diagnosis of what the psychologist was testing as an attribute of personality—may not have been under systematic observation at all. Professor Walters pointed out that we need alternatives to our traditional schemes for analyzing changes in behavior; not the least of our needs is for an explicit recognition of the variation that often exists between the subject's view of his task and the experimenter's.

THE CHILD AS SOLVER OF PROBLEMS

The concept of the child as a constructor as well as a receiver of his environment is an old one. In antique or modern dress, the idea shows several aspects. The child is seen as active; he is seen as possessing an environment that may be quite different from ours (as Yarrow pointed out, the difference is probably greater the younger the child); but, most germane to the problems tackled so effectively by Walters and others in this volume, the child is seen as a definer and solver of problems. Obvious and unamusing examples of the child's confusion in defining problems can be drawn from anecdotes of school-rooms, but my point can be made by reference to more technical and laboratory experimental cases. What is the child's theory of the experiment? I propose that he comes with or quickly develops a hunch about what the experiment is about or what the experimenter is up to. He will then perform according to his hypothesis. If his conception of the experiment is the same as the experimenter's, a primitive postulate of the study is fulfilled; if his conception is different—that is, if the child is bent on solving a problem the experimenter did not pose—then ambiguities, difficult of resolution, are introduced into the interpretation of the child's behavior. It is clearly part of the task of the psychologist of development to probe the problem-making propensities of the children he studies.

THE CONSTRUCTION AND
SELECTION OF ENVIRONMENTS

The child changes, develops, and learns by organizing his behavior and aspects of his environment into systems or structures. He is limited early on by relatively little variation in his behavioral capabilities. The sucking, grasping, looking, hearing infant — to borrow Piaget's elemental reflexes — can handle only a small range of phenomena or, in a different vocabulary, only a small range of variability, a short list of problems. With growth, his competence enlarges as a complex function of maturation — the availability of behavioral systems like standing and walking — and, most critically for our concerns, by the nature of the problems posed to him by his inanimate environment and the people around him. It should be a truism that we — animals, children, and adult human beings — solve only the problems that we encounter or that are presented to us. Moreover, we can solve only the problems for which we have been prepared. Sometimes the deprivation study, because it has no linkage with the earlier problems of the child, is akin to presenting problems in calculus to a person who does not comprehend elementary arithmetical notation. Too often, as Professor Walters noted, the child is "uncertain how he should behave." There are several implications of a view of the child that emphasize his development as dependent on his encounters with increasingly more demanding problems. Two such implications should be stated.

First, as Yarrow has pointed out, the mother can be seen as a poser of problems and a guardian against variability for which the child is not ready. In subtle ways, many of which have not been given systematic study, the teaching parent grades input to match or to lead slightly the child's current capacity to manage variability. The definition of benign environments for the young child's learning can best be undertaken, not in terms of under- or over-stimulation, perhaps not even in terms of available rewards and punishments, but rather in terms of the child's present cognitive structure and the *relevance* of stimulation — or, better, problems — to his present structure.

Second, and conceptually even more troublesome, the child can be seen as a *selector of environments*. As his competence develops, the human child, like the animal child, becomes increasingly better able to handle particular environments or particular aspects of environments. Schneirla has assembled convincing illustrations of the ways in which animal groups are differentially sensitive to certain parts of their environment, perform more effectively in certain environments, and tend to select those environments best suited for their capacities. I maintain that the child, by his history, is also responsively tuned to certain parts or certain aspects of what we — as ultimate epistemologists — call the world. For example, a child who does not possess the common social skills of the usual kindergarten child of the dominant culture will perform poorly in the environment of kindergarten and will also tend to interpret kindergarten as it fits his cognitive capacities or theories of the world: he will tend to move toward a different environment (or construct a different psychological environment) that better suits his cognitive structure.

Thus, when we maintain that a behavioral pattern is reversible or irreversible, we are making a very complicated statement about what procedures we have used to influence the pattern. It may be that some responses, and especially the ones that interest us in controlling behavior in the world of schools and therapy and social interaction, cannot be readily modified by changes in motivational state or in the contingencies of reward and punishment. To reverse or modify a behavioral pattern or a cognitive structure, we not only may have to reinforce differentially certain responses; we may have to retrain or reselect a child's environment. Put even more briefly, we can say little about irreversibility of behavioral patterns until we have better theories of the environment.

Social Conditions, Physiology, and Role Performance

P. HERBERT LEIDERMAN

Dr. René Dubos,[4] in a paper entitled "Science and Man's Nature," points out that "although everyone recognizes that the very existence of natural phenomena and of living organisms is the manifestation of the interplay between their constituent parts under the influence of environmental factors, hardly anything is known of the mechanisms through which natural systems function in an integrated manner." While most biological and social scientists are fundamentally concerned with organism–environment interactions, it is unusual for members of these groups to cross disciplines either conceptually or methodologically. Recent work[9] indicates that methodological integration utilizing biological and social science techniques in behavioral research is in a nascent stage. Conceptual integration is rarer. In my opinion, the essay by Walters in this volume represents one of the few current attempts at both conceptual and methodological integration.

Walters' integration of the biological and behavioral domain is through the concept of arousal. He uses the term, interchangeably, to describe both physiological and psychological states. It is important to distinguish between behavioral and physiological arousal, since the two terms, although suggesting a close conceptual relationship, involve quite different levels of discourse. Behavioral arousal or activation, as used by E. Duffy,[5] the chief popularizer of the concept, was his attempt to describe the intensive, rather than the directional, aspects of behavior. Activated or aroused behavior was assumed to reflect drive or motivational state, and could be represented along a continuum from such quiescent states as sleep at one end to elation or mania at the other. The concept, as originally enunciated by psy-

P . H E R B E R T L E I D E R M A N Associate Professor of Psychiatry, Stanford University School of Medicine, Palo Alto, California

chologists, did not initially prove to be productive of further research, mainly because of difficulties in measurement and the absence of a neurological basis for the construct. The discovery by Moruzzi and Magoun[11] of the ascending reticular activating system and subsequent research findings by Lindsley[10] provided a neurological substrate. This discovery also suggested the possibility that psychophysiological techniques might be used to reflect central nervous system arousal and that both of these physiological processes might be related to behavioral arousal. Many of the problems involved in the use of the concept of arousal revolve around the issues of whether the central neurophysiological processes reflect hypothetical psychological states and whether peripheral autonomic or hormonal measures can be substituted for direct measure of central nervous system activity.

In several of the studies reported by Walters, states of increased arousal are assumed to result from manipulation of antecedent conditions — such as social isolation or threat of shock — without direct measurement of arousal states. Thus, when Walters uses the term arousal, he may be referring to a hypothesized behavioral state, which should not be confused with the central state as measured by electrophysiological methods. Walters does employ physiological measures in some of his studies, typically peripheral automatic indicators such as heart rate and skin resistance. In his use of such measures, he assumes that these indicators mirror states of arousal, either behavioral or cortical. That this assumption is unwarranted is pointed out by Lacey,[6] who emphasizes the necessity to distinguish between electrocortical, autonomic, and behavioral arousal. Furthermore, Lacey points out that the correlation between various autonomic measures is low. Skin resistance and heart rate, two of the measures used by Walters, have consistently shown low correlation. There is no reason to expect that they should covary, at least under conditions of minimal stress, since heart rate and skin potential are both neuroanatomically and neurophysiologically distinct. Heart rate is under dual control, parasympathetic and sympathetic, and is thus a heavily dampened feedback control system; skin potential and skin resistance, on the other hand, although slightly different in their response patterns, have only a single innervation through the sympathetic system.

To complicate the picture further, the relationship between the autonomic nervous system on one hand and the endocrine and biochemical systems on the other is even more obscure at present. The few studies that have been done show that correlations between biochemical substances such as free fatty acids, catecholamines, and heart rate are low. In a recent study by A. Shapiro,[14] comparing responses of monozygotic and dizygotic twins to physical and psychological stimuli, not only were the correlations between autonomic indexes low, but heart rate showed the least response to environmental influence, whereas free fatty acids and catecholamines were more responsive. On the basis of these findings, I would suggest caution in the use of any single peripheral physiological measure as the index of psychological states, unless it can be demonstrated to reflect changes in the organism in response to environmental stimulation or is functionally related to the particular behaviors being examined.

One solution to the dilemma of assessment of the state of arousal is, of course, direct experimental manipulation of the state with the measurement of the appropriate physiological responses. Schachter[13] did just this by giving epinephrine injections to his experimental subjects at the same time as he manipulated the social environment. Similarly, Welch[16] used pharmacological means to manipulate arousal in rats in his studies of the relationship between arousal and social conditions of individual and group living. Both of these studies are excellent models for research on the relationship between physiological arousal and psychological states, and demonstrate the power of the pharmacological method in experimental psychological research.

Besides the conceptual problem of specificity of physiological response as an index of a general state of arousal, the problem of statistical treatment of results must also be considered. Baseline measures of physiological processes are essential because of individual differences. This problem immediately raises several questions. What is the relationship between response measures and basal measures? Does the law of initial values apply? Should continuously recorded measurements be employed or will sampled measurements suffice? Some of these issues are discussed in Oken and Heath[12] and Leiderman and Shapiro,[8] and I raise them to point out that physiological data have a degree of complexity that demands as much attention as the analysis of psychological data, something not adequately considered by Walters in his paper.

Having discussed the conceptual background of Walters' work in reference to the concept of arousal, I shall now take up some of his substantive observations, particularly in relationship to my own work. Walters reports his observations under three major headings, and I shall deal with them in turn. The first section discusses arousal-induction through brief social isolation. The main thrust of the studies reported in this section was to contrast the hypothesis of Gerwirtz — that social drive increased after social deprivation, thus facilitating social learning — with his own hypothesis that social deprivation leads to increased arousal, and hence facilitates learning independent of social reinforcement. Arousal in these studies is a presumed state, arising from the experimental situation of social isolation. This presumption of increased arousal under conditions of social isolation is the point I wish to discuss.

In my own work,[7] isolation of young men under conditions of sensory deprivation for periods as long as six hours, using heart rate and skin potential as indexes of arousal, yielded equivocal findings. Observations of young women in social isolation for periods of two hours, with some sensory stimulation, also produced equivocal results. Cohen,[2] in his summary of the physiological studies of social isolation and sensory deprivation, emphasizes the contradictory aspects of these studies as far as physiological arousal is concerned. I need not further belabor the point that we cannot assume any simple relationship between arousal and isolation without some independent assessment of the arousal state. Walters supports this cautionary comment when he states that isolation per se is not a source of arousal, but may become so when the individual perceives the situation as a potential source of threat.

In his discussion of the arousal-reduction effects of affiliation, Walters asks the question, "In what manner does the presence or absence of others modify the motivational level of an individual and thus influence his behavior under specific stimulus conditions?" In the studies reported in this section, arousal was induced by means of a shock-threat situation and measured by means of heart-rate changes. Ignoring the methodological problems attendant upon the use of a single physiological response parameter as an index of arousal and the fact that significance was achieved at the 10 per cent level, he found that arousal was lower under conditions of affiliation, although only when affiliates themselves did not appear aroused. Perhaps germane to the question of affiliation and arousal is the study reported by Shapiro, Leiderman, and Morningstar,[15] in which they contrasted individuals working together in a group and working alone. Skin potential and heart-rate responses were the indexes of arousal. The results indicate that those individuals performing the task in a group showed a higher skin potential than did those doing the task alone, while heart rate tended in the opposite direction. Since the heart-rate changes were not significant, the authors tentatively conclude that performance under group conditions is accompanied by higher levels of arousal.

To illustrate further the complexity in the relationship between arousal and affiliation, we made an additional analysis of the data of the preceding study. Since each subject appeared both alone and in a group—some initially alone and others initially in a group—we asked what influence the order of conditions might have on the physiological responses. When the subjects appeared initially in a group, followed by being alone, the correlation for skin-potential level between the two sessions was high. If the reverse occurred, the correlation was low. For heart rate, the order appeared to make no difference, the correlations being relatively high in both circumstances. Thus, not only isolation and interaction have some influence on arousal, as measured by skin potential, but the ordering of these experiences also influences arousal levels.

The section on arousal and imitation, perhaps more satisfying to me in that Walters used physiological parameters extensively, was less satisfying as far as results are concerned. He attempted to test the hypothesis that higher levels of arousal would lead to increased imitative or modeling behavior. In an ingenious experimental procedure in which he manipulated arousal independently of conformity behavior, he found that modeling behavior increased under conditions of nonconformity but was not directly related to levels of arousal as measured by heart-rate changes. The use of heart-rate decrease as an index of lower arousal certainly can be questioned, especially in light of the findings of Lacey,[6] who reports that cardiac deceleration accompanies increased attention to the external environment. According to Lacey's findings, we should expect a decrease in heart rate with increased attention to the picture tasks of Walters. This cardiovascular change may be unrelated to behavioral arousal or to physiological arousal as measured by other indicators.

Studies of conformity behavior that can be considered akin to modeling behavior, although other physiological parameters were used, have been reported by Bogdonoff, et al.,[1] and Costell and Leiderman.[3] Bogdonoff, et al.,[1] used the Crutchfield modification of the Asch situation in a social conformity experiment. They reported that friends confronted with a conformity task had lower levels of arousal than did a group of strangers confronted with this same task. They measured changes in the plasma-free fatty-acid level, which is considered to be indicative of high levels of arousal, and concluded that conformity behavior led to lower arousal levels.

In an attempt to replicate and extend the findings of Bogdonoff, et al., Costell and I[3] studied conformity behavior using a modification of the Asch situation that permitted the study of both majority and minority roles in a social group. Skin-potential level was used as the index of arousal. We found that minority-role individuals who maintained nonconformity in the face of unanimous majority pressure habituated in their skin-potential response more slowly (indicative of higher arousal) than did those individuals who conformed to the group pressure. Consistent with this observation, majority subjects confronted with a nonconforming member habituated more rapidly, indicating lower arousal. If it can be assumed that, when a majority responds similarly while facing a nonconforming minority member there is a tendency to greater modeling, the data on both minority and majority subjects suggests that modeling is accompanied by lower levels of arousal. This result, which appears somewhat at variance with Walters' proposed hypothesis, probably can be attributed to the different physiological techniques employed to measure arousal. If we assume that heart rate is an inadequate measure of arousal in a perception experiment that demands external attention, the findings on conformity are remarkably consistent, and we can conclude that conformity and/or modeling behavior leads to lower levels of arousal. Whether high levels of arousal, independently produced, lead to subsequent increased conformity remains unanswered.

Now I should like to turn to a clinical problem with which I am currently concerned. I believe it is directly relevant to one issue raised by Walters — social learning under a condition in which a state of high arousal can be assumed. I refer to the development of the social relationship between a mother and her infant, along with appropriate maternal behavior, in the immediate postpartum period — a period of presumed high arousal. This problem came to my attention through a pediatrician, Dr. Marshall Klaus, former head of the Premature Research Center Nursery at Stanford, who observed that mothers of premature infants did not seem to be as capable in their mothering behavior as did mothers of full-term infants. He observed that they seemed to have more difficulty in the routine care of their infants, expressed greater concern for their welfare, appeared to hold them differently, and reported greater amounts of illness in their infants.

At this point, I should explain that the usual care of the premature infant in the United States, under conditions of modern hospital technology, requires immediate separation of the mother from her child. Frequently, the mother may not even catch a glimpse of her infant if she is not awake during the delivery. The newborn is whisked away by the pediatrician, who applies the best current techniques to deal with immediate physiological problems. Depending on weight, stage of development, and the presence of congenital abnormalities, the infant survives under skilled pediatric care and without any ministrations of his mother.

A group of us — Dr. C. Barnett, an anthropologist, Mrs. R. Grobstein, a social worker, and I, along with Dr. Klaus considered whether the maternal behavior reported by Dr. Klaus can be the result of environmental conditions of the premature nursery in the immediate postpartum period, rather than, as had been suggested in previous studies, that the mothers of prematures were "rejecting" their maternal role. Stated in another way, we asked if the attitude and behavior of mothers of premature infants was chiefly a function of the environmental conditions being imposed on them. We decided to test this hypothesis by permitting mothers to enter the nursery in the immediate postpartum period to handle and, when possible, take care of their infants.

In the clinical phase of this study, we established the feasibility of this relatively novel arrangement for the mothers and their infants, without introducing infection into the nursery or interfering with activities of the pediatric and nursing staffs. During the clinical phase, we also were able to satisfy ourselves that this new arrangement produced changes of attitude and maternal behavior in some mothers. We are currently embarked on a more formal experimental study, wherein we manipulate the nursery at periodic intervals. For part of the year, the usual regimen of separation of mother and infant is maintained. This regimen alternates with periods during which mothers are permitted to be in close contact with their infants. Under both nursery conditions, we examine maternal attitudes and feelings, make direct observations of maternal caretaking behavior in the hospital and follow-up observations in the home, and assess infant growth and development for two years following discharge from the Premature Research Unit.

This study provides the opportunity to test Walters' theoretical model with an important functional behavior — maternal behavior. If learning a social behavior is enhanced by arousal, we would expect that those mothers who are in close contact with their infants in the immediate postpartum period would "*learn*" maternal behaviors more readily, presuming that arousal is highest at that time. This capacity to learn would decrease with increasing separation, presuming a decrease of arousal over time in the postpartum period. On this basis, we would predict that social learning after separation would be less adequate than social learning immediately after birth. On the other hand, using the social drive model, separation over time should increase social drive; therefore, social learning after a period of separation should be more adequate because social drive should be highest. While I do not expect that, in such a complex clinical study, we shall achieve sufficiently definitive results to choose one model over the other, the applicability of a laboratory-derived theoretical formulation to problems in the real world is heartening, indeed.

However, I should point out here, as I did in my critique of Walters' work, that we lack direct measures of arousal. Unlike the presumed arousal involved in experimental manipulation in Walters' work, we have a natural biological event, the birth of an infant, to bring about conditions of high arousal in the mother. One might ask what direct measures of biological arousal could be employed. I would re-emphasize that arousal measures appropriate for the behavior under evaluation might be the ideal choice. Measurement of the release of such hormones as progesterone, estrogen, and prolactin might be the most desirable way to assess the level of arousal of maternal behavior; this would replace such nonspecific indications as heart rate, skin potential, catecholamine or corticoid production, and the like. If these female hormones do reflect higher states of arousal, it is interesting to speculate whether maternal arousal could be maintained by pharmacological injection, even in the face of removal of the infant as a stimulus. Perhaps states of arousal can be induced by pharmacological as well as by behavioral means in mothers who are deficient in their expression of maternal behavior in the postpartum period. If so, the pharmaceutical industry might be induced to become concerned with the *enhancement* of maternal behavior rather than with the prevention of maternity.

In closing, I want to compliment Dr. Walters for showing the way to imaginative and conceptually relevant biosocial research. I hope that some of the other work I have presented suggests additional approaches to some of the problems he raised. Although the statement of Dubos that I quoted at the beginning — "hardly anything is known of the mechanism through which natural systems function in an integrated manner" — can stand almost unmodified, Walters' paper does represent some progress in our understanding of the mechanisms involved with organism-environment interactions. Nonetheless, integration between social conditions, physiological processes, and role performance remains an elusive goal for biosocial researchers.

On Cultural Deprivation

JEROME KAGAN

DISCUSSION

When is Infant Stimulation Effective?
URIE BRONFENBRENNER   251

Perception, Cognitive Maps, and Covert Behavior
LEONARD S. COTTRELL, JR.   257

The choice of the adjective "deprived" to define the poverty-burdened children of our community is not entirely fortunate, for it maintains the bias that the psychological profile of the middle-class child should be the reference standard in evaluating the psychological organization of other groups. This error of the middle-class anchor may set constraints on the variables we study in lower-middle-class children and blind us to deficiencies in the intellectual armor of the middle-class child, especially the consequences of the undue emphasis on purely verbal modes of decoding experience. We shall, therefore, revert to the older terminological distinction that talked of lower-middle-class, middle-class, and upper-middle-class groups, where education and occupation are viewed as the primary criteria for class membership. This paper attempts three goals: (a) to consider a set of assumptions about cognitive development; (b) to discuss the profile of known and supposed differences between lower-middle-class and middle-class children and (c) while meeting these two requirements, to fold in results that have emerged from our own work with infants and school age children.

JEROME KAGAN   William James Hall, Harvard University, Cambridge, Mass.

SOME INITIAL ASSUMPTIONS
CONCERNING MENTAL GROWTH

The beginning student is told that there are three major functional divisions of the cerebral cortex — sensory, motor, and association areas. Each system is assigned a topographical location, a set of unique links within the central nervous system, and an isomorphic relation to the psychological phenomena of sensation, action, and thought. The distinction between action on the one hand, and the sensory, perceptual, and conceptual phenomena on the other, seems to be the more vital dichotomy, for an individual consists, in the most abstract sense, of a pair of parallel organizations of cognitive and behavioral structures.

Although we shall return to the significance of this division later, the reader is reminded that some psychologists do not view these functions as being as separate as we have implied. Most Russian psychologists are publicly committed to the belief that the child acquires many cognitions via action — a modern reinterpretation of Watson's notion of thought as internalized skeletal motor discharge. The proposition that perceptual structures are interiorized actions is a basic notion in Piaget's description of the sensory-motor period. This particular melody is more subtle in American work, but is still detectable, for preschool educators chant support for "learning by doing." Moreover, the classic notion that a new unit of learning is a stimulus-response connection tempts one to conclude that if no response occurs, no learning occurs. Despite many excellent experiments to the contrary, including Solomon's demonstration that acquisition of a conditioned leg withdrawal can occur in a curarized animal, the assumption that learning can occur without an overt action remains controversial.

There are three reasons for taking time to emphasize the division between perceptual and conceptual processes in contrast to action, where we mean by action "a public piece of behavior," not an autonomic reaction or an evoked potential. From a developmental perspective, many cognitive structures are acquired that do not necessarily appear in overt behavior. Second, any behavior is, at best, an imperfect index of the nature of the structure. Finally, a particular behavior may and often does reflect different cognitive structures. Let us consider some illustrations of the above statements.

The child's comprehension of language develops long before he utters meaningful speech. The possession of different schemata for mother's versus a strange woman's face can be detected through studies of cardiac reactions several months before the child clearly indicates in public form (e.g., through anxiety toward strangers) that he has developed different schemata for these two people. The behavioral events to which we ordinarily have easy access do not typically mirror the complexity of the cognitive structure the child has developed, and are imperfect indexes of these structures. The child's drawings or speech, even when elicited under optimal motivational conditions, are not faithful to his ideas. The five-year-old's drawing of a man typically shows the arms emerging from the head, but he does not perceive humans this way, as a perceptual recognition test will quickly show. The young child who can point to a violation of a standard or laugh at something incongruous is often unable to tell us what the standard is or reproduce the essence of the incongruity. Finally, even when a response is tied closely to one particular structure it can owe its allegiance to another. The four-month-old infant smiles when he recognizes a face, a ten-month-old smiles in the service of a social communication. But the smiles may look the same to an observer. The four-month-old infant babbles as an accompaniment to motoric excitement or because he wants to reach a toy. A six-year-old boy hits a peer because he dislikes him or because he is asserting his masculinity. The act alone does not contain all the information necessary to identify the appropriate cognitive structure to which it belongs.

THE NATURE OF SCHEMATA

The organization and nature of mental structures that translate experience and reduce uncertainty comprise our core concern. These structures consist, in large measure, of images and semantic forms arranged in configurations of varying complexity. An analogy to organic chemistry may be helpful. Each protein molecule has a definite structure of known elements. The chemist calls his particular structure a molecule; we call each of our mental structures a "schema." If a schema is purely perceptual, i.e., an image, it is a partial representation of the external event, not an exact replica. If the schema consists primarily of symbols — words and numbers — then it has a pivot or core symbol around which the other elements are organized. Each schema, be it an image, a symbol or a combination of both, has a psychological center which we shall designate as its "distinctive features." A schema is a condensation of an external event and, like a caricature, is defined by a set of distinctive features. If the distinctive features change, the schema changes. The four-month-old schema of a human face probably consists of an oval and two symmetrically placed eyes. A distinctive feature of a human form for a one-year-old child appears to be the head; transformations which involve it elicit greater changes in cardiac deceleration and fixation times than changes in the body.

A two-year-old with an unusually rich language repertoire furnished some anecdotal support for this idea. The child was shown a series of three-dimensional male forms about 12×3 inches. One stimulus was a regular man to which she said, "That's a boy." A second form involved one transformation on this stimulus in which the head was removed from the neck and placed between the man's knees. To this form she said, "He's in his legs," and each time she saw this form (three times) she repeated this statement. To a figure of a lamb with no head at all she said, "The lamb's gone, Mommy." Both the man and the lamb seemed to be defined by the "head." Unfortunately, we know very little about the distinctive features of other events and can only guess at them. One of our central tasks is the invention of principles that will designate the distinctive features for given experiences.

The child is most ready to assimilate information that is congruent with or at least only moderately discrepant from his schema for an event. An event whose distinctive features are dramatically different from those of his schema will not be assimilated and is likely to be ignored. Thus, the structure of the materials presented to lower-middle-class or middle-class children is of critical significance.

The power of various stimuli to recruit and maintain attention changes with development. The three major forces are (a) high rate of change in the physical parameters of the stimulus; (b) discrepancy from an existing schema; and (c) degree to which the event releases a "dense" set of cognitive structures. These conditions are differently effective during the opening three years of life, and, heuristically, can be viewed as additive.

Physical Parameters

The earliest determinant of attention, from an ontogenetic point of view, is high rate of change in the physical parameters of a stimulus. Lights that blink on and off are more likely to capture the newborn's attention than a steady light source. Intermittent tones are more attention-getting than continuous ones; visual events with high black-white contour contrast possess more power to recruit sustained attention than stimuli with minimal contour contrast.[2,12] These conditions produce distinctiveness naturally. They elicit attention without prior learning. But they are most likely to hold the stage solo during the first 12 to 16 weeks.

Role of Discrepancy

A second class of conditions that produces distinctiveness is the product of experience. Selectivity and maintenance of attention appear to be curvilinearly related to the degree to which the features of an event are a distortion or discrepancy from an established schema. The four-month-old will look longer at a photograph of a face — regular or disfigured — than he will at a randomly generated figure with a high degree of black-white contrast. Table I shows the average first fixation times of two independent groups of four-month-old infants either to a set of nine different random shapes containing 5, 10, or 20 turns, or the four achromatic faces, illustrated in Figures 1 and 2, pp. 216–217.

The infants shown the faces displayed significantly longer fixation times — and, incidentally, larger cardiac decelerations — than those who viewed the randomly generated black and white designs. Existing data suggest that this difference is not present at birth.[2] The child

TABLE I

Fixation times (in seconds) and deceleration responses
(in beats per minute) to achromatic faces and random shapes

	First fixation	*Total fixation*	*Cardiac deceleration*
Random shapes (all 9 forms)	4.4	11.1	2.8
Photo regular face	10.8	22.0	8.4
Schematic regular face	10.9	21.1	8.6
Photo irregular face (collage)	8.2	19.4	6.7
Schematic irregular face (collage)	8.1	19.5	5.9

must develop some primitive schema for a human face before the representations contained in the achromatic faces gain their attention-getting effect.

Density of Associations

The third determinant of sustained attention begins to assume importance at about one year, and rests on the richness or density of

FIGURE 1   Sample of random shape shown to 4-month-old infant.

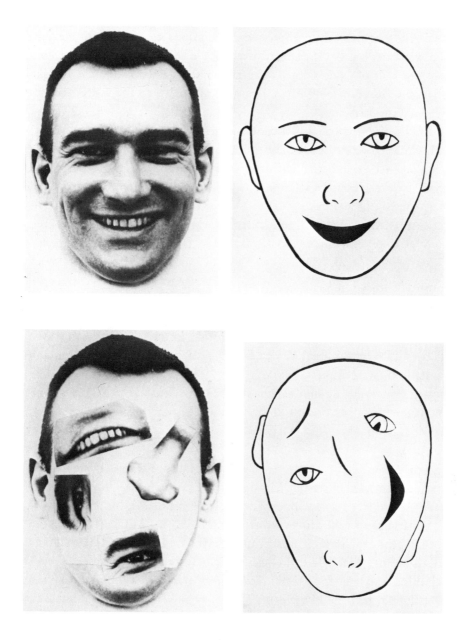

FIGURE 2   Four achromatic facial stimuli shown to infants: photo regular, schematic regular, photo scrambled, schematic scrambled.

available cognitive hypotheses or associations to a particular event. To what degree does a stimulus release a lengthy, repeated or continuing nest of associations? The richer the network of such associations the longer the child will remain attentive to the stimulus that released the structures.

Another empirical illustration of these determinants may be helpful. If one presents a set of stimuli of increasing discrepancy from a standard to verbalizing children of different ages, the older child should devote longer attention to the more discrepant events than does the younger child.

In a recent study,[3] a set of human forms and faces were presented to one-, two-, and three-year-old boys and girls in Cambridge, Massachusetts and Ticul, Mexico (on the Yucatan peninsula). There were four stimuli in each series. The "man" series was achromatic and contained a penciled drawing of a regular man (REG), a man with head and trunk (TRUNK), a man's form collaged with limbs, head, and trunk scrambled (SCR), and an amorphous free form of the same area as the other three (FF). A "face" series was painted flesh color and contained five stimuli — a man's face (REG), a man's face with one eye in the center of the forehead (CYC), a blank face (BL), a scrambled face with eyes, nose, and mouth in irregular positions (SCR), and a free form of the same general area and coloration as the four faces (FF).

The American children saw Caucasian faces and forms, the Mayan Indian children from the Yucatan saw Mayan faces and forms prepared especially for the investigation. The stimuli in each series were presented in several different orders and each stimulus was presented for 30 seconds with an interstimulus period of 15 seconds. The "man" series was presented first, the "face" series second. For both series, each stimulus was seen four times (total of 16 trials for the "man" series; 20 trials for the "face" series). Table II presents the average first fixation times to each of the stimuli by age and cultural setting.

The major finding was that while the regular face or man elicited the longest first fixation at one year of age, the "scrambled" face and "scrambled" man elicited the longest fixation at three years of age (age by stimulus interaction significant at $p < .01$ for man series and

TABLE II

Average first fixation time (in seconds) to man and face
series by age and culture (Ticul, Mexico, and Cambridge, Mass.)

	1 yr.		2 yrs.		3 yrs.	
	Ticul	Camb.	Ticul	Camb.	Ticul	Camb.
MAN						
REG	4.68	5.27	4.78	6.73	7.59	8.09
TRUNK	3.88	4.50	4.37	6.26	5.28	7.17
SCR	3.86	4.19	6.00	7.16	8.57	11.70
FF	3.35	4.10	4.86	6.08	5.58	5.98
FACE						
REG	5.16	4.06	5.45	5.54	7.52	6.66
CYC	3.09	3.39	4.90	5.15	6.35	6.91
BL	2.97	3.25	4.13	5.08	5.79	5.37
SCR	4.85	3.94	5.53	6.27	9.65	9.02
FF	3.79	3.90	4.59	5.28	6.14	6.78

$p < .05$ for face series). That is, the major change with development
was a disproportionate increase in duration of attention to the scrambled man and face. As the child's schema developed, the discrepancy
between his schema of a man and the scrambled pattern decreased and
his available association increased. At age three the scrambled forms
were moderate discrepancies from the set of distinctive features that
defined a man's face or form. When he was one year old the collaged
human forms were both too discrepant and released fewer implicit
hypotheses than they did at age three, and consequently produced
shorter attention.

Note that the Cambridge fixation times are longer than those of
the Yucatan children. Many of the Cambridge children were upper
middle class, while the Yucatan subjects were peasant Indians living
in a small village. It is important to note that the form of the age
curve was identical for both cultural groups. The slightly longer fixation times of the Cambridge children is interpreted as the result of
the richer language repertoire for the urban group. The child's at-

tention remains riveted when an event elicits a chain of associations and the volume of such emissions covaries with the richness of the repertoire. The Yucatan children had a sparse language reservoir in contrast with the Cambridge children. These data suggest that the root determinant of recruitment and maintenance of attention to a common event is similar across cultures. Differences are in degree, not kind.

Consider now a more elegant demonstration of the notion that attentional investment varies with the relation between schemata and event. Three-month-old children were exposed at home to a novel mobile (Figure 3) five to six days a week for four weeks. Each mother was instructed to hang the mobile in front of her infant's face for about half an hour each day, but only when the child was in a good mood, when he was neither hungry nor tired. One month later, when the infants were four months old, the child came to the laboratory and was shown the original mobile he had seen at home (model O) and three transformations he had never seen (1, 2, 3, in Figure 3). Each of the four stimuli was shown four times in random order and four different orders of presentation were used. The control group of four-month-old infants who had never seen any of the stimuli was tested in the same way. Figure 4 illustrates the cardiac deceleration to the four stimuli.

The magnitude of cardiac deceleration was larger in reaction to the transformations than to the original stimulus and maximal to the second and third order transformations for the experimentally exposed girls (F=5.81, p<.05 for difference in linear trend[10]), whereas there were no differences among stimuli for the control infants. The transformations were moderately discrepant from the original mobile to which the infant had been exposed. This result obtained only for girls. We know that girls are more precocious than boys, and we interpret this sex difference as indicating that the schema for the original mobile was better formed among the girls.

First fixation times were consistently lower to all stimuli for the experimental subjects of both sexes (F=6.87, df=1/41, p<.05). This result is concordant with the general assumption that familiarity with a class of stimuli leads to shorter fixation times. The mobile-

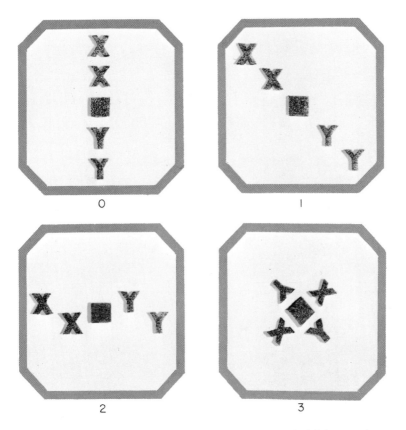

FIGURE 3 Mobile stimuli shown to 3-month-old children at home with transformations — 0 is experimental mobile shown at home; stimuli 1, 2, and 3 are the transformations seen only in the laboratory.

experienced girls displayed a fixation pattern that resembled the cardiac data in Figure 4, but the differences among stimuli were not as pronounced and appropriate interactions and trends were not statistically reliable. Hence, fixation time was not as sensitive as cardiac deceleration to the transformations. Moreover, these data support previous work suggesting that when an infant or child is surprised by a stimulus a cardiac deceleration is a likely accompaniment to that experience.

Cognitive growth resembles a traveling wave. With each succeeding set of experiences, distinctive features change and prepare the child

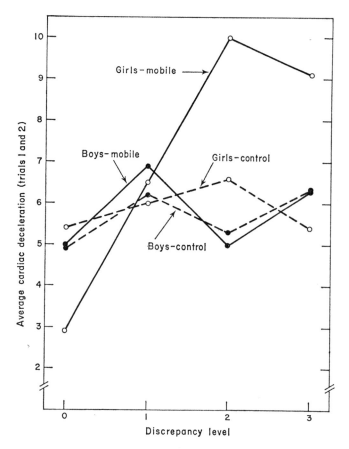

FIGURE 4 Mean cardiac deceleration to mobile seen at home and to the three discrepant transformations.

to decode and attend to an event that he was unable to assimilate at an earlier time. At this moment we have only the simplest procedures to examine the detailed structure of a child's schema. A useful strategy is to posit, a priori, a set of distinctive elements, present transformations on those elements to the child, and note which ones elicit changes in the reactions that accompany attention.

HOW ARE SCHEMATA ESTABLISHED?

What are the conditions that lead to the establishment of a schema and to changes in a schema? Piaget's description of cognitive development cannot be regarded as a complete theory because there are in-sufficiently detailed statements concerning the conditions that cause the child to relinquish one set of operations or rules for another. Our contemporary understanding of cognitive growth resembles the state of chemical theory in the seventeenth century when a scientist could point to obvious changes in the color, weight, smell, or texture of materials as a result of an intrusion, either natural or purposive, but could not explain what happened.

A detailed consideration of the existing and potential differences between lower-middle-class and middle-class children proceeds best in a theoretical context, and we shall entertain some hypotheses re-garding the growth and alteration of schemata.

PRINCIPLE 1   Any change in the features that define a schema re-quires the selective attention of the child. Without investment of at-tention there is no alteration in a schema.

PRINCIPLE 2   Selectivity of attention is related in part to the distinc-tiveness of an event. This is a restatement of Helson's notion that an effective stimulus is discrepant from the subject's adaptation level. Distinctiveness is too general a term, and one must stipulate some of the conditions that create distinctiveness. If a fourth-grade classroom has a green blackboard and all others in the school have black black-boards, the child entering this room for the first time will be likely to orient to the green board and his schema for this room is apt to pivot on the green board; for the other classrooms, the schema will be organized around different elements. Stated in more formal terms, elements with high information will be most likely to attract atten-tion and form the core of established schemata.

Another basis for acquired distinctiveness derives from conditions in which attainment of a goal is contingent upon detecting a partic-ular element. In discrimination learning the child becomes aware of a new distinctive feature because solution of a problem demands se-lective attention to that critical element. Similarly, any event that is linked with a distinctive internal signal, such as an affective experi-ence, will acquire distinctiveness.

Finally, distinctiveness can be established through verbal communication, through an instruction that informs the child of the distinctive element. The mother tells her four-year-old who has just called a goat a dog, "No, that's not a doggie; see the horns, a doggie does not have horns." A schema has been changed and the distinctive features of the schema for dog have been altered permanently.

IMPLICATIONS FOR CLASS DIFFERENCES

Let us consider some class differences in cognitive functioning in light of the above two principles. As part of an extensive longitudinal investigation, and using education as the criterion, we have seen more than 160 first-born Caucasian infants from lower-middle-class, middle-, and upper-middle-class families. Lower-middle-class infants were from families in which one or both parents had not completed high school and whose fathers were in unskilled occupations. Upper-middle-class infants came from families in which both parents were at least college graduates. The lower-middle-class group was not representative of the urban slum family that comprises the core of the group typically called "deprived," because the former had employed fathers in the home and income levels were higher than those in inner-city slums.

At four months of age each infant was shown two visual episodes in the laboratory. In the first episode, each child was shown four different achromatic slides of human faces four times. The slides were a photograph of a male face, a schematic outline of a male face, a collage of the photograph of the face, and a collage of the schematic face (see Figure 2). Each stimulus was presented for 30 seconds with a 15-second rest interval between each stimulus, during which the visual field was partially illuminated. The stimuli were presented 20 inches from the plane of the child's face by a slide projector electronically programed for the correct intervals of stimulus presentation and interstimulus period. The 16 stimulus presentations were preceded by one buffer stimulus, which was an achromatic photograph of a male with one eye.

After a short recess the child was shown a series of three-dimensional sculptured faces painted flesh color, four presentations each of four different faces: a regular male face; a collage of that face with eyes, nose, and mouth rearranged; a regular face with no eyes; and a blank face without eyes, nose, or mouth (Figure 5). Each stimulus was presented for 30 seconds with a 15-second rest interval between each stimulus, during which the visual field was homogeneously white. This series was also preceded by a three-dimensional buffer stimulus. The major variables coded for both visual episodes were duration of each fixation of the stimulus, smiling, vocalization, and change in heart rate during the first fixation.

A word about the cardiac response variable: the children's resting heart rates ranged between 120 and 180 beats per minute with an average of about 145 beats. The infants were never tested when they were upset, and no dramatic fluctuations in heart rate occurred during the experiment. The major variable of interest was the magnitude of the cardiac deceleration during the first fixation of the stimulus. The heart rate was most likely to begin its descent during the first five or six seconds of the first fixation (see Figure 6, p. 227, for a typical deceleration response). The use of cardiac deceleration as a correlate of attentional processes is based on the original work of Lacey,[7] Lacey, Kagan, Lacey, and Moss,[8] and previous investigations of cardiac changes to visual input in infants.[9]

If the child did not show a cardiac deceleration, the most frequent alternative was no change in heart rate. Acceleration to onset of the first fixation was not a common event and usually occurred when the child was startled, motorically active, or cried. Cardiac acceleration is not on a continuum with deceleration, and we shall not be concerned with it in this paper. The index of deceleration was computed in the following manner. The mean of the three lowest contiguous heart beats during the five seconds prior to the first fixation was regarded as the base value. The mean of the three lowest contiguous heart beats during the first fixation was the heart rate value for the stimulus. The stimulus value was then subtracted from the base value to arrive at the deceleration score. If the difference was positive (i.e., the base was higher than the fixation value), that difference was scored as the magnitude of cardiac deceleration. If the differences were zero or positive, a score of zero was coded. Table III presents the average first fixation times to the first two series of each episode by

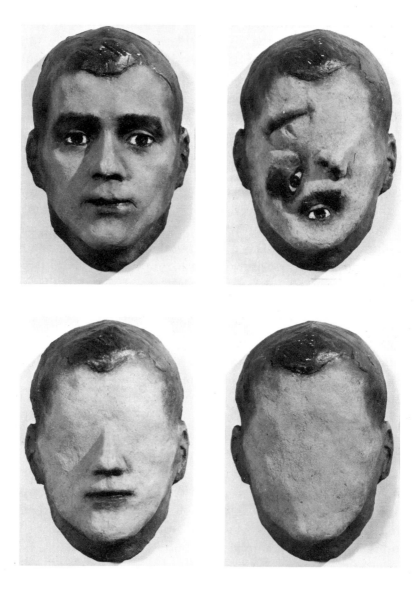

FIGURE 5   Three-dimensional faces shown to the infants in the laboratory — regular, scrambled, no eyes, and blank.

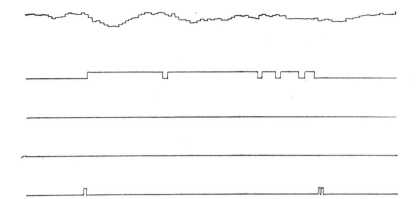

FIGURE 6 Sample of typical deceleration response during a first fixation in a four-month-old infant; top line is heart rate; second line indicates fixation; third line, smiling; fourth line, vocalization; fifth line, onset and termination of stimuli.

stimulus (trials 1–8), as well as the mean first fixation times to all 16 trials for each of the two episodes (p. 228). Family educational level had no significant effect on fixation time.

Table IV (p. 229) presents the cardiac deceleration data by stimulus for each sex and educational level (the score is the mean of the two largest decelerations to each stimulus in the series).*

The children from the lowest educational level consistently displayed the smallest cardiac decelerations to all the stimuli (13 of the 16 comparisons involving the achromatic and three-dimensional faces between the least- and best-educated families revealed smaller decelerations for the infants of the former group). The differences were

* We performed a nonparametric analysis with chi square. In these analyses we chose absolute rather than shifting (i.e., relative) levels of deceleration for cutting points, and we retained the same cutting points for all analyses. We divided the distribution of decelerations into three categories — zero to 2, 3 to 7, and equal to or greater than 8 beats. We viewed decelerations of one or two beats as essentially insignificant, and most likely to be due to error. The choice of the interval 3 to 7 beats was based on the fact that the majority of the decelerations typically fall in this range. But most of them were not accompanied by any other obvious signs of attention or surprise in the child. Decelerations greater than 7 beats were most often associated with facial or motoric responses indicating a surprise or attentive posture. Decelerations over 7 beats are least likely to be false positives and we have the greatest faith that decelerations of this magnitude reflect a special cognitive reaction to the stimulus.

TABLE III

Average first fixation times (trials 1–2)
to achromatic and three-dimensional faces

		Education of parents			
		Less than high school	High school graduate	Part college	College graduate or more
Boys		N=16	N=24	N=24	N=15
	Photo Regular	10.9	10.7	11.9	9.5
	Schematic Regular	12.3	11.5	13.5	9.8
Achromatic	Photo Scrambled	9.8	8.8	8.0	8.2
Faces	Schematic Scrambled	9.6	7.8	8.3	5.9
	Mean of all 16 trials	8.9	8.4	9.3	7.6
	Regular	7.8	10.2	10.3	9.4
Three	Scrambled	9.4	11.5	11.1	9.7
Dimensional	No Eyes	5.4	7.7	6.5	7.8
Faces	Blank	3.5	5.7	5.2	4.5
	Mean of all 16 trials	5.8	8.3	7.3	7.6
Girls		N=12	N=18	N=25	N=17
	Photo Regular	9.8	7.5	11.5	9.6
	Schematic Regular	11.7	7.2	10.6	9.7
Achromatic	Photo Scrambled	7.3	4.9	8.6	7.9
Faces	Schematic Scrambled	9.3	6.5	8.1	7.7
	Mean of all 16 trials	7.5	5.4	8.7	7.8
	Regular	9.4	7.9	9.0	10.9
Three	Scrambled	12.8	10.1	9.4	10.0
Dimensional	No Eyes	6.2	5.4	7.9	6.6
Faces	Blank	4.6	4.6	5.0	5.4
	Mean of all 16 trials	7.3	6.3	6.9	7.0

most marked for the "blank" three dimensional face — a stimulus clearly discrepant from the regular human face.

It should be noted that there was a great deal of variability in the deceleration scores (the range, for example, was from zero to 30 beats).

Table V presents the proportion of each sex and educational group

TABLE IV

Mean of the two largest decelerations
to the achromatic and three-dimensional faces

	Education of parents				
	Less than high school	High school graduate	Part college	College graduate or more	Significance level
Boys	N=15	N=17	N=15	N=12	
Photo Regular	5.3	8.2	8.4	8.6	
Schematic Regular	5.3	10.0	9.2	6.1	
Photo Scrambled	4.3	6.0	5.3	7.3	
Schematic Scrambled	4.4	7.5	5.3	4.2	
4 largest decelerations	7.9	11.9	11.1	10.5	
Regular	5.1	7.5	6.5	7.1	
Scrambled	4.1	7.7	9.0	5.7	
No Eyes	5.1	7.9	7.3	4.9	
Blank	1.5	6.5	6.0	4.1	F=3.18, p<.05
4 largest decelerations	7.1	10.9	10.9	8.5	
Girls	N=11	N=16	N=18	N=11	
Photo Regular	6.9	6.6	7.3	5.2	
Schematic Scrambled	4.4	6.2	7.0	5.7	
Photo Scrambled	2.9	4.0	6.3	5.9	
Schematic Scrambled	3.1	5.4	5.3	6.7	
4 largest decelerations	6.7	9.6	10.2	8.5	
Regular	5.1	6.0	10.1	6.8	
Scrambled	7.1	5.5	8.0	7.4	
No Eyes	4.9	5.4	5.8	5.5	
Blank	1.9	4.0	5.9	5.3	F=2.58, p=.06
4 largest decelerations	8.5	8.4	11.0	10.3	

TABLE V

*Per cent of each group showing cardiac decelerations of 0–2
(no deceleration); 3–7 (moderate deceleration) and equal to or greater than
8 beats (high deceleration) to faces. (each value rounded to whole numbers.)*

		Girls			Boys			Total Sample			
		Education of parents			Education of parents			Education of parents			
	Decel	Low	Mod	High	Low	Mod	High	Low	Mod	High	
Achromatic faces											
Photo	None	30	40	20	33	14	18	32	27	19	
(Regular)	Mod.	40	10	26	47	50	18	44	30	22	
	High	30	50	54	20	34	64	24	43	59	
Schematic	None	40	17	28	28	4	12	33	10	20	
(Regular)	Mod.	50	31	36	44	46	44	46	45	40	
	High	10	52	36	28	50	44	21	45	40	
Photo	None	80	35	20	33	25	12	52	30	16	
(Scrambled)	Mod.	10	41	40	54	54	50	36	47	45	
	High	10	24	40	13	21	38	12	23	39	$\chi^2=10.53$, df$=4$, p$<.05$
Schematic	None	50	16	20	27	25	25	36	21	22	
(Scrambled)	Mod.	40	44	47	46	47	50	44	45	48	
	High	10	40	33	27	28	25	20	34	30	
3-Dimensional faces											
Regular	None	46	18	12	33	24	18	39	21	14	
	Mod.	36	35	44	50	36	41	43	36	43	
	High	18	47	44	17	40	41	18	43	43	
Scrambled	None	36	22	25	50	24	23	43	24	24	
	Mod.	36	35	37	33	28	35	35	31	36	
	High	28	43	38	17	48	42	22	45	40	
No Eyes	None	36	17	19	33	28	23	34	23	21	
	Mod.	45	52	56	58	28	54	53	18	55	
	High	19	31	25	9	44	23	13	59	24	
Blank	None	82	35	25	67	35	29	74	33	27	
	Mod.	9	39	50	33	39	42	22	35	46	
	High	9	26	25	0	26	29	4	32	27	$\chi^2=15.40$, df$=4$, p$<.01$

showing no deceleration (zero, one, or two beats), moderate decelerations (three to seven beats) or large decelerations (eight or more) to each of the stimuli. Chi square tests appear when they were significant. In this analysis, we pooled the two average educated groups to yield three groups — a poorly educated group (less than high-school graduation), moderately educated group (high-school graduation and part college), and a well- or highly educated group (both parents at least college graduates).

Each of the eight stimuli yielded the same trend. The infants of the poorly educated parents were less likely than those of the better educated to have large decelerations (greater than seven beats), and typically contained more subjects showing no deceleration. The trend was similar for both sexes. When the data were pooled for sex, significant chi-square values emerged for the collaged photograph in the achromatic series (chi square=10.53, p<.05); and for the blank, three-dimensional face (chi square=15.40, p<.01).

Note that there were no differences among the educational groups in average heart rate during the base period. The means were similar and averaged between 140–145 bpm.

When the middle range of deceleration (two to seven beats) was omitted, and we considered only no deceleration or large decelerations for the two extreme educational groups, the results, of course, were more dramatic and significant chi squares emerged for the collaged photograph (chi square=9.00, p<.01), the three dimensional blank face (chi square=6.65, p<.01); the achromatic photograph of the regular face (chi square=3.84, p<.05); and the three dimensional regular face (chi square=5.72, p<.05). In every one of the eight comparisons, more infants of the well-educated than of the least-educated showed decelerations over seven beats.

How are these findings to be interpreted? We first need a brief discussion of the meaning of the fixation and cardiac deceleration responses. As stated earlier, fixation time during the period 3–12 months appears to be curvilinearly related to the degree of discrepancy between schema and stimulus, with a broad, flat area covering a large set of stimuli, each of which is discrepant from an existing schema. Figure 7 illustrates the hypothetical relation between duration of

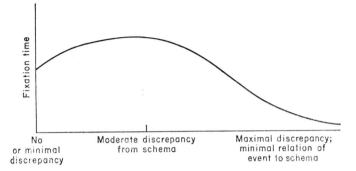

FIGURE 7 Hypothetical relation between fixation time and discrepancy from child's schema.

fixation time (primarily the first fixation) and discrepancy from a schema.

This hypothetical relation predicts that the infant will display equivalent fixation times to a band of stimuli that are different from each other, and each is differentially discrepant from the presumed existing schema. There is empirical support for this proposition. The reader will recall from the data in Table I that fixation times to the photograph of the male face and to the schematic outline of the male face were equivalent, despite gross differences in contrast and shading. Moreover, fixation times to the collages of these two stimuli were shorter than they were to the regular faces (as might be expected on the basis of their greater discrepancy), but were equivalent to each other. Fixation times of the one-, two-, and three-year-old children tested in Cambridge and Yucatan, summarized in Table II, are also confirmatory. The fixation times to regular man and "trunk" in the "man" series were not significantly different from each other. Similarly, first fixation times were equal to the regular and cyclops faces at each of the three ages. Additional data from our laboratory also confirm this generalization.

Cardiac deceleration, on the other hand, seems to bear a more specific relation to the schema-stimulus discrepancy. Maximal cardiac deceleration apparently occurs in response to a small band of stimulus discrepancies that are relatively close to the child's schema — stimuli that involve changes in only one or two aspects or components of the set of distinctive features that define the schema. The reader will recall the mobile study in which a schema for a novel stimulus was established experimentally in three-month-old infants. The largest deceleration, one month later, occurred in response to the stimuli that were transformations of the original. Figure 8 shows a hypothetical relation between magnitude of cardiac deceleration and discrepancy from schema.

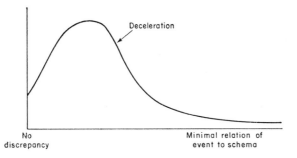

FIGURE 8   Hypothetical relation between cardiac deceleration and discrepancy from child's schema.

The critical deduction from the two hypothetical curves is that when one is dealing with a set of stimuli that are somewhat similar to each other, but are differentially discrepant from a schema (i.e., none is so discrepant that it has no cognitive links to a schema) the child with a better-articulated schema is likely to show larger deceleration to these stimuli than one with a poorly articulated schema, because the discrepant stimulus is, for the former, closer to his schema. Thus, he is more likely to be surprised. Note that this prediction is based on the critical assumption that all the stimuli are indeed discrepant. If the child's schema is so well articulated that the event is immediately assimilable, then, of course, there will be no deceleration. Recall that the girls in the mobile study showed minimal deceleration to the stimulus to which they were exposed at home.

Let us now return to the finding that lower-middle-class infants had smaller decelerations to the face stimuli than did middle-class subjects. If we assume that the children from the least-educated parents have a less well-articulated schema of a face than have middle-class infants, the former should not display large decelerations to representations of faces, especially to those that are grossly discrepant, such as the collaged photograph and the blank face.

Figure 9 illustrates the hypothetical position of the two groups on the curves for fixation time and deceleration. Note that the faces are assumed to be less discrepant from the schema of the upper-middle-class infants and that therefore these subjects are likely to show larger decelerations than the poorly educated group. But the fixation times

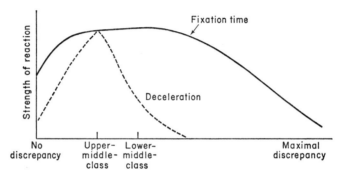

FIGURE 9 Hypothetical position of poorly and well-educated infants at 4 months of age on the discrepancy continuum for faces.

should be essentially equivalent for both groups. The lower-middle-class infant looks as long or longer at the faces, but does not decelerate because the face is not close enough to his schema to elicit a recognitory reaction and an accompanying cardiac deceleration. (Fewer infants of poorly educated families smiled at the collage of the achromatic photograph than did infants from well educated families [chi square=4.19, p<.05]. Since the smile at four months can be regarded as an index of a recognitory reaction, the smile and deceleration data are concordant.) The favored explanation for this difference is that the mother's face has been a more distinctive stimulus for the upper-middle-class child. We believe that well-educated parents engage in more frequent, distinctive, face-to-face contact with their children, and are thus more likely to create conditions that will make the parent's countenance a distinctive stimulus. In a moment we shall consider some empirical support for this idea.

DIFFERENCES IN LANGUAGE DEVELOPMENT

The most dramatic differences between lower-middle-class and middle-class children of preschool or school age involve language skills. Documentation for this conclusion is everywhere (see Cazden-Courtney[1]). A fast and often glib interpretation of the difference rests on the belief that lower-middle-class parents talk less often to their children. This may be too simple an interpretation. We certainly do not wish to reject this idea totally, but to balance it with the possibility that lower-middle-class children are not so much deprived of parental vocalization as they are deprived of distinctive vocalization. "Distinctive vocalization" refers to speech directed at the infant and not accompanied by other sensory inputs that might distract the infant. The lower-middle-class child does not receive distinctive verbal stimulation from adults and, as a result, is less likely to attend to human speech.

Consider the following empirical support for this statement. When about half (77) of the children described earlier were four months old, they were observed with their mothers in the home for a day. Each mother was told to act naturally with her child. She was to attend to her daily routine as if the observer were not present. Although this instruction is impossible to follow in the literal sense, the two observers felt that most mothers were relatively natural. A selected set of mother and child variables were discretely coded every five seconds. The observer wore a small, inconspicuous, battery-powered device in her ear. This produced a brief auditory signal every five seconds and the observer recorded, in five-second units, variables that belonged to a prearranged code. Some of the variables included: mother vocalize to infant, mother touch infant, mother vigorously manipulate infant, mother pick up infant, child vocalize, child extend limbs, and child thrash.

When one computes the percentage of time the mother vocalized to the infant, regardless of what else she was doing, there was only a slight and nonsignificant tendency for the upper-middle-class mothers to vocalize more often than lower-middle-class or middle-class mothers to their daughters (28 per cent of the time for upper-middle-class versus 19 and 14 per cent for lower-middle-class and middle-class mothers respectively). There were even less striking class differences for sons. When we examined the distinctiveness of the mothers' vocalization, more dramatic differences appeared. In a second analysis we computed the proportion of vocalizations from mother to child that occurred alone, in a distinctive context; when the mother simply was close by and not touching, tickling, or picking up the infant. Table VI contains class differences in maternal distinctive vocalization.

College-educated mothers were more likely than less well-educated mothers to vocalize to their daughters in a distinctive manner (t= 2.75, p<.05 for the difference between the mothers with less than high-school education and mothers with college degrees). These data

TABLE VI

Differences in maternal distinctive vocalization to infant as a function of education level

Education of mother	Girls			t low vs. high	p
	Low	*Middle*	*High*		
Per cent distinctive vocalization	5.0	5.0	10.5	2.75	< .05
Per cent non-distinctive vocalization	10.8	12.1	17.0		
Education of mother	Boys				
	Low	*Middle*	*High*		
Per cent distinctive vocalization	6.0	5.1	5.2		
Per cent non-distinctive vocalization	15.0	15.7	14.1		

suggest that the lower-middle-class girl is not so much deprived of vocal stimulation from the mother as she is deprived of distinctive vocal stimulation. Some of the instances of distinctive maternal vocalization were direct responses to the child's babbling. In a third analysis, we noted each time the child vocalized (frets, whines, and cries were not counted) and asked what happened during the next 10 seconds. Did the mother respond in any way to the child's vocalization and, if so, what was the nature of her response? Table VII contains

TABLE VII

Per cent of time mother responded to infant's vocalization

Education of mother	Girls			t low vs. high	p
	Low	*Middle*	*High*		
Distinctive vocalization	12.1	11.0	21.0	2.06	= .06
Non-distinctive vocalization	4.2	8.0	3.1		
No response	78.4	77.9	61.0	2.20	< .05
Per cent of time child vocalized	13.6	16.9	14.2		

Education of mother	Boys		
	Low	*Middle*	*High*
Distinctive vocalization	19.1	15.2	12.7
Non-distinctive vocalization	12.0	17.3	11.1
No response	63.6	65.4	71.1
Per cent of time child vocalized	10.9	14.2	15.1

the proportion of time the mothers of each educational group responded to the child's vocalization with a distinctive vocalization, a vocalization that accompanied tactile or visual input, and the proportion of time the mother made no response within 10 seconds of the child's vocalization. The best-educated mothers of girls were more likely to respond to the child's vocalizations with a vocal response and were less likely to ignore the infant $(t=2.20, p<.05)$. The lower-middle-class girl vocalized as often as the upper-middle-class girl, but the lower-middle-class mother was more likely to ignore her daughter. As in the earlier analysis, there were no class differences among boys. The effect of class on reciprocal vocal interchange between mother and child held only for girls.

The upper-middle-class daughter seems to receive more distinctive vocalization from her mother than both the lower-middle-class girl or any son and, as many studies have shown, has the most precocious language development of any category of child. The sex difference in maternal predisposition to respond vocally to the infant's babbling is supported by Moss's[11] report that the middle-class mothers of infant girls are more likely to imitate their daughters than their sons.

Let us describe a hypothetical lower-middle-class and upper-middle-class girl's experience. The upper-middle-class child is lying in her crib in her bedroom on the second floor of a suburban home. She wakes, the room is quiet, her mother is downstairs baking. The infant studies the crib and her fingers. Suddenly the quiet is broken as the mother enters and speaks to the child. This auditory intrusion is maximally distinctive and likely to orient the infant to her mother and to the vocalization. If the child responds vocally, the mother is apt to continue the dialogue. Contrast this set of events with those that occur to an infant girl in Harlem lying on a couch in a two-room apartment with the television going and siblings peering into her face. The child lies in a sea of sound, but, like the sea, it is homogeneous. The mother approaches the child and says something to her. This communication, however, is minimally distinctive from background noise and, as such, is not likely to recruit the infant's attention. Many of the infant's vocalizations during the day are not likely to be heard by anyone nor are they likely to elicit a special response. The fundamental theme of this argument seeks to minimize the importance of absolute amount of stimulation the child receives and spotlights instead the distinctiveness of that stimulation.

MAINTENANCE OF ATTENTIONAL INVESTMENT

Distinctiveness of events recruits the child's attention and can maintain it for 5, 10, or even 20 seconds. But sustained attention for minutes requires more than discrepancy; it requires the possession of structures or chains of cognitive units that are specifically elicited by the event. When one sees a three-year-old devote a half hour to exploration of an old telephone, we are tempted to smile and mumble something about the child's natural curiosity. But long periods of sustained involvement are neither inherent in the event nor part of the child's natural equipment. Sustained involvement is dependent on the child's having previously acquired a set of hypotheses and reactions; a set of associations to the event; a structured set of schemata appropriate to the object. If this prior learning has not occurred, a 30-minute exploration will have been reduced to less than 30 seconds. I recall a teacher bringing in a dozen packs of Cape Cod seaweed stuffed with attractive samples of shells of diverse species. She gave each pair of six-year-old children one of these attractive toys and withdrew, expecting them to display their natural curiosity. Each child devoted less than 10 seconds to the material before returning to his previous game. The child had no complex questions to ask of the shells, few hypotheses to emit, no rich set of responses to release upon this material. As a result, there was no sustained attention — no curiosity.

CHANGE OF SCHEMATA AND STRUCTURES

As indicated earlier, we have no adequate theory of schema change. The discussion that follows is intended only as an introduction, and not as a finished set of propositions. The discussion may be aided if the reader holds in mind an image of an adult with a poorly articulated schema for the dashboard of a car. The initial schema is a series of protrusions, sections of glass and shiny knobs. What are the conditions that will change this schema and alter the relative distinctiveness of elements in the array?

The Role of Habituation

If a person attends for a long period of time to a particular event, he will gradually habituate to one set of features. If the conditions are such that the individual is either motivated to continue, or the event is attractive enough to maintain his attention, eventually a different set of distinctive features will be noticed. The child who is allowed or has the opportunity to engage in long periods of sustained involvement with a toy or object should habituate to the initial set of distinctive features and discover a new set. The child who is not allowed, does not prefer, or initially is not capable of a long period of sustained attention to an event, will be less likely to make that discovery.

There are, of course, dramatic individual differences in the tendency to display long periods of sustained involvement with objects. Earlier work in our laboratory demonstrated that lower-middle-class, school-age children were more likely to be impulsive in problems with response uncertainty, more likely to show short decision times when faced with a problem. This predisposition to act, at the sacrifice of continued scanning of alternatives, lowers the probability that the lower-middle-class child will detect a new feature, perhaps the feature that unlocks the problem. The idea that long periods of study facilitate changes in a schema resembles the worn maxim that a creative idea requires a long period of incubation. The mind scans the older features, wearing a path until it notices a new element, and finally gives birth to a new structure.

Contingencies of Reward and Punishment

The most frequent conditions for change in a schema are related to goal attainment. If attention to a cue is instrumental in attaining a goal or avoiding an unpleasant event, distinctiveness is automatically enhanced and a new element will dominate the set of distinctive features. It may be that the lower-middle-class, preschool child typically is not required to master instrumental skills, especially language skills, as frequently as is the middle-class child. The development of speech furnishes one of the best examples of the differential operation of this principle. The middle-class mother, as Roger Brown and others have noted, corrects the child's speech and often will not give desirable goals unless the child pronounces a word correctly. The three-year-old points to the candy and the middle-class mother says, "What do you say? Say candy," and withholds the prize until the child complies. This mother's anxious preoccupation with mastery and the independence it implies pushes the child to attend to new features in order to solve instrumental problems.

The Power of Language

A final condition for schema change resides in the power of words. The lower-middle-class child does not have a large reservoir of words to comprehend communications and he lives in a milieu in which adults are not likely to use words to point out distinctive features.

Habituation, goal attainment, and language catalyze change in the distinctive features of a schema. The lower-middle-class child seems to be deprived of experience related to all three of these processes.

THE MOTIVATIONAL BASES OF COGNITIVE DEVELOPMENT

This discussion has centered primarily on the dynamics of cognitive structures; on schemata and their change. We must now consider a second constellation of forces that recruit and maintain attention, forces usually referred to as socialization or personality dimensions. The role of motives, standards, and sources of anxiety is most closely related to the dynamics surrounding reward and punishment. If the child wishes to obtain a particular goal and if attention is required in order to attain the goal, the child is likely to pay the price.

We usually assume that a motive for a goal increases the probability that the child will attend to cues that are instrumental in attaining the goal. This principle holds for all children. Differences between lower-middle-class and middle-class children are likely to reside with the specific goal each seeks and, more specifically, with particular instrumental procedures used to acquire the goals. Some of the psychological goals that children seek include:

1 signs of positive evaluation, recognition, attention by particular adults; by peers;
2 instrumental aid;
3 maximization of perceived similarity to a desirable model;
4 autonomy of action;
5 dominance of others;
6 genital stimulation;
7 congruence with standards, especially standards for sex-appropriate behaviors; mastery of specific skills or tasks;
8 signs of pain or unhappiness in another (i.e., hostility);
9 reduction of uncertainty; reduction of anxiety;
10 avoidance of failure, pain, and punishment.

At this level of abstraction, children are remarkably similar. But the specific social contexts in which the child resides establish different contracts with children. As a result, children differ in the primacy of each of these goals (i.e., their hierarchical organization) and the means by which they attain them.

The middle-class parent who values intellectual development barters a demand that the child master language and academic skills in return for continued signs of positive evaluation. The lower-middle-class parent more often insists on generalized obedience in return for avoidance of painful punishment. The lower-middle-class child is more likely to hear, "Don't be bad," whereas the middle-class child encounters, "Don't make a mistake, don't bring home a bad report card." Each child imprints on the parent's major concern. The middle-class child is apt to learn strong anxiety over failure at an academic task; the lower-middle-class child learns to be anxious about "getting caught" after a violation of a prohibition on aggression or destruction.

EXPECTANCY OF FAILURE VERSUS ANXIETY OVER FAILURE

Expectancy of failure is a subjective estimate of the probability of success or failure on a task. Anxiety over failure, which involves uncomfortable feelings, requires possession of high standards of performance as well as an expectancy of failure. High expectancy of failure in an area that a person does not value does not elicit anxiety. The middle-class child is more likely to possess high standards than the lower-middle-class child, and, as a result, is more likely to be anxious about failure. High anxiety over failure leads the middle-class child to behave in a way that helps to protect him from the failure experience. One of the most adaptive strategies to minimize failure is to place strong inhibition upon impulsively given answers. The middle-class child is likely to inhibit a response, to brood excessively before reporting an answer. The lower-middle-class child offers his answers impulsively, in part because he cares less about a mistake. He has less reason to inhibit a response.

We have administered perceptual discrimination tasks with response uncertainty to lower-middle-class and middle-class children in grades one through five. Figure 10 illustrates two sample items from the Matching Familiar Figures test. The child is asked to select the

Figure 10 Sample items from the Matching Familiar Figures test.

one tree or toy from the set of six trees or six toys that are identical to the standard. Average response time to the child's first solution hypothesis and error scores across the 12-item test reveals that response times are typically faster and error rates typically higher for lower-middle-class than for middle-class children.

Sigel has given conceptual sorting tasks to five-year-old Negro children from lower-middle-class and middle-class backgrounds, and the results are similar. The lower-middle-class children offered concepts impulsively. They did not take time to analyze the stimuli and did not give analytically-based concepts that middle-class children begin to produce at five years of age.[13]

When six- and seven-year-old children begin to learn to read, an impulsive attitude, based on minimal anxiety over error commission, leads to errors. The initial grapheme will be misread, a suffix dropped or added. In one study, first-grade children were evaluated with respect to their tendency to respond impulsively or with reflection on the Matching Familiar Figures test. The child with unusually fast decision times (an average of five seconds) and many errors (usually two errors per item) was classified as impulsive. The child with long decision times (more than 15–20 seconds) and few errors (less than one per item) was called reflective.

The children were asked to recognize words by selecting the one word of five presented that matched the word read aloud by the examiner. For example, the child would be shown a card on which the five words — noon, moon, boom, soon, and mean — were printed. The examiner would say the word "moon" and the child had to point to the correct word on the card. The point biserial correlations between the reflection-impulsivity dimension and recognition errors were .34 ($p < .05$) for boys, and .59 ($p < .001$) for girls. Most of the children were seen one year later when they were in the second grade. At this time they were asked to read four paragraphs aloud. The impulsive children made more errors than the reflectives, even when verbal intelligence was controlled. The impulsive children were more likely to add or drop suffixes, misread initial graphemes, or interchange internal letters.[5] Since an impulsive attitude is more prevalent among lower-middle-class children, it is always a potential contributor to poor reading performance.

It is important to note that although the classification "impulsive" is based on the molar variables of decision time and errors, the more molecular scanning strategies of the impulsive child are consonant with the grosser variables. In a recently completed investigation, school-age children were classified impulsive or reflective on the basis of errors and response time on the standard Matching Familiar Figures test which we use for categorizing children on this dimension. (This work is Miss Diana Drake's doctoral dissertation.) These children were then placed in the apparatus designed by Mackworth, which permits coding of the subject's eye movements while scanning a visual display. The children were shown a standard and four variants and given the same instruction as used on the original test. However, this time the child's eye movements were being photographed. During the first six seconds of stimulus exposure, the impulsive child made fewer comparisons of homologous areas in the variants, suggesting that the impulsive child does not adopt as systematic a search strategy as does the reflective.

A central determinant of impulsivity is minimal anxiety over making a mistake, which depends upon standards of correctness. The fragility of a consistently high standard of correctness is seen clearly in the two-year-old child. We have been administering perceptual tests to 27-month-old children of middle- and lower-middle-class membership. One of the most striking aspects of the children's behavior is that their involvement and concern with being correct hangs precariously on a slim motivational thread. As long as they are performing adequately and are told or sense that they are correct, they continue to be affectively involved and try to find the disguised standard in an Embedded Figures task. However, after one failure — or, for the more zealous, two failures — enthusiasm is transformed dramatically to apathy. Most children begin to respond impulsively or leave their chairs and wander around the room. It is usually very difficult to bring the child back to the task once he has had one or two failure experiences. A concern with correct performance is a standard that is acquired only gradually, and in its early development is easily dissolved. When it is not operative, impulsivity or apathy are typical reaction patterns to problems with a correct solution. The lower-middle-class child of preschool age typically has not acquired a strong standard of quality for intellectual skills. The child must develop a desire to be correct and there is some evidence suggesting that the middle-class child, as young as 27 months, derives more joy from mastery. We have recently administered our own version of an Embedded Figures task to 42 children, 27 months of age. There is no dramatic class difference in the quality of performance, but the middle-class children are more likely to smile spontaneously when they detect the correct answer — when they spot the standard in the disguised array. The lower-middle-class child smiles less often, suggesting that "being correct," in an artificial problem-solving situation, is less satisfying; that it is less of a victory than it is for the child whose parents have a college education.

Many of the intellectual tasks the culture requires of children have a minimal meaning. These tasks are infused with value by a uniquely human form of alchemy — an adult who has acquired value announces his concern about mastery of that task. The lower-middle-class child may be missing the experience of a valued adult communicating concern about correctness of behavior and rewarding such correctness affectively. This deprivation could lead to an impulsive orientation.

One of the implications of this discussion is that remedial work with lower-middle-class children should consider specific training in reflection as a first step in rehabilitation. This training can be effective. Recent studies from our own and other laboratories have demonstrated that impulsive children can be trained to inhibit fast decision times. In one study we took a direct approach and told the child he could not answer until a signal was given. He was forced to inhibit a response for a fixed duration. After three forty-minute training sessions another observer returned to test the child, and we discovered that the training had led to dramatically slower decision times, in contrast to a control group of impulsive children who experienced no training. The response times of the trained children were approximately twice those of the untrained impulsive children.[6] Wright and Briggs have also found that reflective children can be shaped through direct tutoring, and Debus has found that exposure to a reflective model can lengthen decision times in third-grade children. (The results of Wright and Briggs and of Debus are not yet in published form.) Thus, the disposition to be impulsive is subject to training. In some cases, it might be wiser first to train the child with a reading problem to be reflective and subsequently to initiate specific tutoring in letter and word recognition.

THE ROLE OF THE MODEL

There are two major mechanisms by which motives, behaviors, standards, and anxieties are established—reward and punishment contingencies, and imitation of a desirable model. The attributes of the lower-middle-class model, as well as the strength of the lower-middle-class child's desire to be like the model, differ from those of the middle-class child. Children and adults want to maximize similarity to adults who command power, status, and instrumental competence. The child desires these goals but he does not know how to obtain them. He behaves as if he believes that if he made himself similar to the models who appear to possess these resources, he might share vicariously in the model's power, status, and competence. If the models display an interest in the mastery of intellectual skills, the child will attempt to mimic such mastery. The absence of this dynamic in many lower-middle-class families is partially responsible for the fact that their children are less highly motivated to master academic skills. Such parents may exhort the child to work hard for grades, but the child does not perceive his parent as a person who publicly engages in or expresses a value in intellectual mastery. As a result, the child cannot view mastery of intellectual skills as a way of gaining the adult resources of power and competence that he perceives his parent to possess.

He selects, instead, the activities that the parents seem to value most. Moreover, as he approaches the prepubertal years and is better able to evaluate with objectivity the attributes of the model, he realizes the model's relative incompetence. He becomes aware that his parents are less in command of desirable resources than are the parents of middle-class children, and his motivation to maximize similarity to the model decreases.

THE ROLE OF PEERS

The peer group is not unimportant in the development of standards and motives surrounding intellectual mastery. The child selects models from the peer group once he begins school. As with the family, the lower-middle-class peer group is biased strongly against school achievement and pushes traditional sex role identification. Thus, both the family and peer vectors act in concert to devalue the attractiveness of academic achievement. The fact that the lower-middle-class child and adult emphasize sex typing with greater zeal than do middle-class adults and children has serious consequences for school performance. The child of six years wants to maximize his similarity to a standard of sex-role appropriateness. The child has learned that he or she is called a boy or a girl and rushes to elaborate this operational definition. How does the child decide what events, objects, or actions are masculine or feminine? The child works by a reliable formula. He implicitly computes the ratio of males to females associated with the event or action. If the ratio is lopsided in one direction, that activity is assigned the sex role of the majority party. Rowing a boat is masculine, sewing is feminine. Any five-year-old will tell you this. School is usually classified as feminine because in over 90 per cent of the primary grades in this nation, the activity of the room is monitored by a woman.

A recent study of first- and second-grade children is relevant here. The purpose of the study was to determine if children view school objects as masculine or feminine. One cannot ask a child this question directly for he will regard it as nonsense. A moderate disguise is necessary and seems to work. A child was told he was going to be given some pictures that belonged to one of two groups. One group was called by one nonsense syllable, a second group by another. The child had to figure out which nonsense word was appropriate. The children were then shown individual pictures that were obviously masculine or feminine in their connotation. Within five or ten minutes most of the children had learned to apply the correct nonsense word to obviously masculine or feminine objects. Once the child had learned a new label for masculinity or femininity he was shown pictures of objects normally associated with a schoolroom (a page of arithmetic, a book, a blackboard). Most of the boys and girls in the primary grades were more likely to call most of the school objects feminine rather than masculine. (Dr. Kazuo Miyake has gathered data indicating that on the island of Hokkaido in northern Japan, where more than half of the elementary school teachers are men, there is no excess proportion of boys to girls with reading problems. The percentages are equivalent for the sexes. In the United States, however, where male teachers are a rarity in grades 1, 2, and 3, the ratio of boys to girls with reading problems is typically five or six to one.) As the children become older, this tendency decreases; older children associate acquisition of knowledge with the masculine vocations of science, medicine, and business.

One implication of these data argues for the wisdom of segregating the sexes, especially in the primary grades. In a sex-segregated class the child might learn to maximize the masculinity of the school experience. This change in school structure is obviously more critical for the lower-middle-class child because of the stricter sex typing among that group. The presence of a man in the classroom would obviously be optimal, but even changing the content of the reading curriculum should have some benefit.[4]

Aside from the importance of modeling, peers mediate other mechanisms that engage the motive to master academic tasks. Most children, especially boys, have a strong motive for power, a desire to play the dominant role in the interpersonal dyad. The uncorrupted sign of power for all children is strength. Strength is the only legitimate currency of power which cannot be corrupted, and children recognize this principle. The culture, in its wisdom, preaches substitute signs for power. Prowess at athletics, skill in adult activities, signs of intelligence, all can function as badges of potency if the group accepts that currency. The middle-class child is likely to find himself in a peer group where the right to dominate is given to the child with good grades, to the child with a quick answer, to the child with a catalogue of facts. Lower-middle-class peer cultures rarely adopt this translation of power. Thus, the child is deprived of a primary motive to master intellectual skills.

SUMMARY AND IMPLICATIONS

Each child requires a set of schemata to decode experience, distinctive events to promote the growth and alteration of schemata, a perception of similarity to a model or group whom the child views as possessing attributes he values, a set of goals promoted by people from whom the child wants a positive evaluation and, finally, some degree of certainty about each day. Some children are deprived of all of these ingredients; some get one or more of these supplies. It is possible to arrange the environment to improve the cognitive structure of the developing child by altering the distinctiveness of cues. However, it would be more profitable, in the long run, to alter the value of intellectual mastery by persuading the child that attainment of academic skills increases his similarity to desirable models and is instrumental in the attainment of tangible goals he desires. Attainment of this end requires more than casual tutorial contact or novel curriculum reform. To achieve it, we require a more serious intervention into the social ecology in which these children spend most of their day. The ability to read, spell, and multiply are artificial skills to which the child does not initially assign much worth. A human catalyst, who carries value, provides the best strategy of transferring involvement to this endeavor. We should reflect long over whether we want the children from lower socioeconomic groups to adopt the middle-class value system. If the answer is affirmative, we must initiate strategies appropriate to the enormity of the task and not deceive ourselves about the therapeutic value of weak intervention procedures.

When Is Infant
Stimulation Effective?

URIE BRONFENBRENNER

One of the adventures of scientific inquiry is to encounter work by others which corroborates one's own ideas and provokes their further development. I am indebted to Professor Kagan for this kind of gratifying experience. Recently I completed an extensive critical review[2] of studies of early deprivation in mammals with the ambitious aim of determining what basic principles of psychological development could be derived from this substantial but, as I discovered, highly variable body of research. The strategy called for deriving hypotheses on the basis of the more systematic and experimentally oriented animal research and then attempting to cross-validate the resultant generalizations on such data on humans as were available. One of the major difficulties encountered, of course, was the sparsity of adequate research in the latter category, most of the published studies being primarily clinical and often impressionistic in character.

It was therefore with some feeling of excitement that, on reading Professor Kagan's paper, I found experimental studies that provided systematic evidence from human subjects bearing directly on three major interrelated conclusions of my own analysis. In brief form, these conclusions may be stated as follows:

PROPOSITION I Psychological development of particular behavioral capacities in the infant is brought about through the infant's participation in progressively more complex patterns of reciprocal interaction with the mother (or substitute caretaker).
PROPOSITION II The infant's participation in progressively more complex patterns of interaction with the mother also has the effect of strengthening his dependency drive toward the mother.
PROPOSITION III The strengthening of the dependency drive, in turn, ac-

URIE BRONFENBRENNER Department of Child Development, Cornell University, Ithaca, New York

celerates the infant's psychological development by motivating him to be attentive and responsive to those aspects of the mother's behavior which signal probable satisfaction or frustration of his dependency drive.

The first proposition finds strong support in two major findings of Kagan's study of the sources of the poorer language development of the lower-middle-class child.

1   The lower-middle-class mother differed from her middle-class counterpart primarily in making less use of "distinctive vocalization," that is, utterances unaccompanied by other acts such as caressing the baby or picking him up. In other words, there were instances in which the infant's attention was engaged by a uniquely vocal pattern of behavior.
2   Lower-middle-class mothers were less likely to respond at all or to react with a distinctive vocalization when their infants vocalized spontaneously. (This relation held only for mothers of girls.)

Also consistent with Proposition I is Professor Kagan's interpretation of the larger heart decelerations of middle- vs. lower-middle-class infants in reaction to facial stimuli. "The favored explanation for this difference," he states, "is that the mother's face has been a more distinctive stimulus for the upper-middle-class child. We believe that well-educated parents engage in more frequent, distinctive, face-to-face contact with their children, and are thus more likely to create conditions that will make the parent's countenance a distinctive stimulus."

The second and third propositions are supported not so much by Kagan's empirical findings as by his interpretations of them. For example, he says: "The lower-middle-class child may be missing the experience of a valued adult communicating concern about correctness of behavior and rewarding such correctness affectively."

Of course, our third proposition goes beyond or — more accurately — before the parent's conscious efforts to mold the child's behavior. It asserts that attachment propels the child to engage in reciprocal response to the parent's actions and thus to learn how to carry out such responses on his own.

In this more general form, the principle is not only fully consistent with Kagan's data but also illuminates some of the seeming inconsistencies in those data. For example, there is the problem posed by the striking sex differences in his own experiments and those of others that he cites. Thus the relationships of social class to maternal vocalization holds only for girls. Conversely, social class differences in manipulation of toys emerge for boys but not for girls. Without discounting the probable mediating role of genetic factors in producing these interaction effects, one can also point to sex differences in socialization practices which, in the light of Proposition III, would lead to the pattern of results found by Professor Kagan. Thus a number of studies[1] document the tendency for parents to be more affectionate with girls than with boys, particularly in the early years of life. The result is an earlier development of a stronger dependency drive, which, in turn, is probably a contributing factor to the greater responsiveness of females to the socialization process. In contrast, boys are treated more permissively — a circumstance that would facilitate the development of autonomous exploratory behavior and manipulation of the environment.

If, as Professor Kagan and I both believe, the development of dependency drive on the one hand and control and richness of the young child's physical environment on the other are differentially distributed by class, it follows from the preceding analysis that the former would be especially critical in accounting for the accelerated language development of middle-class girls, and the latter in explaining the more wide-ranging exploratory manipulative activity of middle-class boys.

The facilitating function of dependency drive in social learning may also be reflected in another class-associated developmental effect documented in Kagan's research. He reports that, by the age of four months, middle-class infants showed significantly greater cardiac deceleration to facial stimuli than did children of the same age from lower-middle-class families, but that there was no such effect when the stimuli represented more random shapes. In other words, the reaction was specific to a representation of the human face. Professor Kagan interprets this phenomenon as a function of a greater tendency on the part of middle-class parents to engage in face-to-face contact with the child. An alternative — or, perhaps more correctly, a complementary—hypothesis emphasizes the role of a motivational component contributed by the dependency drive. Although corresponding data are not yet available for human subjects, Harlow and Zimmerman[4] have demonstrated that infant monkeys brought up by real or surrogate mothers develop an emotional attachment that is reflected in a strong visual preference for the "mother figure"; that is, given the opportunity to select from a variety of visual stimuli, the infant spends more time looking at the particular form to which he has developed an attachment.

If an analogous process occurs in the human species, we would expect the development of a special responsiveness to facial stimuli to vary directly with the strength of the dependency drive. A stronger dependency drive in middle-class infants would produce the differential perceptual reactions described by Professor Kagan.

Finally, at the most speculative level, the heightened specific reaction of four-month-old infants to scrambled vs. regular *human* features may also involve an emotional component deriving from the dependency drive. If it is correct that expressions of displeasure and anger typically involve a moderate distortion of regular facial and bodily features, then, to a child who has developed a strong dependency relation, a scrambled human stimulus may connote rejection and will, as a result, provoke anxiety and enhanced attention.

Let it be understood that these interpretations of Professor Kagan's findings in terms of dependency drive are not intended to supplant his own explanations couched primarily in terms of stimulus familiarity. Our intent is merely to call attention to another class of variables that might be contributing to the same effect. These variables are motivational and emotional factors deriving from the infant's dependency relationship with the mother, which, by the time he is four months of age, can develop considerable intensity and drive strength.

In Professor Kagan's study, the experimental and motivational variables are correlated so that it becomes impossible to assess the independent effect of each. Nor is this situation unique. On the contrary, among the dozens of studies examined in connection with the review mentioned at the outset of this paper, there was hardly an instance in which variation in the dependency relationship between caretaker and child was not accompanied by a similar change in the amount of stimulation given to the child. For example, the social position most conducive to the development of a dependency relationship, that of an only child in a nuclear family, turns out also to be the position in which the infant receives the most vocal stimulation from the mother—more than twice as much as a youngest child or an infant in a well-staffed kibbutz.[3] Correspondingly, as early as six months of age, only children vocalized twice as much as their age-mates among kibbutz infants or among last-borns in a nuclear family.

Perhaps the most dramatic example of this seemingly enforced correlation comes from the surely heroic doctoral research of Rheingold,[5] who took on the task of caring single-handed for four six-month-old infants at a time for a period of eight weeks. With the aim of assessing the effects of single vs. multiple mothering, she compared the psychological development of eight children she cared for, four at a time, to that of eight other infants in the same institution attended by fourteen "constantly changing mothers." Although she worked a seven-and-one-half-hour day and had to divide her attention among four charges, time-sampling studies indicated that the single caretaker offered substantially more stimulation to each child than did the multiple caretakers, two or three of whom might be in the room at the same time. For example, the infants with the single caretaker were played with three to five times as often, talked to four to six times as often. In addition to being more socially responsive than the controls, the experimental subjects showed a significant difference in vocalizing behavior. The number of their vocalizations increased over the course of the experiment, whereas the number of vocalizations of the control subjects appeared to decrease after the fifth week.

The observed covariation between the intensity of the dependency relationship and the level of stimulation given the child is, of course, completely consistent with the circular relationship between these two variables posited in our second and third propositions. In the presence of such a correlation, it is impossible to assess the independent role of either variable in the psychological development of the child. To gauge the specific impact of the dependency relationship on the development of, say, vocalization, it would be necessary to find two different levels of dependency relationship in which the intensity of stimulation offered to the child was substantially the same. Given the general correlation between the two sets of variables, one can expect to locate such an exception to the rule only in some special combination of circumstances in which one external factor operates to decrease the high level of stimulation normally associated with high dependency relationship, while another external factor enhances the lower level of stimulation typically found in a less intimate relationship.

I have been able to find only one instance in the research literature in which this unique combination of conditions is approximated. Among the contrasts reported by Gewirtz and Gewirtz[3] in their observational study of caretaker and infant behavior during the first year of life is that between one group of babies being brought up in a well-staffed kibbutz and another consisting of youngest children being raised in their own homes. The frequency with which an adult talked to an infant was identical in these two settings, but the percentage of interactive vocalization (i.e., response to an adult's utterance) was higher among the youngest children raised in a family setting (30 per cent) than among their age mates in the kibbutz (21 per cent). Even more striking were the data on caretaker and infant smiling in the two situations. Although infants in the kibbutz were smiled at almost twice as often as youngest children in a family setting, the latter group exhibited as high a proportion of interactive smiles (i.e., returning a smile with a smile) as did the kibbutz infants (80 per cent and 84 per cent respectively).

We have marshalled the evidence for the influence of the dependency relationship on psychological development, not because it contradicts Professor Kagan's conclusions but because it supplements them in an important way. The importance becomes evident when we follow Kagan's commendable example of considering the practical implications of his research for compensatory education programs. For if our analysis is valid, it means that, to be fully effective, these programs must not only provide the appropriately and progressively more complex stimuli advocated by Professor Kagan; they must also perpetuate and permit further development of a dependency relationship, preferably toward a single caretaker — the child's mother. This, in turn, implies active involvement of the mother in interaction with the child both in the pre-school setting and at home. Moreover, given the fact, documented by Professor Kagan and others, of the lower level of stimulation — particularly verbal stimulation — typically provided by lower-middle-class mothers, we face the necessity of designing programs and activities eliciting change — not directly in the child's behavior, but in the behavior of his mother. This is an area in which we have little knowledge even at the anecdotal, let alone the scientific, level. It is to be hoped that investigators of Professor Kagan's imagination will broaden their interests to include the design and assessment of strategies for modifying the behavior of those who, as his present research indicates, are the most important determiners of the nature and rate of infant development — the children's own mothers.

Perception, Cognitive Maps, and Covert Behavior

LEONARD S. COTTRELL, JR.

My preliminary cognitive map of Professor Kagan's paper may be traced crudely in "five distinctive features" somewhat as follows:

1. In the first four pages he is chiefly concerned with giving the "bum's rush" to behaviorists who insist that perception and cognition always must involve some form of behavior. He concludes with the pious, not to say sanctimonious, prediction that the noxious influences of the behaviorists are happily declining.

2. Having waved his wand and banished behaviorists, he then af-

LEONARD S. COTTRELL, JR. Department of Sociology, University of North Carolina, Chapel Hill, North Carolina.

firms that cognitive schemata, which consist largely of what he describes as "images and semantic forms arranged in configurations of varying complexity," may be learned and modified without behavioral components being essential to the process.

At this point, it should be noted that the image or semantic form of my cognition is a little blurred. Dr. Kagan never makes it quite clear enough to me what he means by behavior. He sometimes limits the term with the adjective "overt"; at other times he seems to include all operant manifestations inside as well as outside the skin. (In the general discussion following my comments at the conference on which this book is based, Professor Kagan defined as behavior "anything overt enough to be observed." While this clarifies his position, it is hardly satisfactory to those who insist upon the necessity for assuming a behavioral component of perceptual and cognitive phenomena. To such investigators, covert muscular activity, including those conditions referred to as set, is behavioral or distinguished from whatever is meant by "purely mental." Indeed, some, while disclaiming a naive Watsonian behaviorism, contend that a substantial part of what is experienced as thinking is essentially behavioral.)

3. He adduces evidence that lends plausibility to the concept of cognitive schemata as major elements in mental development and learning, and then proceeds to demonstrate the utility of his concept. In doing this, he advances some intriguing hypotheses as to the processes by which cognitive schemata emerge and change.

4. Within the framework thus evolved in phase 3, he then addresses the problem of identifying class differences in cognitive schemata and reports findings of comparative studies that strongly support not only the fact of significant differences, but indicate that differences appear very early in the life cycle. Implied, if not explicitly suggested, is the view that the management of the development and changes of cognitive schemata is a strategic point of intervention for ameliorating the handicaps of cultural deprivation of the lower classes.

5. At this point, the cognitive schema that was emerging in my mind of Professor Kagan's cognitive schema, purged of the behavioral dross, received a severe jolt. Whereas Professor Kagan appeared in the beginning to have banished the behaviorists to outer darkness, it now

seems that he had merely swept them under the rug. For when he began to deal with the practical problems of developing competent cognitive schemata, this development was found to be enmeshed in complex interpersonal processes. Indeed, when the author indicates such a desirable condition as the posture or set of ego's expectancy of success, which in turn reflects the expectations entertained by the teacher and/or the parent, he comes very close to the position of that arch social behaviorist, George H. Mead, who held that the cognitive schema we call the self is an internalized interpersonal behavioral system. The author's recognition of the critical importance of such interactive processes and products as internalization of identity models, parent-child relations, and impact of peer expectations and norms suggests that perhaps one of the essential deprivations of the lower-middle-class child is an interpersonal one.

To be sure, Professor Kagan can rightly argue that the interpersonal and intrapersonal behavioral processes are not essential components of a cognitive schema as such, but are positive or negative motivating conditions impelling toward or away from effort and achievement of the desired cognitive structure he has held to be a separable entity.

This, then, was my somewhat dissonant cognitive map of Dr. Kagan's presentation. He may see it as a caricature or he may not even grant it that status. In any case, it may be of some help if I elaborate, although necessarily briefly, on some of the features of my perception of his presentation. In so doing, I may make it easier for Dr. Kagan to correct my perception, and indeed to do some correcting myself.

Let me return, then, to my reading of the introductory section of the paper. First I offer at least mild apologies for appearing to involve our biologist colleagues in a family quarrel between the pure cognitionists and the less pure behaviorists. It would indeed be unseemly to inject this as a major issue into this particular volume. On the other hand, I am sure that those whose major focus is on the organism as such will and do see profitable lines of investigation emerging from the issues posed by Dr. Kagan's opening remarks.

In any case, good manners notwithstanding, I feel constrained to enter some objections to so peremptory a dismissal of behavioral components of what the organism experiences as perceiving, cognitive structuring, and comprehending. Far from being on their way out of this field of theory and research, the behaviorists, equipped with greatly refined equipment, are increasingly involved with work that is very much to the point.

Thirty-five years ago Edmund Jacobson was observing the interesting correspondences between muscular activity involved in "imagined" or "thought-about" behavior and that shown in actual overt movements of the muscles in question. As you will remember, the instrumentally revealed patterns and sequences of imagined movements were the same as those shown in the overt movements, except for the latter's greater amplitudes. For some reason, the leads opened up by Jacobson's work did not receive the attention they deserved, no doubt because of the lack of technological development. Now, with present electronic development, it is possible again to attack the interrelations of the "mental" and "behavioral" with hopes of greater penetration. That this is taking place can be seen in such useful reviews as that by Ralph F. Hefferline, to be found in the collection of papers on *Experimental Foundations of Clinical Psychology* (1962), edited by Arthur J. Bachrach.

Certainly we are already at the point where our conceptions of the behavioral components of so-called "mental" constructs must be much more sophisticated than what appears to me to be implied by Dr. Kagan's use of the term. For example, he observes: "From a developmental perspective, many cognitive structures are acquired that do not necessarily appear in overt behavior." True, if we limit ourselves to overt manifestations, but how much do we know of what is taking place beneath the skin, behaviorally speaking? The behaviorists are certainly going to move strongly toward finding out. Again, he says: ". . . any behavior is, at best, an imperfect index of the nature of the [cognitive] structure." True, and still true even if we were able to detect all of the covert operant accompaniments of the allegedly separable cognitive structure. I fail to see why we cannot allow a behavioral caricature of a perceived event just as Professor Kagan allows a cognitive schema to be "a condensation of an external event and, like a caricature . . . defined by a set of distinctive features."

This same limited concept is implied in his assumption that the observed cognitive activity of infants, reported later in his paper, carries no skeletal muscular accompaniments. This is not to claim they *do*, so much as to call for observation to determine what does happen.

In this connection, let me refer to the intriguing work of Professor Francis H. Palmer of the City University of New York. He is not actually addressing the problem of the nonbehavioral and behavioral components of cognitive elements in his research. Rather, in his effort to develop an adequate conceptual equipment in two- and three-year-old children, he appears to be operating on the assumption that functional cognitive systems comprise an inextricable mix of perceptual and behavioral components. Thus, in teaching his young subjects concepts such as "up" and "down" he gives them behavioral experiences along with the verbal concept. He uses the same kind of procedure with "in," "out," "tall," "short," etc. The very explicit instructions to the child's teacher leave little doubt in my mind that cognitions then induced have substantial behavioral components. How much of *what,* he leaves to the theorists and experimenters. He is bent upon testing the effectiveness of enhancing the basic conceptual equipment of the two- and three-year-old child, as manifested by his later school performance.

In this connection, I am reminded of some relevant ancedotal material, which I am emboldened to offer by Professor Kagan's example. An 18-month-old boy with early signs of verbal facility was fascinated by his father's carpentry tools. Frequently, to the parents' annoyance, he would pull the tools out of their box under the table and strew them around the apartment. His interest was nevertheless capitalized upon to expand his vocabulary, and tools were duly named and in time correctly tagged by the youngster. Long before he was physically able to use the hammer properly, he knew the word and recognized the sight of the tool. Some time around the age of two-and-a-half years he was observed trying to use the heavy hammer to hit a piece of board. It took two hands and the results were not too precise. When he was asked what he was doing, he replied that he was daddy. About the same time, a friend of the family gave the child a toy consisting of a small mallet and some blocks and pegs for pounding. For a time he played with these materials as he had played with ordinary blocks, and made no use of the mallet for pounding. However, upon being told that the mallet was a hammer, he immediately proceeded to pound vigorously, using one hand and demonstrating his understanding of the meaning of the term.

The pay-off of this cognitive-behavioral achievement came one day when the father and son were putting up a pup-tent in the yard. The father, while attempting to peg the corners of the tent, remarked, "We need a hammer." However, he made no move to go back to the apartment to obtain the tool. The child, who was three years of age at the time, offered his father a round stone he had been rolling around on the ground nearby and said, "This is a hammer," meanwhile demonstrating by pounding a stake. The father completed the scene by using the stone to tap the pegs securely into the ground.

Without gainsaying all the faults and pitfalls of anecdotal evidence, this incident is at least suggestive of the complex behavioral, perceptual, and interpersonal elements that made up the youngster's cognitive structure of the hammer. I am inclined to suspect that, to make the connection between whatever semantic and image elements constituted his "cognitive schema" of hammer and round stone, the child must also have had the covert behavioral mobilization of hammer into which the stone fitted and was therefore cognized as hammer.

In my own work over the years, my chief interest has been in processes and products of social interaction: interpersonal, intrapersonal, inter- and intragroup. This interest has had theoretical and practical relevance for me in fields as separated as marital interaction and psychological warfare (although, come to think of it, I'm not so sure these two fields are so terribly far apart, at that). As you would expect, given my bias, I have regularly been forced to deal with cognitive constructs of these phenomena largely in behavioral terms. The self, the self-other system, the role, the situation, are cognitive schemata, but difficult to conceive except in behavioral terms—and I mean behavior, not merely symbols of behavior. Symbols and images are involved, of course, but are behavioral in content. My past work has depended upon qualitative descriptive methods and has not had the benefit of rigorous experimental design or advanced technology. Actually, the essential position, which I laid out in propositional form in the early 1940s, has never been rigorously tested. Recently, when I was expressing regrets at having been so long diverted from such testing, I was reassured by Dr. Jacob Davidowitz, one of Professor Hefferline's collaborators, who commented that I hadn't lost much time, because the level of technology needed to test my propositions had only recently been achieved. My present intention is to take advantage of the advances in technical equipment to test some of the core assumptions of the social behaviorist position.

It is again with some sense that apologies are called for that I realize I have spent a disproportionate time on the introductory portion of Dr. Kagan's paper. However, I apparently had to do this and, indeed, my remarks are relevant to the main body of the paper. However, in questioning the adequacy of his conceptual position, it should be clear that I am not suggesting that his resarch is trivial; far from it. I am impressed, as is the author, with the evidence of early cognitive structure, with the cross-cultural and cross-class differences and similarities that he has found. Even more impressive is the early age at which these differences appear. Incidentally, the early-age aspect of the findings poses the most perplexing and possibly insoluble problems for those who insist on behavioral components of cognitive structures. Even so, I contend that the difficulties should not inhibit the attempt to discover the relationships, and I would anticipate substantial enrichment and enhancement of the significance of differences that Dr. Kagan has so ably demonstrated.

Having said this, it must immediately be admitted that the difficulties of implementing such demands are such that we may well have to continue segmental investigations as if there is, in fact, a separable cognitive and behavioral domain. This will not necessarily be harmful if we can avoid becoming entrapped by our own limited conceptualizations. This is especially important when we attempt to apply theory to the design of action programs — in this case to overcome what are regarded as cultural deprivations. As Dr. Kagan suggests in the latter section of his paper, interpersonal behavioral processes may be the strategic areas of deprivation and targets for remedial action, even though one may regard such behavioral processes, as he does, as *serving* rather than as *a part of* cognitive development.

It is interesting to note that here, as in many similar situations, diverse theoretical positions find themselves bedfellows in the same practical action program. Again reference is made to the experimental program being conducted by Professor Palmer.

In closing, I wish to follow the excellent lead Professor Kagan has given us in the concluding sentences of his paper. I join him in pointing to the necessity for a greatly broadened perspective and a strategy appropriate for attacking the relevant problems. Given the limits of time and specific focus of interests represented in this volume, we have concentrated on a limited aspect of the general problems of cultural environment and its impact on the human organism. It is quite understandable that the sciences of human behavior, including human biology, would gravitate to and feel more confident and secure in studying and theorizing about the concrete individual organism or segments thereof. However, it is quite evident from Professor Kagan's reported experience, and reflections upon that experience, that we cannot make meaningful and relevant investigations of the individual organism without a competent grasp of the supra-individual contexts in which the organism must act and survive.

This in no wise minimizes the urgent need to press our studies of the processes of the individual soma and psyche, but simply adds the equally urgent need to look at these processes in the perspectives of the impinging contexts. This is not only to make our research more productive of knowledge and theory, but to give our work strategic relevance to the significant problems confronting human existence today.

Dr. Kagan's paper points to the necessity for more adequate contextual perspectives for research on human behavior; it also suggests the need for more competence among disciplinary specialists for relating theory and methodology in ways that make joint attacks on important problems realistic and effective. Behavioral science disciplines have not yet reached the level of development at which they can undertake major integrated projects.

Dr. Alvin M. Weinberg, Research Director of the Oak Ridge National Laboratories, has pointed out that most of the problems confronting mankind today require massive mobilization of scientific, engineering, and administrative skills for what he calls coherent programs. In a recent conversation I had with him, we discussed the successful integration of the knowledge and operating skills that has resulted in the agro-industrial programs now ready to make massive conversions of large desert areas in the world into productive agricultural and industrial regions. In fact, the process is already under way. He expressed concern over our limited capabilities for dealing with the social aspects of this development and, indeed, with all the rapid, massive, technological changes now, and even more in the future. He commented that he found it not too difficult to recruit and integrate coherent task forces in the physical sciences and engineering, but had met with little success in trying to integrate the behavioral sciences.

Biologists are not too difficult, but psychologists and social scientists are not adept in gearing their interests, theories, and methods to the kinds of undertakings Dr. Weinberg has to mount. The massive problems of developing and applying the necessary knowledge for coping with population control, for a workable system of social integration and mobility, for socialization and the development of social competence, of achieving a working basis for orderly relations among the nations, suggest the awe-inspiring dimensions of the problems the human sciences must somehow master.

It seems a long way from the cognitive schemata of Dr. Kagan's four-month-old subjects to the achievement of a workable world community, or even a competent community on the Lower East Side of New York City. But it is not so remote when one thinks a bit about it. If the universe was conceived in the mind of God and He is now deceased, then it behooves man to find out how to equip himself with a maximally effective cognitive grasp of the universe in whose destiny he must now participate on his own.

References

DAVID C. GLASS. *Preface*

1 KESSLER, ALEXANDER. Social behavior and population dynamics: evolutionary relationships, *Biology and Behavior: Genetics* (David C. Glass, editor), New York, Russell Sage Foundation and The Rockefeller University Press, 1967, pp. 169–177.
2 GLASS, DAVID C., J. E. SINGER, and L. FRIEDMAN. The psychic costs of adaptation to an environmental stressor. (In preparation)

JOAQUÍN CRAVIOTO. *Nutritional Deficiencies and Mental Performance in Childhood*

1 AGUILAR, R. Estudios sobre avitaminosis y las perturbaciones del crecimiento en los niños hipoalimentados, *Gac. Méd. Méx.*, 1945, Vol. 75, pp. 25–40.
2 ALEKSEEVA, I. A. and S. I. KAPLANSKAYA-RAISKAYA. The methionine effect upon the higher nervous activity of rats in protein deficiency, *Vop. Pitan.*, 1960, Vol. 19, No. 1, pp. 45–48.
3 AMBROSIUS, K. D. El comportamiento del peso de algunos organos en niños con desnutrición de tercer grado, *Bol. Med. Hosp. Infantil (Mex.)*, 1961, Vol. 18, pp. 47–52.
4 AUTRET, M. and M. BEHAR. Sindrome pluricarencial infantil (kwashiorkor) and its prevention in Central America, *FAO Nutr. Stud.*, No. 13, Rome, 1954.
5 BALDWIN, JAMES MARK. Mental Development in the Child and the Race, New York, Macmillan, 1897.
6 BARRERA-MONCADA, G. Estudios sobre Alteraciones del Crecimiento y del Desarrollo Psicológico del Sindrome Pluricarencial (kwashiorkor), Caracas, Editorial Grafos, 1963.
7 BAYLEY, NANCY. Value and limitations of infant testing, *Children*, 1958, Vol. 5, pp. 129–133.
8 BENGOA, JOSÉ MARÍA. Nutrition advisor, W.H.O., Geneva, Switzerland. Personal communication.
9 BIRCH, HERBERT G. and M. E. BITTERMAN. Reinforcement and learning: the process of sensory integration, *Psychol. Rev.*, 1949, Vol. 56, pp. 292–308.
10 BIRCH, H. G. and M. E. BITTERMAN. Sensory integration and cognitive theory, *Psychol. Rev.*, 1951, Vol. 58, pp. 355–361.
11 BIRCH, HERBERT G. and LILLIAN BELMONT. Auditory-visual integration, in-

telligence and reading ability in school children, *Percept. Motor Skills*, 1965, Vol. 20, pp. 295–305.

12 BIRCH, H. G., J. CRAVIOTO, and C. MASS. A cross-cultural comparison of auditory-visual integrative development in children. Unpublished.

13 BIRCH, HERBERT G. and ARTHUR LEFFORD. Two strategies for studying perception in "brain-damaged" children, *in* Brain Damage in Children: Biological and Social Aspects (Herbert G. Birch, editor), Baltimore, Williams and Wilkins, 1964, p. 46.

14 BIRCH, H. G. and A. LEFFORD. Visual differentiation, intersensory organization and voluntary motor control, *Mon. Soc. Res. Child Devel.*, Vol. 32 (No. 2), Serial 110, 1967.

15 BOURLIÈRE, F. and S. PAROT. Le viellissement de deux populations blanches vivant dans des conditions écologiques très differentes, étude comparative, *Rev. Franc. Etud. Clin. Biol.*, 1962, Vol. 7, pp. 629–635.

16 BOWLBY, J. Critical Phases in the Development of social responses in man and other animals (J. M. Tanner, editor), *in* Prospects in Psychiatric Research, Oxford, England, Blackwell, 1952.

17 CABAK, VERA and R. NAJDANVIC. Effect of undernutrition in early life on physical and mental development, *Arch. Dis. Child.*, 1965, Vol. 40, pp. 532–534.

18 CHEUNG, M. W., D. I. FOWLER, P. M. NORTON, S. E. SNYDERMAN, and L. E. HOLT, JR. Observations on amino acid metabolism in kwashiorkor (a preliminary report), *J. Trop. Pediat.*, 1955, Vol. 1, pp. 141–147.

19 CRAVIOTO, J. Consideraciones epidemiológicas y bases para la formulación de un programa de prevención de la desnutrición, *Bol. Med. Hosp. Infantil (Mex.)*, 1958, Vol. 15, pp. 925–940.

20 CRAVIOTO, JOACHÍN. Appraisal of the effect of nutrition on biochemical maturation, *Am. J. Clin. Nutr.*, 1962, Vol. 11, pp. 484–492.

21 CRAVIOTO, JOACHÍN. Application of newer knowledge of nutrition on physical and mental growth and development, *Amer. J. Public Health*, 1963, Vol. 532, pp. 1803–1809.

22 CRAVIOTO, J., H. G. BIRCH, and C. ESPINOSA. Early malnutrition and auditory visual integration in school-age children, *J. of Special Educ.*, 1967, Vol. 2, pp. 75–82.

23 CRAVIOTO, JOACHÍN, HERBERT G. BIRCH, ELSA R. DE LICARDIE, and LYDIA ROSALES. The ecology of infant weight gain in a pre-industrial society, *Acta Paediat. Scand.*, 1967, Vol. 56, pp. 71–84.

24 CRAVIOTO, J., F. GOMEZ, R. RAMOS-GALVÁN, S. FRENK, E .LÓPEZ-MONTAÑO, and N. GARCÍA. Protein metabolism in advanced malnutrition: concentrations of free amino-acids in blood plasma, *Pediatria Internazionale*, 1959, Vol. 9, pp. 21–37.

25 CRAVIOTO, JOACHÍN, ELSA R. DE LICARDIE, and HERBERT G. BIRCH. Nutrition, growth and neurointegrative development: an experimental and ecologic study, *Pediatrics*, 1966, Vol. 38 (No. 2, Part II), pp. 319–320.

26 Cravioto, Joachín, Carmen Lila de la Pena, and Guillermo Burgos. Fat metabolism in chronic, severe malnutrition: lipoprotein in children with kwashiorkor, *Metabolism*, 1959, Vol. 8, pp. 722–730.

27 Cravioto, J., L. Rivera, J. L. Pérez Navarrete, J. González, L. Vega, A. Vilchis, R. Arrieta, and E. Santibañez. "Operación Zacatepec IV" ensayo de sistematización del concepto de enfermedad trasmisible, *Bol. Ofic. Sanit. Panamer.*, 1962, Vol. 53, pp. 136–144.

28 Cravioto, Joachín and Beatriz Robles. Evolution of adaptive and motor behavior during rehabilitation from kwashiorkor, *Amer. J. Orthopsychiat.*, 1965, Vol. 35, pp. 449–464.

29 Cravioto, J., L. Vega, and J. J. Urrutia. "Operación Nimiquipalg I" — mortality and natality in the Guatemalan Highlands, *Guatemala Pediatrica*, 1964, Vol. 4, pp. 38–49.

30 Dean, R. F. A. The effects of malnutrition on the growth of young children, *Bibl. Pediat.*, 1960, Vol. 5, pp. 111–122.

31 Dean, R. F. A. and R. G. Whitehead. The metabolism of aromatic aminoacids in kwashiorkor, *Lancet*, 1963, Vol. 1, pp. 188–192.

32 Eisenberg, Leon. Behavioral manifestations of cerebral damage, *in* Brain Damage in Children: Biological and Social Aspects (Herbert G. Birch, editor), Baltimore, Williams and Wilkins, 1964, pp. 61–73.

33 Escobedo, M. and J. Cravioto. Influencia de la desnutrición en el metabolismo de la fenilalanina, *Proc. Mexican Society for Pediatric Research, 18th Meeting*, Cuernavaca, México, June, 1964.

34 Faladé, S. Le Development Psychomoteur du Jeune Africaine Originaire du Senegal au cours de sa Première Année, R. Foulon, Paris, France, 1955.

35 Flexner, Josefa B., Louis B. Flexner, and Eliot Stellar. Memory in mice as affected by intracerebral puromycin, *Science*, 1963, Vol. 141, pp. 57–59.

36 Geber, Marcelle and R. F. A. Dean. The psychological changes accompanying kwashiorkor, *Courrier*, 1956, Vol. 6, pp. 3–14.

37 Geber, Marcelle and R. F. A. Dean. The state of development of newborn African children, *Lancet*, 1957, Vol. 1, pp. 1216–1219.

38 Gesell, Arnold and Catherine S. Amatruda. Developmental Diagnosis; Normal and Abnormal Child Development, New York, Hoeber, 1941.

39 Gómez, Federico, Rafael Ramos-Galván, Joachín Cravioto, and Silvester Frenk. Malnutrition in infancy and childhood with special reference to kwashiorkor, *Advances Pediat.*, 1955, Vol. 7, pp. 131–169.

40 Gómez, F., R. Ramos Galván, S. Frenk, J. Cravioto Muñoz, R. Chavez, and J. Vazquez. Mortality in second and third degree malnutrition, *J. Trop. Pediat.*, 1956, Vol. 2, pp. 77–83.

41 György, Paul. The late effects of early nutrition, *Amer. J. Clin. Nutr.*, 1960, Vol. 8, pp. 344–345.

42 Harris, Albert J. How to Increase Reading Ability, New York (second edition), Longmans Green, 1947, p. 9.

43 Held, Richard and Alan Hein. Movement produced stimulation in the de-

velopment of visually guided behavior, *J. Comp. Physiol. Psychol.*, 1963, Vol. 56, pp. 872–876.

44 HERTZIG, MARGARET E. and HERBERT G. BIRCH. Neurologic organization in psychiatrically disturbed adolescent girls, *Arch. Gen. Psychiat.*, 1966, Vol. 15, pp. 590–598.

45 HIERNAUX, J. Weight/height relationship during growth in Africans and Europeans, *Hum. Biol.*, 1964, Vol. 36, pp. 273–293.

46 JELLIFFE, D. B. and H. F. WELBOURN. Clinical signs of mild-moderate protein-calorie malnutrition of early childhood, *in* Symposium on Mild-Moderate Forms of Protein-calorie Malnutrition, Swedish Nutr. Foundation, Göteborg and Bastad, August, 1962.

47 KAGAN, J. and H. A. Moss. Parental correlates of child's I.Q. and height: A crossvalidation of the Berkeley growth study results, *Child. Develop.*, 1959, Vol. 30, pp. 325–332.

48 KEYS, ANCEL, JOSEF BROVEK, AUSTIN HENSCHEL, OLAF MICKELSEN, and HENRY LONGSTREET TAYLOR. The Biology of Human Starvation, Vol. II, Minneapolis, Univ. of Minnesota Press, 1950.

49 KNOBLOCH, HILDA and BENJAMIN PASAMANICK. Environmental factors affecting human development, before and after birth, *Pediatrics*, 1960, Vol. 26, pp. 210–218.

50 KNOBLOCH, HILDA and BENJAMIN PASAMANICK. Predicting intellectual potential in infancy. Some variables affecting the validity of developmental diagnosis, *Amer. J. Dis. Child.*, 1963, Vol. 106, pp. 43–51.

51 KUGELMASS, I. NEWTON, LOUISE E. POULL, and EMMA L. SAMUEL. Nutritional improvement of child mentality, *Amer. J. Med. Sci.*, 1944, Vol. 208, pp. 631–633.

52 KUMMATE, J., C. MARISCAL, J. HIKIMURA, and P. YOSHIDA. Desnutrición e inmunidad. 1.—Complemento hemolítico en niños desnutridos, *Bol. Med. Hosp. Infantil (Mex.)*, 1964, Vol. 21, pp. 427–434.

53 LEITCH, I. Growth and health, *Brit. J. Nutr.*, 1951, Vol. 5, pp. 142–151.

54 LICARDIE, E. R., H. G. BIRCH, and J. CRAVIOTO. Adaptive and motor organization of full-term new born Guatemalan infants. Unpublished.

55 LOWREY, R. S., W. G. POND, R. H. BARNES, L. KROOK, and J. K. LOOSLI. Influence of caloric level and protein quality on the manifestations of protein deficiency in the young pig, *J. Nutr.*, 1962, Vol. 78, pp. 245–253.

56 MARTÍNEZ, P. D., R. RAMOS GALVÁN, and R. DE LA FUENTE. Los factores ambientales en la pelegra de los niños de México, *Bol. Med. Hosp. Infantil (Mex.)*, 1951, Vol. 6, pp. 743–749.

57 McCANCE, R. A. Food, Growth and Time, *Lancet*, 1962, Vol. 2, p. 621–626.

58 McCANCE, R. A. Some effects of undernutrition, *J. Pediat.*, 1964, Vol. 65, pp. 1008–1014.

59 MEREDITH, HOWARD V. Stature and weight of children of the United States with reference to the influence of racial, regional, socioeconomic, and secular factors, *Amer. J. Dis. Child.*, 1941, Vol. 62, pp. 909–932.

60 Nissen, H. W., S. Machover, and Elaine F. Kinder. A study of performance tests given to groups of native African Negro children, *Brit. J. Psychol.*, 1935, Vol. 25, pp. 308–355.

61 Olarte, J., J. Cravioto, and M. C. B. Campos. Inmunidad en el niño desnutrido. 1. Producción de antitoxina diftérica, *Bol. Med. Hosp. Infantil (Mex.)*, 1956, Vol. 13, pp. 467–471.

62 Pérez-Navarrete, J. L., F. L. Vega, A. Vilches, R. Arrieta, E. Santibañez, L. Rivera, and J. Cravioto. "Operacion Zacatepec" V — Longitudinal study of rural children during the first year of life, *Bol. Med. Hosp. Infantil (Mex.)*, 1960, Vol. 17, pp. 283–296.

63 Platt, B. S., G. Pampiglione, and R. J. C. Stewart. Experimental protein-calorie deficiency, clinical, electroencephalographic and neuropathological changes in pigs, *Develop. Med. Child Neurol.*, 1965, Vol. 7, pp. 9–26.

64 Pratt, C. W. M. and R. A McCance. Severe undernutrition in growing and adult animals. 6. Changes in the long bones during the rehabilitation of cockerels, *Brit. J. Nutr.*, 1961, Vol. 15, pp. 121–129.

65 Ramos-Galván, R. Communication to the PAHO Scientific Group on Research in Protein-Calorie Malnutrition, Bogota, March, 1964.

66 Ramos-Galván, R., J. Cravioto, G. Gutierrez, F. Gómez, and S. Frenk. "Operacion Zacatepec" III. — Comparación de un Método indirecto y otro directo, en la evaluación del estado de nutrición de los niños de una comunidad rural, *Bol. Med. Hosp. Infantil (Mex.)*, 1958, Vol. 15, pp. 855–873.

67 Ramunni, M. and G. Moretti. Significado e limiti dei tossi ematici di lipasi, lizozima e potere complementare in rapporto allo stato di nutrizione, *G. Mal. Infett. Parasit.*, 1960, Vol. 12, pp. 75–77.

68 Rivers, W. H. R. Vision *in* Reports of the Cambridge Anthropological Expedition to Torres Straits (A. C. Haddon, editor), Vol. II, Part 1, Cambridge, Cambridge Univ. Press. 1901, pp. 8–140.

69 Robles, B., J. Cravioto, L. Rivera, A. Vilches, E. Santibañez, L. Vega, and J. L. Pérez-Navarrete. "Operacion Zacatepec VI" — Influence of certain ecologic factors on the behavior of children in rural Mexico, *IX Reunión Asoc. Méx. de Investigación Pediátrica,* Cuernavaca, México, 1959.

70 Robles, B., R. Ramos-Galván, and J. Cravioto. Valoración de la conducta del niño con desnutrición avanzada y de sus modificaciones durante la recuperación, *Bol. Med. Hosp. Infantil (Mex.)*, 1959, Vol. 16, pp. 317–341.

71 Scott, J. P. Critical periods in behavioral development, *Science*, 1962, Vol. 138, pp. 949–958.

72 Scott, J. P. Theory of critical periods, *Monogr. Soc. Res. Child Develop.*, 1963, Vol. 28, No. 1, pp. 31–34.

73 Scrimshaw, Nevin S., Moises Behar, Carlos Pérez, and Fernando Viteri. Nutritional problems of children in Central America and Panama, *Pediatrics*, 1955, Vol. 16, pp. 378–397.

74 Segall, Marshall H., Donald T. Campbell, and Melville J. Herskovits.

Cultural differences in the perception of geometric illusions, *Science*, 1963, Vol. 139, pp. 769–771.

75 Sherrington, Charles S. Man on his Nature, New York, Macmillan, *and* Cambridge, Cambridge Univ. Press, 1941, pp. 278–279.

76 Stoch, M. B. and P. M. Smythe. Does undernutrition during infancy inhibit brain growth and subsequent intellectual development? *Arch. Dis. Child.*, 1963, Vol. 38, pp. 546–552.

77 Thompson, William R. Influence of prenatal maternal anxiety on emotionality in young rats, *Science*, 1957, Vol. 125, pp. 698–699.

78 Vasile, B. Il potere complementere del siero di sangue nei lattanti con disturbi di nutrizione, *Pediatria*, 1929, Vol. 37, pp. 1059–1066.

79 Widdowson, Elsie M., J. W. T. Dickerson, and R. A. McCance. Severe undernutrition in growing and adult animals, 4. The impact of severe undernutrition on the chemical composition of the soft tissues of the pig, *Brit. J. Nutr.*, 1960, Vol. 14, pp. 457–471.

80 Widdowson, Elsie M. and R. A. McCance. The effect of finite periods of undernutrition at different ages on the composition and subsequent development of the rat, *Proc. Roy. Soc. (Biol.)*, 1963, Vol. 158, pp. 329–342.

81 Wilson, Dorothy, Ricardo Bressani, and Nevin S. Scrimshaw. Infection and nutritional status. 1. The effect of chicken pox on nitrogen metabolism in children, *Amer. J. Clin. Nutr.*, 1961, Vol. 9, pp. 154–158.

82 Woodworth, R. S. Racial differences in mental traits, *Science*, 1910, Vol. 31, pp. 171–186.

ACKNOWLEDGMENTS

This work was supported in part by grants from the Association for the Aid of Crippled Children, New York, N.Y., The Nutrition Foundation, Inc., the Williams Waterman Fund for the Combat of Dietary Diseases, the Gerber Baby Fund, and La Cooperativa Emiliano Zapata, Zacatepec, Morelos, México. We would also like to express our appreciation to the Director and Staff of the American School of Guatemala for their cooperation in allowing us to study their pupils.

Richard H. Barnes. *Behavioral Changes Caused by Malnutrition in the Rat and Pig*

1 Barnes, R. H., S. R. Cunnold, R. R. Zimmermann, H. Simmons, R. B. MacLeod, and L. Krook. Influence of nutritional deprivations in early life on learning behavior of rats as measured by performance in a water maze, *J. Nutrition*, 1966, Vol. 89, pp. 399–410.

2 Barnes, R. H., A. U. Moore, I. M. Reid, and W. G. Pond. Learning behavior following nutritional deprivations in early life, *J. Am. Diet. Assn.*, 1967, Vol. 51, pp. 34–39.

3 BARNES, R. H., I. M. REID, W. G. POND, and A. U. MOORE. The use of experimental animals in studying behavioral abnormalities following recovery from early malnutrition, *in* Calorie and Protein Deficiencies (R. A. McCance and E. M. Widdowson, editors), London, J. and A. Churchill (in press).

ACKNOWLEDGMENTS

This research was supported in part by funds provided through the State University of New York and Public Health Service Research Grant No. HD02581–07 from the National Institutes of Health.

EDWARD A. SUCHMAN, *Sociocultural Factors in Nutritional Studies*

1 JOHN CASSEL. Social and cultural implications of food and food habits, *American Journal of Public Health,* 1957, Vol. 47, pp. 732–740.

WILLIAM A. MASON. *Early Social Deprivation in the Nonhuman Primates: Implications for Human Behavior*

1 CLARK, W. E. LE GROS. The Antecedents of Man, Edinburgh, Edinburgh Univ. Press, 1959, *also* Chicago, Quadrangle Books, 1960.
2 DAVENPORT, RICHARD K., JR. and EMIL W. MENZEL, JR. Stereotyped behavior of the infant chimpanzee, *Arch. Gen. Psychiat.,* 1963, Vol. 8, pp. 99–104.
3 DE BEER, SIR GAVIN. Embryos and Ancestors (3rd edition), London, Oxford Univ. Press, 1958.
4 HARLOW, HARRY F., ROBERT O. DODSWORTH, and MARGARET K. HARLOW. Total isolation in monkeys, *Proc. Natl. Acad. Sci., U.S.,* 1965, Vol. 54, pp. 90–97.
5 HARLOW, HARRY F. and MARGARET KUENNE HARLOW. Social deprivation in monkeys, *Sci. Am.,* 1962, Vol. 207, No. 5, pp. 137–146.
6 HARLOW, HARRY R. and ROBERT R. ZIMMERMANN. The development of affectional responses in infant monkeys. *Proc. Am. Phil. Soc.,* 1958, Vol. 102, pp. 501–509.
7 HOCKETT, CHARLES F. Animal "languages" and human language, *Human Biol.,* 1959, Vol. 31, pp. 32–39.
8 JENSEN, GORDON D. and CHARLES W. TOLMAN. Mother-infant relationship in the monkey, *Macaca nemestrina:* the effect of brief separation and mother-infant specificity, *J. Comp. Physiol. Psychol.,* 1962, Vol. 55, pp. 131–136.
9 KAUFMAN, I. CHARLES and LEONARD A. ROSENBLUM. Depression in infant monkeys separated from their mothers, *Science,* 1967, Vol. 155, pp. 1030–1031.
10 KUTTNER, ROBERT. An hypothesis on the evolution of intelligence, *Psychol. Rept.,* 1960, Vol. 6, pp. 283–289.
11 MASON, WILLIAM A. The effects of social restriction on the behavior of rhesus

monkeys: I. Free social behavior, *J. Comp. Physiol. Psychol.*, 1960, Vol. 53, pp. 582–589.

12 MASON, WILLIAM A. The effects of social restriction on the behavior of rhesus monkeys: III. Dominance tests, *J. Comp. Physiol. Psychol.*, 1961, Vol. 54, pp. 694–699.

13 MASON, WILLIAM A. Social development of rhesus monkeys with restricted social experience, *Percept. Motor Skills*, 1963, Vol. 16, pp. 263–270.

14 MASON, WILLIAM A. Determinants of social behavior in young chimpanzees, *in* Behavior of Nonhuman Primates (Allen M. Schrier, Harry F. Harlow, and Fred Stollnitz, editors), Vol. 2, New York, Academic Press, 1965, pp. 335–364.

15 MASON, WILLIAM A. The social development of monkeys and apes, *in* Primate Behavior (Irven DeVore, editor), New York, Holt, Rinehart and Winston, 1965, pp. 514–543.

16 MASON, WILLIAM A. Motivational aspects of social responsiveness in young chimpanzees, *in* Early Behavior: Comparative and Developmental Approaches (Harold W. Stevenson, Eckhard H. Hess, and Harriet L. Rheingold, editors), New York, Wiley, 1967, pp. 103–126.

17 MASON, WILLIAM A. and PHILLIP C. GREEN. The effects of social restriction on the behavior of rhesus monkeys: IV. Responses to a novel environment and to an alien species, *J. Comp. Physiol. Psychol.*, 1962, Vol. 55, pp. 363–368.

18 MASON, WILLIAM A. and JOHN H. HOLLIS. Communication between young rhesus monkeys, *Anim. Behav.*, 1962, Vol. 10, pp. 211–221.

19 MASON, WILLIAM A. and R. R. SPONHOLZ. Behavior of rhesus monkeys raised in isolation, *J. Psychiat. Res.*, 1963, Vol. 1, pp. 299–306.

20 MEIER, GILBERT W. Other data on the effects of social isolation during rearing upon adult reproductive behaviour in the rhesus monkey (*Macaca mulatta*), *Anim. Behav.*, 1965, Vol. 13, pp. 228–231.

21 MEIER, GILBERT W. and RALPH J. BERGER. Development of sleep and wakefulness patterns in the infant rhesus monkey, *Exptl. Neurol.*, 1965, Vol. 12, pp. 257–277.

22 MENZEL, EMIL W., JR. Patterns of responsiveness in chimpanzees reared through infancy under conditions of environmental restriction, *Psychol. Forsch.*, 1964, Vol. 27, pp. 337–365.

23 MILLER, R. E., W. F. CAUL, and I. A. MIRSKY. The communication of affects between feral and socially-isolated monkeys. *J. Personality Soc. Psychol.*, 1967, Vol. 7, pp. 231–239.

24 SCHULTZ, ADOLPH H. Postembryonic age changes, *in* Primatologia I. (H. Hofer, A. H. Schultz, and D. Starck, editors), Basel, S. Karger, 1956, pp. 887–959.

25 SEAY, BILL and HARRY F. HARLOW. Maternal separation in the rhesus monkey, *J. Nerv. Ment. Dis.*, 1965, Vol. 140, pp. 434–441.

26 SIMPSON, GEORGE GAYLORD. The Meaning of Evolution, New York, New American Library, 1951.

27 THOMPSON, WILLIAM R., RONALD MELZACK, and T. H. SCOTT. "Whirling behavior" in dogs as related to early experience, *Science*, 1956, Vol. 123, p. 939.

28 WALLACE, ALFRED RUSSEL. The Malay Archipelago, London, Macmillan, 1869, *also* New York, Dover Publications, 1962.

ACKNOWLEDGMENT

Preparation of this chapter and research by the author reported here were supported in part by funds received from National Institutes of Health Grant FR00164-05.

LEON J. YARROW. *The Crucial Nature of Early Experience*

1 BELL, R. Q. The problem of direction of effects in research on parents and children. Paper presented at meeting of Society for Research in Child Development, Minneapolis, 1965.

2 BOWLBY, J. Maternal care and mental health, Monograph No. 2, World Health Organ., 1951.

3 FANTZ, ROBERT L. and SOULA NEVIS. Pattern preferences and perceptual-cognitive development in early infancy, *Merrill-Palmer Quart. Behav. Develop.*, 1967, Vol. 13, pp. 77–108.

4 HARLOW, H. F. The development of affectional patterns in infant monkeys, *in* Determinants of Infant Behavior (B. M. Foss, editor), New York, Wiley, 1961, pp. 75–97.

5 HARLOW, HARRY F. and MARGARET K. HARLOW. The affectional systems, *in* Behavior of Nonhuman Primates (Allan M. Schrier, Harry F. Harlow, and Fred Stollnitz, editors), Vol. 2, New York, Academic Press, 1965, pp. 287–334.

6 MACFARLANE, J. W. Perspectives on personality consistency and change from the Guidance Study, *Vita Humana*, 1964, Vol. 7, pp. 115–126.

7 MASON, WILLIAM A. Determinants of social behavior in young chimpanzees, *in* Behavior of Nonhuman Primates (Allan M. Schrier, Harry F. Harlow, and Fred Stollnitz, editors), Vol. 2, New York, Academic Press, 1965, pp. 335–364.

8 MASON, W. A., RICHARD K. DAVENPORT, JR., and EMIL W. MENZEL, JR. Early experience and the social development of rhesus monkeys and chimpanzees, *in* Early Experience and Behavior: The Psychobiology of Development (G. Newton and S. Levine, editors), Springfield, Ill., C. C Thomas, 1968, pp. 440–480.

9 MOSS, H. A. and J. KAGAN. Report on personality consistency and change from the Fels Longitudinal Study, *Vita Humana*, 1964, Vol. 7, pp. 127–139.

10 MURPHY, L. B. Factors in continuity and change in the development of adaptational style in children, *Vita Humana*, 1964, Vol. 7, pp. 96–114.

11 SANDER, L. W. Issues in early mother-child interaction, *J. Am. Acad. Child Psychiat.*, 1962, Vol. 1, No. 1, 141–166.

12 YARROW, L. J. Maternal deprivation: toward an empirical and conceptual reevaluation, *Psychol. Bull.*, 1961, Vol. 58, pp. 459–490.

13 Yarrow, L. J. Measurement and specification of the early infant environment, *World Health Organ. Public Health Papers*, 1964, Vol. 24, pp. 138–146.

14 Yarrow, L. J. Personality consistency and change: an overview of some conceptual and methodological issues, *Vita Humana*, 1964, Vol. 7, 67–72.

15 Yarrow, L. J. An approach to the study of reciprocal interactions in infancy. Paper presented at meeting of Society for Research in Child Development, Minneapolis, 1965.

16 Yarrow, L. J. and Marion S. Goodwin. Some conceptual issues in the study of mother-infant interaction, *Am. J. Orthopsychiat.*, 1965, Vol. 35, pp. 473–481.

17 Yarrow, L. J. and M. R. Yarrow. Personality continuity and change in the family context, *in* Personality Change (P. Worchel and D. Byrne, editors), New York, Wiley, 1964, pp. 489–523.

ACKNOWLEDGMENTS

Portions of this research were conducted under Research Grant 3M-9077 from the National Institute of Mental Health, U.S. Public Health Service.

Peter Marler and Andrew Gordon. *The Social Environment of Infant Macaques*

1 Andrew, R. J. The origin and evolution of the calls and facial expressions of the primates, *Behavior*, 1963, Vol. 20, pp. 1–109.

2 Andrew, R. J. Vocalization in chicks, and the concept of "stimulus contrast," *Anim. Behav.*, 1964, Vol. 12, pp. 64–76.

3 Berlyne, D. E. Conflict, Arousal, and Curiosity, New York, McGraw-Hill, 1960.

4 Bernstein, I. S. and W. A. Draper. The behavior of juvenile rhesus monkeys in groups, *Anim. Behav.*, 1964, Vol. 12, pp. 84–91.

5 Bernstein, I. S. and W. A. Mason. Group formation by rhesus monkeys, *Anim. Behav.*, 1963, Vol. 11, pp. 28–31.

6 DeVore, I. Mother-infant relations in free-ranging baboons, *in* Maternal Behavior in Mammals (H. L. Rheingold, editor), New York, Wiley, 1963, pp. 305–335.

7 Eisenberg, J. F. and R. E. Kuehn. The behavior of *Ateles geoffroyi* and related species, *Smithsonian Misc. Collections*, 1966, Vol. 151, pp. 1–63.

8 Furness, W. H. Observations on the mentality of chimpanzees and orangutans, *Proc. Am. Phil. Soc.*, 1916, Vol. 55, pp. 240–246.

9 Hinde, R. A., T. E. Rowell, and Y. Spencer-Booth. Behaviour of socially living rhesus monkeys in their first six months, *Proc. Zool. Soc., Lond.*, 1964, Vol. 143, pp. 609–649.

10 Hinde, R. A. and Y. Spencer-Booth. The behavior of socially living rhesus

monkeys in their first two and a half years, *Anim. Behav.*, 1967, Vol. 15, pp. 169–196.

11 IMANISHI, KINJI. Identification: a process of socialization in the subhuman society of *Macaca fuscata*, *Primates*, 1957, Vol. 1, pp. 1–29; *translated in* Japanese Monkeys (Kinji Imanishi and Stuart A. Altmann, editors), Alberta, Canada, Univ. of Alberta Press, 1965, pp. 30–51.

12 IMANISHI, KINJI. The origin of the human family: a primatological approach, *translated in* Japanese Monkeys (Kinji Imanishi and Stuart A. Altmann, editors), Alberta, Canada, Univ. Alberta Press, 1965, pp. 113–140.

13 IMANISHI, KINJI and STUART A. ALTMANN (EDITORS). Japanses Monkeys, Alberta, Canada, Univ. of Alberta Press, 1965.

14 ITANI, JUNICHIRO. On the acquisition and propagation of a new food habit in the troop of Japanese monkeys at Takasakiyama, *Primates*, 1958, Vol. 1, pp. 84–98; *translated in* Japanese Monkeys (Kinji Imanishi and Stuart A. Altmann, editors), Alberta, Canada, Univ. of Alberta Press, 1965, pp. 52–65.

15 ITANI, JUNICHIRO. Paternal care in the wild Japanese monkeys, *Primates*, 1959, Vol. 2, pp. 61–93.

16 JAY, PHYLLIS. Mother-infant relations in langurs, *in* Maternal Behavior in Mammals (H. L. Rheingold, editor), New York, Wiley, 1963.

17 JAY, PHYLLIS. Field studies, *in* Behavior of Nonhuman Primates (Allan M. Schrier, Harry F. Harlow, and Fred Stollnitz, editors), Vol. 2, New York, Academic Press, 1965, pp. 525–591.

18 JAY, PHYLLIS. The common langur of North India, *in* Primate Behavior (Irven DeVore, editor), New York, Holt, Rinehart and Winston, 1965, pp. 197–249.

19 JOLLY, A. Lemur Behavior, Chicago, Univ. of Chicago Press, 1966.

20 KAWAI, MASAO. On the rank system in a natural group of Japanese monkeys: I. Basic rank and dependent rank, *Primates*, 1958, Vol. 1, pp. 111–130; *translated in* Japanese Monkeys (Kinji Imanishi and Stuart A. Altmann, editors), Alberta, Canada, Univ. of Alberta Press, 1965, pp. 66–86.

21 KAWAI, MASAO. On the rank system in a natural group of Japanese monkeys: II. In what pattern does the ranking order appear on and near the test box? *Primates*, 1958, Vol. 1, pp. 131–148; *translated in* Japanese Monkeys (Kinji Imanishi and Stuart A. Altmann, editors), Alberta, Canada, Univ. of Alberta Press, 1965, pp. 87–104.

22 KAWAI, MASAO. Newly-acquired pre-cultural behavior of the natural group of Japanese monkeys on Koshima Island, *Primates*, 1965, Vol. 6, pp. 1–30.

23 KAWAMURA, SHUNZO. The matriarchal social order in the Minoo-B group: a study on the rank system of Japanese macaques, *Primates*, 1958, Vol. 1, pp. 131–148; *translated in* Japanese Monkeys (Kinji Imanishi and Stuart A. Altmann, editors), Alberta, Canada, Univ. of Alberta Press, 1965, pp. 105–112.

24 KIMBLE, G. A. Hilgard and Marquis' Conditioning and Learning, New York, Appleton-Century-Crofts, 1961.

25 KOFORD, C. B. Ranks of mothers and sons in bands of rhesus monkeys, *Science*, 1963, Vol. 141, pp. 356–357.

26 KOFORD, C. B. Population changes in rhesus monkeys: Cayo Santiago, *Tulane Studies in Zoology*, 1966, Vol. 13, pp. 1–7.

27 LANYON, W. E. The ontogeny of vocalizations in birds, *in* Animal Sounds and Communication (W. E. Lanyon and W. N. Tavolga, editors), Washington, D.C., American Institute of Biological Sciences, 1960, pp. 321–347.

28 LENNEBERG, E. H. Biological Foundations of Language, New York, Wiley, 1967.

29 LINDBURG, D. A field study of behavior of the rhesus macaque. Ph.D. thesis, Univ. of California, 1967.

30 LORENZ, K. The comparative method in studying innate behavior patterns, *Symp. Soc. Exptl. Biol.*, 1950, Vol. 4, pp. 221–268.

31 MAIER, N. R. F. and T. C. SCHNEIRLA. Principles of Animal Psychology, New York, McGraw-Hill, 1935.

32 MARLER, P. Inheritance and learning in the development of animal vocalization, *in* Acoustic Behavior of Animals (R. G. Busnell, editor), Amsterdam, Elsevier, 1963, pp. 225–243 and 794–797.

33 MARLER, PETER and WILLIAM J. HAMILTON, III. Mechanisms of Animal Behavior, New York, Wiley, 1966.

34 NISBETT, R. and A. GORDON. Self-esteem and susceptibility to social influences, *J. Personality Soc. Psychol.*, 1967, Vol. 5, pp. 268–276.

35 NISSEN, H. W. Social behavior in primates, *in* Comparative Psychology, 3rd edition (C. P. Stone, editor), Englewood Cliffs, N.J., Prentice Hall, 1951, pp. 423–457.

36 ROWELL, T. E., R. A. HINDE, and Y. SPENCER-BOOTH. "Aunt"-infant interaction in captive rhesus monkeys, *Anim. Behav.*, 1964, Vol. 12, pp. 219–226.

37 SADE, D. S. Some aspects of parent-offspring and sibling relations in a group of rhesus monkeys, with a discussion of grooming, *Am. J. Phys. Anthropol.*, 1965, Vol. 23, pp. 1–17.

38 SADE, D. S. Ontogeny of social relations in a group of free-ranging rhesus monkeys (*Macaca mulatta* Zimmerman). Unpublished thesis, Univ. of California, 1966.

39 SADE, D. S. Determinants of dominance in a group of free-ranging rhesus monkeys, *in* Social Communication Among Primates (S. A. Altmann, editor), Chicago, Univ. of Chicago Press, 1967, pp. 99–114.

40 SADE, D. S. Inhibition of son-mother mating among free-ranging rhesus monkey. Address to American Academy of Psychoanalysis, Detroit, Michigan, May 7, 1967.

41 SCHNEIRLA, T. C. An evolutionary and developmental theory of biphasic processes underlying approach and withdrawal, *in* Nebraska Symposium on Motivation (Marshall R. Jones, editor), Lincoln, Neb., Univ. of Nebraska Press, 1959, Vol. 7, pp. 1–42.

42 SCHNEIRLA, T. C. Aspects of stimulation and organization in approach/withdrawal processes underlying vertebrate behavioral development, *in* Advances in the Study of Behavior (Daniel S. Lehrman, Robert A. Hinde, and Evelyn Shaw, editors), New York, Academic Press, 1965, pp. 2–74.

43 STELLAR, E. Drive and motivation, *in* Handbook of Physiology (J. Field, editor), Sec. 1, Vol. 3, Washington, D.C., American Physiological Society, 1960, pp. 1501–1527.

44 SUGIYAMA, Y. Bibliography of the study of primate behavior in Japan, *in* Japanese Monkeys (Kinji Imanishi and Stuart A. Altmann, editors), Alberta, Canada, Univ. of Alberta Press, 1965, pp. 141–151.

45 THIELCKE, G. Ergebnisse der Vogelstimmen-Analyse, *J. Ornithol.*, 1961, Vol. 102, pp. 285–300.

46 THORPE, W. H. Bird Song: The Biology of Vocal Communication and Expression in Birds, 2nd edition, Cambridge, Cambridge Univ. Press, 1961.

47 THORPE, W. H. Learning and Instinct in Animals, Cambridge, Mass., Harvard Univ. Press, 1963.

48 TOKUDA, K. Dominance-subordinate relationships in a society of the wild Japanese monkeys, *Biol. Sci.,* 1955, Vol. 7, pp. 48–53.

49 TOKUDA, K. A study of the sexual behavior in the Japanese monkey troop, *Primates*, 1961–62, Vol. 3, No. 2, pp. 1–40.

59 WUNDT, W. M. Grundzuge der physiologischen Psychologie? Leipzig, Engelmann, 1874.

51 YAMADA, M. A study of blood-relationship in the natural society of the Japanese macaque. An analysis of co-feeding, grooming, and playmate relationships in Minoo-B troop, *Primates*, 1963, Vol. 4, pp. 43–65.

52 YERKES, ROBERT M. and BLANCHE W. LEARNED. Chimpanzee Intelligence and Its Vocal Expression, Baltimore, Williams and Wilkins, 1925.

53 YERKES, ROBERT M. and ADA W. YERKES. The Great Apes, New Haven, Conn., Yale Univ. Press, 1929.

I. ARTHUR MIRSKY, *Communication of Affects in Monkeys*

1 ADER, ROBERT. Early experience and adaptation of stress, *Assoc. Res. Nerv. Ment. Dis.*, 1966, Vol. 43, pp. 292–306.

2 BOLK, L. Das Problem der Menschwerdung, Haarlem, Bohn; Jena, Fischer, 1926.

3 BRIDGER, WAGNER H. Ethological concepts and human development, *in* Recent Advances in Biological Psychiatry (J. Wortis, editor), Vol. 4, New York, Plenum Press, 1962, pp. 95–107.

4 BRUCH, HILDE. Changing approaches to the study of the family, *Psychiat. Res. Rept.*, 1966, No. 20, pp. 1–7.

5 BUTLER, NICHOLAS MURRAY. Anaximander on the prolongation of infancy in man, *in* Classical Studies in Honour of Henry Drisler, New York and London, Macmillan, 1927.

6 DE BEER, G. R. Embryology and Evolution, London, Oxford Univ. Press, 1930.

7 FISKE, JOHN. Outlines of Cosmic Philosophy, 8th edition, Boston, Houghton Mifflin, 1874, *also* New York, Columbia Univ. Press, 1894.

8 Fiske, John. The Meaning of Infancy, Boston, Houghton Mifflin, 1909.

9 Hutt, Corrinne and Christopher Ounsted. The biological significance of gaze aversion with particular reference to the syndrome of infantile autism, *Behav. Sci.*, 1966, Vol. 11, pp. 346–356.

10 Levine, Seymour. Psychophysiological effects of infantile stimulation, *in* Roots of Behavior (Eugene L. Bliss, editor), New York, Harper, 1962, pp. 246–253.

11 Lidz, Theodore, Stephen Fleck, and Alice R. Cornelison. Schizophrenia and the Family, New York, Intern. Univ. Press, 1965.

12 Mason, William A. The effects of social restriction on the behavior of rhesus monkeys. I. Free social behavior, *J. Comp. Physiol. Psychol.*, 1960, Vol. 53, pp. 582–589.

13 Mason, William A. The effects of social restriction on the behavior of rhesus monkeys. II. Tests of gregariousness, *J. Comp. Physiol. Psychol.*, 1961, Vol. 54, pp. 287–290.

14 Mason, William A. Determinants of social behavior in young chimpanzees, *in* Behavior of Nonhuman Primates (Allan M. Schrier, Harry F. Harlow, and Fred Stollnitz, editors), Vol. 2, New York, Academic Press, 1965, pp. 335–364.

15 Miller, James G. Toward a general theory for the behavioral sciences, *Am. Psychologist*, 1955, Vol. 10, pp. 513–531.

16 Miller, Robert E., James H. Banks, Jr., and Nobuya Ogawa. Role of facial expression in "cooperative-avoidance conditioning" in monkeys, *J. Abnorm. Soc. Psychol.*, 1963, Vol. 67, pp. 24–30.

17 Miller, R. E., W. F. Caul, and I. A. Mirsky. The communication of affects between feral and socially-isolated monkeys, *J. Pers. Soc. Psychol.*, 1967, Vol. 7, pp. 231–239.

18 Mitchell, G. D., E. J. Raymond, G. K. Ruppenthal, and H. F. Harlow. Long-term effects of total social isolation upon behavior of rhesus monkeys, *Psychol. Rept.*, 1966, Vol. 18, pp. 567–580.

19 Montagu, M. F. Ashley. Anthropology and Human Nature, Boston, Porter Sargent, 1957.

20 Ostow, Mortimer. The biological basis of human behavior, *in* American Handbook of Psychiatry (Arieti Silvano, editor), Vol. 1, New York, Basic Books, 1959, pp. 58–87.

21 Pratt, Charles L. and Gene P. Sackett. Selection of social partners as a function of peer contact during rearing, *Science*, 1967, Vol. 155, pp. 1133–1135.

22 Róheim, G. The Riddle of the Sphinx, London, Hogarth Press, 1934.

23 Róheim, Géza. Psychoanalysis and Anthropology: Culture, Personality and Unconscious, New York, Intern. Univ. Press, 1950.

24 Rosenzweig, Mark R. Environmental complexity, cerebral change, and behavior, *Am. Psychologist*, 1966, Vol. 21, pp. 321–332.

25 Rowland, G. L. The effects of total social isolation upon learning and social behavior in rhesus monkeys. Unpublished Ph.D. dissertation, Univ. Wisconsin, 1964.

26 Sackett, Gene P. Response of rhesus monkeys to social stimulation presented by means of colored slides, *Percept. Motor Skills*, 1965, Vol. 20, pp. 1027–1028.

27 Schneider, von, Ernst. Hemmung und Verdrängung, *Schweiz. Z. Psychol.*, 1947, Vol. 6, pp. 54–63.

28 Singer, Margaret Thaler and Lyman C. Wynne. Thought disorder and family relations of schizophrenics. IV. Results and implications, *Arch. Gen. Psychiat.*, 1965, Vol. 12, pp. 201–212.

29 Spitz, René A. The First Year of Life, New York, Intern. Univ. Press, 1965.

Richard H. Walters. *The Effects of Social Isolation and Social Interaction on Learning and Performance in Social Situations*

1 Amoroso, D. M. The effects of anxiety and socially-mediated anxiety reduction on paired-associated learning. Unpublished Ph.D. thesis, Univ. Waterloo, 1966.

2 Bandura, Albert. Social learning through imitation, *in* Nebraska Symposium on Motivation (Marshall R. Jones, editor), Lincoln, Neb., Univ. Nebraska Press, 1962, pp. 211–269.

3 Bandura, Albert. Vicarious processes: A case of no-trial learning, *in* Advances in Experimental Social Psychology (Leonard Berkowitz, editor), Vol. 2, New York, Academic Press, 1965, pp. 1–55.

4 Bandura, Albert and Theodore L. Rosenthal. Vicarious classical conditioning as a function of arousal level, *J. Personality Soc. Psychol.*, 1966, Vol. 3, pp. 54–62.

5 Bandura, Albert and Richard H. Walters. Social Learning and Personality Development, New York, Holt, Rinehart and Winston, 1963.

6 Beller, Emanuel K. Dependency and independence in young children, *J. Genet. Psychol.*, 1955, Vol. 87, pp. 25–35.

7 Berlyne, D. E. Conflict, Arousal, and Curiosity, New York, McGraw-Hill, 1960.

8 Bowlby, J. The nature of the child's tie to his mother, *Intern. J. Psychoanal.*, 1958, Vol. 39, pp. 350–373.

9 Easterbrook, J. A. The effect of emotion on cue utilization and the organization of behavior, *Psychol. Rev.*, 1959, Vol. 66, pp. 183–201.

10 Estes, W. K. Learning theory and the new "mental chemistry," *Psychol. Rev.*, 1960, Vol. 67, pp. 207–223.

11 Gewirtz, Jacob L. A program of research on the dimensions and antecedents of emotional dependence, *Child Develop.*, 1956, Vol. 27, pp. 205–221.

12 Gewirtz, J. L. Social deprivation and dependency: a learning analysis, Paper presented at the Annual Meeting of the Am. Psychol. Assoc., New York, 1957.

13 Gewirtz, J. L. Deprivation and satiation of social stimuli as determinants of their reinforcing efficacy, *in* Minnesota Symposium in Child Psychology (J. P. Hill, editor), Vol. 1, Minneapolis, Univ. Minnesota Press, 1967 (in press).

14 Gewirtz, Jacob L. and Donald M. Baer. The effect of brief social deprivation on behaviors for a social reinforcer, *J. Abnorm. Soc. Psychol.*, 1958, Vol. 56, pp. 49–56.

15 Gewirtz, Jacob L. and Donald M. Baer. Deprivation and satiation of social

reinforcers as drive conditions, *J. Abnorm. Soc. Psychol.*, 1958, Vol. 57, pp. 165–172.

16 HARLOW, HARRY F. and MARGARET K. HARLOW. The affectional systems, *in* Behavior of Nonhuman Primates (Allan M. Schrier, Harry F. Harlow, and Fred Stollnitz, editors), Vol. 2, New York, Academic Press, 1965, pp. 287–334.

17 HARTUP, WILLARD W. Nurturance and nurturance-withdrawal in relation to the dependency behavior of preschool children, *Child Develop.*, 1958, Vol. 29, pp. 191–201.

18 HARTUP, WILLARD W. and YAYOI HIMENO. Social isolation vs. interaction with adults in relation to aggression in preschool children, *J. Abnorm. Soc. Psychol.*, 1959, Vol. 59, pp. 17–22.

19 HEBB, D. O. The Organization of Behavior, New York, Wiley, 1949.

20 HEBB, D. O. Drives and the C. N. S. (conceptual nervous system), *Psychol. Rev.*, 1955, Vol. 62, pp. 243–254.

21 HEIDER, FRITZ. The Psychology of Interpersonal Relationships, New York, Wiley, 1958.

22 HULL, CLARK L. Principles of Behavior, New York, Appleton-Century, 1943.

23 JAKUBCZAK, LEONARD F. and RICHARD WALTERS. Suggestibility as dependency behavior, *J. Abnorm. Soc. Psychol.*, 1959, Vol. 59, pp. 102–107.

24 KAUSLER, DONALD H. and E. PHILIP TRAPP. Motivation and cue utilization in intentional and incidental learning, *Psychol. Rev.*, 1960, Vol. 67, pp. 373–379.

25 KESSEN, WILLIAM and GEORGE MANDLER. Anxiety, pain, and the inhibition of distress, *Psychol. Rev.*, 1961, Vol. 68, pp. 396–404.

26 KIESLER, SARA B. Stress, affiliation, and performance, *J. Exptl. Res. Personality*, 1966, Vol. 1, pp. 227–235.

27 KÖHLER, WOLFGANG. The Place of Values in a World of Facts, New York, Liveright, 1938.

28 LEVIN, HARRY and ELINOR WARDWELL. The research uses of doll play, *Psychol. Bull.*, 1962, Vol. 59, pp. 27–56.

29 LOGAN, FRANK A. and ALLAN R. WAGNER. Reward and Punishment, Boston, Allyn and Bacon, 1965.

30 LUMSDAINE, A. A. (editor). Student Response in Programmed Instruction: A Symposium, Washington, D.C., National Academy of Sciences — National Research Council, 1961.

31 MALMO, ROBERT B. Activation: A neuropsychological dimension, *Psychol. Rev.*, 1958, Vol. 66, pp. 367–386.

32 REICHENBACH, HANS. Experience and Prediction: An Analysis of the Foundations and the Structure of Knowledge, Chicago, Univ. Chicago Press, 1938.

33 ROSENBLITH, JUDY F. Learning by imitation in kindergarten children, *Child Develop.*, 1959, Vol. 30, pp. 69–80.

34 RYLE, GILBERT. The Concept of Mind, New York, Barnes and Noble, 1949, *also* London, Hutchison, 1950.

35 SCHACHTER, STANLEY. The Psychology of Affiliation, Stanford, Stanford Univ. Press, 1959.

36 SCHACHTER, STANLEY and JEROME E. SINGER. Cognitive, social, and physiological determinants of emotional state, *Psychol. Rev.*, 1962, Vol. 69, pp. 379–399.

37 SCHAFFER, H. RUDOLPH and PEGGY E. EMERSON. The development of social attachments in infancy, *Monogr. Soc. Res. Child Develop.*, 1964, Vol. 29, No. 3 (Serial No. 94).

38 SCOTT, J. P. Social facilitation and allelomimetic behavior, *in* Social Facilitation and Imitative Behavior: Outcome of the 1967 Miami University Symposium on Social Behavior (E. C. Simmel, R. A. Hoppe, and G. A. Milton, editors), Boston, Allyn and Bacon, 1968, pp. 55–72.

39 SEARS, ROBERT R. Dependency motivation, *in* Nebraska Symposium on Motivation (Marshall R. Jones, editor), Lincoln, Neb., Univ. Nebraska Press, 1963, pp. 25–64.

40 SEARS, ROBERT R., ELEANOR E. MACCOBY, and HARVEY LEVIN. Patterns of Child Rearing, Evanston, Ill., Row, Peterson, 1957.

41 SEARS, R. R., L. RAU, and R. ALPERT. Identification and Child Rearing, Stanford, Calif., Stanford Univ. Press, 1965.

42 SEARS, R. R., J. W. M. WHITING, V. NOWLIS, and P. S. SEARS. Some child-rearing antecedents of aggression and dependency in young children, *Genet. Psychol. Monogr.*, 1953, Vol. 47, pp. 135–236.

43 SPENCE, KENNETH W. Behavior Theory and Conditioning, New Haven, Conn., Yale Univ. Press, 1956.

44 WALTERS, R. H. Basic concepts and principles of personality development, unpublished.

45 WALTERS, R. H. Some conditions facilitating the occurrence of imitative behavior, *in* Social Facilitation and Imitative Behavior: Outcome of the 1967 Miami University Symposium on Social Behavior (E. C. Simmel, et al., editors), Boston, Allyn and Bacon, 1968, pp. 7–30.

46 WALTERS, R. H. and D. M. AMOROSO. Cognitive and emotional determinants of the occurrence of imitative behavior, *Brit. J. Soc. Clin. Psychol.*, 1967, Vol. 6, pp. 174–185.

47 WALTERS, RICHARD H., NORMA V. BOWEN, and ROSS D. PARKE. Influence of the looking behavior of a social model on the subsequent looking behavior of observers of the model, *Percept. Motor Skills*, 1964, Vol. 18, pp. 469–483.

48 WALTERS, RICHARD H., JOHN E. CALLAGAN, and ALBERT F. NEUMAN. Effect of solitary confinement on prisoners, *Am. J. Psychiat.*, 1963, Vol. 119, pp. 771–773.

49 WALTERS, RICHARD H. and G. BRUCE HENNING. Social isolation, effect of instructions, and verbal behaviour, *Can. J. Psychol.*, 1962, Vol. 16, pp. 202–210.

50 WALTERS, RICHARD H. and PEARL KARAL. Social deprivation and verbal behavior, *J. Personality*, 1960, Vol. 28, pp. 89–107.

51 WALTERS, RICHARD H., WILLIAM E. MARSHALL, and J. RICHARD SHOOTER. Anxiety, isolation, and susceptibility to social influence, *J. Personality*, 1960, Vol. 28, pp. 518–529.

52 WALTERS, RICHARD H. and ROSS D. PARKE. Emotional arousal, isolation, and

discrimination learning in children, *J. Exptl. Child Psychol.*, 1964, Vol. 1, pp. 163–173.

53 WALTERS, RICHARD H. and Ross D. PARKE. Social motivation, dependency, and susceptibility to social influence, *in* Advances in Experimental Social Psychology (Leonard Berkowitz, editor), Vol. 1, New York, Academic Press, 1964, pp. 231–276.

54 WALTERS, RICHARD H. and Ross D. PARKE. The role of the distance receptors in the development of social responsiveness, *in* Advances in Child Development and Behavior (Lewis P. Lipsitt and Charles C. Spiker, editors), Vol. 2, New York, Academic Press, 1965, pp. 59–96.

55 WALTERS, RICHARD H. and Ross D. PARKE. The influence of punishment and related disciplinary techniques on the social behavior of children, *in* Progress in Experimental Personality Research (B. A. Maher, editor), Vol. 4, New York, Academic Press, 1968, pp. 179–222.

56 WALTERS, RICHARD H. and EDWARD RAY. Anxiety, social isolation, and reinforcer effectiveness, *J. Personality*, 1960, Vol. 28, pp. 358–367.

57 WHITING, J. W. M. and IRVIN L. CHILD. Child Training and Personality, New Haven, Conn., Yale Univ. Press, 1953.

58 ZAJONC, ROBERT B. Social facilitation, *Science*, 1965, Vol. 149, pp. 269–274.

59 ZAJONC, ROBERT B. Social Psychology: An Experimental Approach, Belmont, Calif., Wadsworth, 1966.

ACKNOWLEDGMENTS

The preparation of this paper was made possible by research grants from the National Research Council of Canada (Grant No. APT-94), the Ontario Mental Health Foundation (Grant No. 42), the Defense Research Board of Canada (Grant No. 9401–24), and the National Institutes of Health, United States Health Service (Grant No. HD01456). Current grant numbers are given. Donald M. Amoroso conducted two of the experiments that are reported in the paper, made helpful comments on an earlier draft, and contributed one paragraph.

D. E. BERLYNE. *Indifferent Exteroceptive Stimulation and Reinforcement*

1 BERLYNE, D. E. Conflict, Arousal, and Curiosity, New York, McGraw-Hill, 1960.

2 BERLYNE, D. E. Motivational problems raised by exploratory and epistemic behavior, *in* Psychology: A Study of Science (S. Koch, editor), New York, McGraw Hill, 1963.

3 BERLYNE, D. E. Curiosity and exploration, *Science*, 1966, Vol. 153, pp. 25–33.

4 BERLYNE, D. E. Arousal and reinforcement, *in* Nebraska Symposium on Moti-

vation (D. Levine, editor), Lincoln, Neb., Univ. Nebraska Press, 1967, pp. 1–110.

5 BERLYNE, D. E. The reward value of indifferent stimulation, *in* Reinforcement (J. T. Tapp and G. W. Meier, editors), New York, Academic Press, 1968 (in press).

6 BERLYNE, D. E., ISOLDE D. V. KOENIG, and T. HIROTA. Novelty, arousal, and the reinforcement of diversive exploration in the rat, *J. Comp. Physiol. Psychol.*, 1966, Vol. 62, pp. 222–226.

7 COPPERMAN, N. Interaction of white noise and MAS scores in paired-associate learning. Unpublished M.A. thesis, Univ. Toronto, 1967.

8 FISKE, DONALD W. and SALVATORE R. MADDI. A conceptual framework, *in* Functions of Varied Experience (Donald W. Fiske and Salvatore R. Maddi, editors), Homewood, Ill., Dorsey, 1961.

9 GRASTYÁN, ENDRE, GYÖRGY KARMOS, LAJOS VERECZKEY, JÁNOS MARTIN, and LÓRAND KELLENYI. Hypothalamic motivational processes as reflected by their hippocampal electrical correlates, *Science*, 1965, Vol. 149, pp. 91–93.

10 GRASTYÁN, ENDRE, GYÖRGY KARMOS, LAJOS VERECZKEY, JÁNOS MARTIN, and LÓRAND KELLENYI. The hippocampal electrical correlates of the homeostatic regulation of motivation, *Electroenceph. Clin. Neurophysiol.*, 1966, Vol. 21, pp. 34–53.

11 HEBB, D. O. Drives and the C. N. S. (conceptual nervous system), *Psychol. Rev.*, 1955, Vol. 62, pp. 243–254.

12 LORE, R. K. Some factors influencing the child's exploration of visual stimuli. Unpublished Ph.D. thesis, Univ. Tennessee, 1965.

13 McMAHON, M. L. The relationship between environmental setting and curiosity in children. Unpublished Master in City Planning thesis, Mass. Inst. Technology, 1966.

14 NICKI, R. M. The reinforcing effect of uncertainty reduction on a human operant. Unpublished Ph.D. thesis, Univ. Toronto, 1968.

15 OLDS, JAMES. Hypothalamic substrates of reward, *Physiol. Rev.*, 1962, Vol. 42, pp. 554–604.

16 OLDS, JAMES and MARIANNE OLDS. Drives, rewards, and the brain, *in* New Directions in Psychology II (Frank Barron, William C. Dement, Ward Edwards, Harold Lindman, Lawrence D. Phillips, James Olds, and Marianne Olds, editors), New York, Holt, Rinehart and Winston, 1965, pp. 327–410.

17 SCHNEIRLA, T. C. An evolutionary and developmental theory of biphasic processes underlying approach and withdrawal, *in* Nebraska Symposium on Motivation (Marshall R. Jones, editor), Lincoln, Neb., Univ. Nebraska Press, 1959, pp. 1–42.

18 SCHNEIRLA, T. C. Aspects of stimulation and organization in approach/withdrawal processes underlying vertebrate behavioral development, *in* Advances in the Study of Behavior (Daniel S. Lehrman, Robert A. Hinde, and Evelyn Shaw, editors), New York, Academic Press, 1965, pp. 2–74.

19 WUNDT, W. M. Grundzüge der physiologischen Psychologie, Leipzig, Engelmann, 1874.

ACKNOWLEDGMENTS

The preparation of this chapter and the research reported in it were supported by Research Grants MH–06324 and MH–12528 from the National Institute of Mental Health, U.S. Public Health Service, No. 70 from the Ontario Mental Health Foundation, APT–73 and APB–73 from the National Research Council of Canada, and a grant from the Ontario Institute for Studies in Education.

P. Herbert Leiderman. *Social Conditions,*
Physiology and Role Performance

1 Bogdonoff, M. D., R. F. Klein, K. W. Back, C. R. Nichols, W. G. Troyer, and T. C. Hood. Effect of group relationships and the role of leadership upon lipid mobilization, *Psychosom. Med.*, 1964, Vol. 26, pp. 710–719.

2 Cohen, Sanford I. Central nervous system functioning in altered sensory environments, *in* Psychological Stress (Mortimer H. Appley and Richard Trumbull, editors), New York, Appleton-Century-Crofts, 1967, pp. 77–122.

3 Costell, R. M. and P. H. Leiderman. Psychophysiological concomitants of social stress: the effects of conformity pressure, *Psychosom. Med.*, 1968, Vol. 30, No. 3, pp. 298–309.

4 Dubos, René. Science and man's nature, *Daedalus*, 1965, Vol. 94, Winter, pp. 223–244.

5 Duffy, E. Activation and Behavior, New York, Wiley, 1962.

6 Lacey, J. L. Somatic response patterning and stress: Some revisions of activation theory, *in* Psychological Stress (M. H. Appley and R. Trumbull, editors), New York, Appleton-Century-Crofts, 1967, pp. 14–37.

7 Leiderman, P. H. Imagery and sensory deprivation, Washington, D.C., U.S.A.F. Tech. Doc. Rept. No. MRL-TDR-62-28, May 1962.

8 Leiderman, P. H. and D. Shapiro. Application of a time-series statistic to physiology and psychology, *Science*, 1962, Vol. 138, pp. 141–142.

9 Leiderman, P. H. and D. Shapiro (editors). Psychobiological Approaches to Social Behavior, Stanford, Calif., Stanford Univ. Press, 1964.

10 Lindsley, D. B. The reticular system and perceptual discrimination, *in* Reticular Formation of the Brain (H. H. Jasper, L. D. Proctor, R. S. Knighton, W. C. Noshay, and R. T. Costello, editors), Boston, Mass., Little, Brown, 1958, pp. 513–534.

11 Moruzzi, G. and H. W. Magoun. Brain stem reticular formation and activation of the EEG., *Electroenceph. Clin. Neurophysiol.*, 1949, Vol. 1, pp. 455–473.

12 Oken, D. and H. A. Heath. The law of initial values; some further considerations, *Psychosom. Med.*, 1963, Vol. 25, pp. 3–12.

13 Schachter, S. The interaction of cognitive and physiological determinants of emotional state, *in* Psychobiological Approaches to Social Behavior (P. H.

Leiderman and D. Shapiro, editors), Stanford, Calif., Stanford Univ. Press, 1964, pp. 138–173.

14 SHAPIRO, A. 1967. Personal communication.

15 SHAPIRO, D., P. H. LEIDERMAN, and M. MORNINGSTAR. Social isolation and social interaction: a behavioral and physiological comparison, *in* Recent Advances in Biological Psychiatry (J. Wortis, editor), Vol. 6, New York, Plenum Press, 1964, pp. 129–137.

16 WELCH, B. L. Psychophysiological response to mean level of environmental stimulation: a theory of environmental integration, *in* Symposium on Medical Aspects of Stress in Military Units (D. McK. Rioch, editor), Washington, D.C., Walter Reed Army Institute of Research, 1965, pp. 39–96.

ACKNOWLEDGMENT

This work is supported by Grant Foundation, New York, and NICHD Grant HD 02636-02.

JEROME KAGAN. *On Cultural Deprivation*

1 CAZDEN-COURTNEY, B. Subculture differences in child language: an inter-disciplinary review, *Merrill-Palmer Quart. Behav. Develop.*, 1966, Vol. 12, pp. 185–219.

2 FANTZ, ROBERT L. and SOULA NEVIS. Pattern preferences and perceptual-cognitive development in early infancy, *Merrill-Palmer Quart. Behav. Develop.*, 1967, Vol. 13, pp. 77–108.

3 FINLEY, G. A. A cross sectional and cross cultural study of young children's attention to familiar and incongruous stimuli. Paper presented at meeting of Society for Research on Child Development, March, 1967.

4 KAGAN, JEROME. The child's sex role classification of school objects, *Child Develop.*, 1964, Vol. 35, pp. 1051–1056.

5 KAGAN, JEROME. Reflection-impulsivity and reading ability in primary grade children, *Child Develop.*, 1965, Vol. 36, pp. 609–628.

6 KAGAN, JEROME, LESLIE PEARSON, and LOIS WELCH. Modifiability of an impulsive tempo, *J. Educ. Psychol.*, 1966, Vol. 57, pp. 359–365.

7 LACEY, JOHN I. Psychophysiological approaches to the evaluation of psychotherapeutic process and outcome, *in* Research in Psychotherapy (Eli A. Rubinstein and Morris B. Parloff, editors), Washington, D.C., Natl. Publ. Co., 1959, pp. 160–208.

8 LACEY, JOHN I., JEROME KAGAN, BEATRICE C. LACEY, and HOWARD A. MOSS. The visceral level: situational determinants and behavioral correlates of autonomic response patterns, *in* Expression of the Emotions in Man (Peter H. Knapp, editor), New York, Intern. Univ. Press, 1963, pp. 161–196.

9 LEWIS, MICHAEL, JEROME KAGAN, HELEN CAMPBELL, and JOHN KALAFAT. The

cardiac response as a correlate of attention in infants, *Child Develop.*, 1966, Vol. 37, pp. 63–72.

10 McCall, R. B. and J. Kagan. Stimulus-schema discrepancy and attention in the infant, *J. Exptl. Child Psychol.*, 1967, Vol. 38, pp. 938–952.

11 Moss, Howard A. Sex, age and state as determinants of mother-infant interaction, *Merrill-Palmer Quart. Behav. Develop.*, 1967, Vol. 13, pp. 19–36.

12 Salapatek, Philip and William Kessen. Visual scanning of triangles by the human newborn, *J. Exptl. Child Psychol.*, 1966, Vol. 3, pp. 155–167.

13 Sigel, Irving E., Larry M. Anderson, and Howard Shapiro. Categorization behavior of lower- and middle-class Negro preschool children; differences in dealing with representation of familiar objects, *J. Negro Educ.*, 1966, Summer, pp. 218–229.

ACKNOWLEDGMENTS

Preparation of this paper was supported in part by research grant MH–8792 from the National Institute of Mental Health and Contract PH43–65–1009 from the National Institute of Child Health and Human Development and a grant from the Carnegie Corporation of New York.

Urie Bronfenbrenner. *When Is Infant Stimulation Effective?*

1 Bronfenbrenner, U. The changing American child, *J. Soc. Issues*, 1961, Vol. 17, pp. 6–18.

2 Bronfenbrenner, U. Early deprivation: a cross-species analysis, *in* Early Experience and Behavior (G. Newton and S. Levine, editors), Springfield, Ill., Charles C Thomas, 1968, pp. 627–764.

3 Gewirtz, H. B. and J. L. Gewirtz. Caretaking settings, background events, and behavior differences in four Israeli child-rearing environments: some preliminary trends, *in* Determinants of Infant Behavior IV (B. M. Foss, editor), London, Methuen, 1967.

4 Harlow, H. F. and R. R. Zimmerman. Affectional responses in the infant monkey, *Science*, 1959, Vol. 130, pp. 421–432.

5 Rheingold, H. L. The modification of social responsiveness in institutional babies, *Monogr. Soc. Res. Child Develop.*, 1956, Vol. 21 (Serial No. 63), pp. 5–48.

Index

Note: Numbers in italics refer to pages on which figures and tables appear

A

adaptation, *see also* monkeys
to inadequate food intake 144–145
to stress 143–144
adaptive behavior, primates 75 ff.
adaptive development
in Guatemalan infants 14, 15, *15*
mental development and, 29–30
adaptive scale scores *15*
adopted children, in longitudinal
studies 108–110
adrenal function v
affiliation, arousal-reduction and
168 ff., 205 ff.
age
adaptive development and *19–20*
adoption and 108–110
attitude toward models and 247–
248
body length and *21*
chronological and mental, malnutrition and 26–28, *26*
chronological, and size 18–21, *21*
class differences in cognition and
263
dominance behavior among monkeys and 120–122
effects of malnutrition and 23, 49
environmental effects and 151–152
intelligence tests and 29
mental development and 28, 152
motor development and *19–20*
reaction to visual stimuli and 104
schema of human form and 214
smiling and 213
social development and *21*
of vocalization, position in family
and 255
aggression
definitions of 157
dominance behavior and 123 ff.
isolation and 163 ff.

aggression (cont'd)
monkeys and 123 ff.
alienation vi, 144 ff.
amino acids, malnutrition and 7
animals, *see also specific types*
crowding and 146
curarized, conditioned leg withdrawal and 212
research in malnutrition with 52 ff.
anxiety
failure and 242 ff.
social isolation, saturation and
164 ff.
verbal retention and 168, *194* ff.
apathy, malnutrition and 144–145
apes, *see* nonhuman primates
arousal, *see also under* monkeys
behavioral and psychological, compared 202 ff.
conformity behavior and 207–208
deprivation syndrome and 89
emotional control and 90–91
epinephrine-induced 179
of erotic responses 175 ff., *178–179*
imitation and 173 ff., 206–207
infantile contact behavior and 76–
77
MAS score and *195*
maternal function and 90
measurement of 203 ff.
modeling behavior and 207–208
in mother, hormones and 210
optimal level of 114, 193 ff., *193*
organization of behavior and 131–
132
physiological index of 166, *170–171*
potential 187 ff., *187*
predisposing states of 115
reduction of, *see* arousal-reduction
reward and 186 ff.
social isolation and 162 ff., 181 ff.,
205

arousal (cont'd)
    statistical treatment of 204–205
    verbal learning and 194 ff., *194*
arousal hypothesis 116
arousal-reduction 78
    affiliation and 168 ff., 205 ff.
    clinging, sucking, grooming, and
        114
    role of mother in 87, *87*
ascending reticular activating sys-
        tem 203
associations, development of 216 ff.,
        216
attention
    alteration of schema and 223
    density of associations and 216 ff.,
        216
    earliest determinant of 215
    discrepancy from established
        schema and 215–216
    distinctiveness of event and 223
    habituation and 240
    maintenance of 239
        and cultural differences 220
    to visual patterns, social class
        and 196
attachment behavior 157–158
auditory stimulation, in infants 14,
        15, 159
auditory-visual integration
    ethnic differences and 45–46
    learning and 51
    malnutrition and 46 ff.
    reading and 44
avoidance
    conditioned 58, *58*, 59
    indifferent exteroceptive stimuli
        and 196
    social isolation and 134 ff.
axolotl, neoteny and 95

                    B
behavior, *see also specific types*
    arousal and 131 ff.
    complexity of environment and
        130 ff., 196
    of culturally deprived children 196
    culture and 151
    definition of 258

behavior (cont'd)
    development of, *see* behavioral
        development
    early experience and 106–107
    effects of crowding on 146–147
    heredity and environment and
        139 ff.
    of malnourished pigs 55–56, *56*
    methodological and metaphysical
        approaches to 198
    methods of analyzing changes in 199
    muscular activity and 260
    neoteny and, *see* behavioral neo-
        teny
    of nonhuman primates 73 ff., 79 ff.,
        91 ff.
    protein-calorie malnutrition and
        3 ff., *24–26*
    related to biology 129–130
    reversible and irreversible 201
    stimulation and repression of 129–
        130
    trends in organization of 97 ff.
    weight and height related to 10
behavioral development
    in newborns 10, 97
    phylogenetic trends in 94
    of primates compared 91 ff., 112
behavioral isomorphism 198
behavioral neoteny 95–96, *96*, 136
behavioristic revolution 198
behaviorists 257 ff.
biochemistry
    learning and 161
    malnutrition and 5 ff., *5 ff.*
biology, related to behavior v, 129–
        130
birds, sound-learning in 128–129
birth control 139, 148
blood cholesterol, malnutrition and 5
body measurements, *see* height;
        weight
Boston slum children, study of habits
        and tastes of 152
brain
    effects of malnutrition on 49–50,
        144
    "reward" and "aversion" systems
        of 187, *187*
    weight, neoteny, and 95

breast-feeding 18
brow ridges, neoteny and 95

C

Cakchiquel Indians, Gesell test scores
    of 18
Cambridge children, study of reac-
    tions to human forms in 218 ff.,
    232 ff., *232, 233*
candy-eating, in monkeys 127
Cape Town, semilongitudinal study
    of mental development in 29
catecholamines, malnutrition and
    204
Cayo Santiago, study of monkeys on,
    117 ff., 122 ff.
central nervous system
    of animals on inadequate diets 50
    arousal and 203
    nutritional deprivation and 30
Chicago school of behavior research
    198
child-care, *see* child-rearing practices;
    maternal care; mother
child-care institutions, research in
    107
child-rearing practices
    in child-care institutions 107
    diet and 64
    in kibbutz 256
    malnutrition and 3
    oversocialized conditions and 148
    social class and 65
childhood, adaptive benefit of pro-
    longing 94–97
children
    adopted, *see* adopted children
    autistic 136
    behavior studies in varied settings
        of 196
    in Boston slums 152
    conditioned responses and protein
        deficiency in 50–51
    construction and selection of en-
        vironments by 200–201
    culturally deprived viii, 211 ff., *see
        also* deprivation; deprivation
        syndrome
    attentiveness to visual patterns
        by 196

children (cont'd)
    mental functioning in vii
    physiological functions of 133
    use of term 211
    development of 9
        barriers to 144–145
        and changes in environment 106–
            107
        desirable models for 247
        educational level of parents and
            28
        infant precocity and 18
        research on nonhuman primates
            and 111–113
        rewards and 185
        role of peers in 248 ff.
    earlier maturation of 142–143
    early verbal facility in 261–262
    effect of early experiences on 106–
        107
    failure and 242 ff.
    first-born, anxiety studies of 168–
        169
    height of, *see* height
    impulsive 244 ff.
    intelligence scores and body meas-
        urements of 19, 21, *22*
    language development in 235 ff.
    learning and social isolation in
        162 ff.
    maintenance of attentional invest-
        ment in 239
    malnourished vii, 22 ff.
        biochemical alterations in 4–5
        IQ scores of 29–30
    and non-nutritional factors re men-
        tal development 28–29
    study plan for 9–10
    survival rates in 8
    mental growth of 212 ff.
    middle-class
        auditory-visual integration study
            in 44 ff.
        compared to lower-middle class
            vii–viii
    Negro, conceptual sorting tasks and
        244
    organismic sensitivities of 102–104
    as problem-solvers 199
    psychological goals of 242

children (cont'd)
  reaction to schema of human form
    in 214, 218 ff.
  research strategy with 107–108
  response times of 246–247
  rural, form recognition by *41*
  separation situations and 107–108
  school-age, *see* school-age children
  social class membership of 64
  social development of 136
  stimuli, novel 220 ff., *221–222*
  urban, form recognition by *43*
chimpanzees, *see also* nonhuman pri-
    mates
  behavioral arousal in 131–132
  limited isolation studies of 90
  neoteny and 95–96, *96*
  as playful parents 95–96, *96*
  primitive infantile responses in 97
  stereotyped movements of 98–99
  walking in 74
class, *see* social class
clasping, in nonhuman primates 78–
    79, *79*
clinging, in nonhuman primates 75–
    78, 115
cognitive behavior
  acquisition of 212, 213, 221–222
  class differences and 224 ff.
  elements involved in 261 ff.
cognitive schemata
  critique of concept of 258 ff.
  definition of 258–259
  as major elements in mental de-
    velopment 258
cognitionists, behaviorists and 259
communication behavior
  in apes 128–129
  deprivation syndrome and 82, *82*,
    91
  distinctiveness and 223
  isolation studies and 135
  of parents 252
  schema changes and 241
  schizophrenic children and 136–137
compulsion, motor activity and 115–
    116
conditioned avoidance tests 58, *58*, 59
conditioned reflexes, malnutrition
    and 50–51

conformity behavior
  arousal and 207–208
  habits and tastes and 152
  in modeling studies 176 ff.
  skin potential level and 207
contact-seeking behavior, in nonhu-
    man primates 76 ff., 83
critical-period hypothesis 11
crowding, social behavior and 146 ff.
crying, in nonhuman primate infants
    75
"culturally deprived" children, *see*
    children, culturally deprived
cultural stimulation, social class and
    65
culture, behavior and perception
    and 151
curiosity, neoteny and 96, *96*
cylinders, cloth covered, as surrogate
    mothers 86

D

death wish 97
dehydration 23
dentine composition of teeth, protein
    malnutrition and 4
dependency drive
  acquired 158–159
  criticism of term 156–158
  definitions of 157
  maternal deprivation and 163
  psychological development and
    252, 256–257
  responsiveness to facial stimuli and
    254
  vocalization and 255 ff.
deprivation, *see also* social isolation
  in nonhuman primates 79 ff., *79,
    81*
  nutritional, *see also* malnutrition,
    in animals 52 ff., *58, 59*
  psychological consequences of 91
  remedial action and 263
  visual 103–104
deprivation syndrome
  excessive arousal and 89
  excessive emotionality and 91
  general classification of *81*
  hyperexcitability and 84–85
  in monkeys 80–81, *81*

deprivation syndrome (cont'd)
  motivational disturbances and 84
  sensorimotor patterns and 89
  sexual performance and 90
  stereotyped movements and 83, *84–85*
  timing of onset of 86
  water regulation and 133–134
development, *see* children, development of
diet, *see also* eating habits; malnutrition; nutrition
  and child-rearing practices 64
  education of mother and 48
  persistence of eating habits and 144–145
  of protein-calorie deficient animals 53 ff., *56* ff.
  social development and 61–62
digit sucking, in nonhuman primates 83
discomfort, human attachment behavior and 159
discrepancy, in infant development 215–216, *216*
discrimination learning, distinctiveness and 223
disease, mental development and 64
dispositional adjectives 157
distinctiveness
  attention span and 239
  acquired 223
  of mother's vocalization 235 ff.
dogs
  isolation-reared 91
  salivary conditioning of 50
doll-play 163
dominance behavior
  in macaques 117 ff.
    age and 121
    incest and 123
    sex and 122 ff.
drawing, cognition and 213
drinking, concentration of solutions and 114
drive, *see* social drive
drought, nutrition and 61
drugs, learning and 190 ff.
dummies, in primate-rearing studies 83 ff., *84* ff.

Duncan Multiple-Range Test 169 ff.

E

East African infants, precocity study of 16
eating habits, *see also* diet; nutrition; malnutrition
  of monkeys 119 ff., 125 ff.
  nutritional deprivation and 53 ff.
  social class and 61 ff.
early experiences
  brain structure and 152
  effects of 141, 151–152
  life-style of organism and 132
  outcome variables of 110–111
economic depression, nutrition and 61
education
  "learning by doing" concept of 212
  malnutrition and vii
  of mother
    and height of child 44, *44*, 52
    and intellectual development of child 28
    maternal vocalization and 235 ff., *236–237*
    neuro-integrative function of child and 48
  of parents
    child's reaction to tests and 246
    cognitive function of infants and 227 ff.
  sex role and 248
  in underground schools 149
electric shock, learning and 169
emotional arousal, *see* arousal
Embedded Figures task 245 ff.
endocrine function, crowding and 146 ff.
environment, *see also* mother; social class; etc.
  behavior and 130 ff.
  changing dynamic character of 106
  construction and selection of 200–201
  diversification of 154
  heredity and 138, 153
  human behavior and 139 ff.
  infant conceptualization and analysis of 104–105

environment (cont'd)
    interactions between stimuli and
        organismic characteristics and
        106
    learning behavior and 197 ff.
    psychomotor precocity and 16–18,
        17
    reaction to visual patterns and 196
    of severely malnourished children
        28–29
    technologized 144 ff.
    in terms of schedules of gratifica-
        tion and frustration 105
enzyme system, malnutrition and 7
epinephrine, arousal and 204
estrogen 210
ethnic origin
    psychomotor organization and 16–
        17, 17
    sensory integrative functioning
        and 45
evolution
    of future man 153
    of ontogenesis of infantile behav-
        ior 130–131
    of primates 92–93, 92–93
    vocal learning and 128–129
experience, see also early experience
    ability to interpret vii-viii
    behavioral development and 79 ff.,
        79
exploratory behavior
    onset in nonhuman primates of 77–
        78
    in malnourished rats 52 ff.
    permissiveness and 253
eye-movements, in modeling studies
    176 ff.

F

faces, see human faces and forms
failure, anxiety and 242 ff.
families, see also children; father;
        mother; parents
    in epidemiological study 68
    nuclear, only child in 255
family relationships
    and malnutrition 3
    among monkeys 119, 123
family tree, primate 93–94

fat absorption, malnutrition and 5
father, child's intersensory perform-
        ance and height of 42, 44
feeding habits, see diet; eating
        habits; malnutrition
feeding test, of monkeys 121
filial response, in nonhuman primates
        78 ff.
first-born, see children, first-born
foetalization, theory of 130
folkways, nutrition and 61
food-attitude test 53 ff.
food consumption surveys 8
food-supplementation program 67, 68
foot, of adult and fetal monkey and
        human 95–96, 96
foster homes 108
free fatty acids, malnutrition and 204

G

galvanic skin response, in modeling
        study 176 ff., 178
7–S gamma–2–globulin, in severe mal-
        nutrition 6
General Systems Theory 130
genes
    life experience and 153–154
    repression and stimulation of 129
    response to environment and 138
genetics, see genes; heredity
Gesell Development Quotients 12,
        12 ff.
    in cross-sectional studies of chil-
        dren 18 ff., 20–21, 24, 24–25
    predictions of mental development
        and 29
    protein-calorie malnutrition and 24
Gestalt psychology 184
gibbons, see also nonhuman primates
    as playful parents 96
goals
    change in schema and 240–241
    of children 241–242
    model-selection and 247–248
great apes, "loosening" of motor pat-
        terns in 99
grooming behavior, in monkeys 118 ff.
growth
    acceleration of 142–143

growth (cont'd)
  of nonhuman primates compared
    to man 94
Guatemalan infants, in nutrition and
    behavior study 10 ff., *16*, 67–68

H

habituation, change of schema and
    239–240
hand-clapping 99
haptic-kinesthetic test series 34 ff., *41*
heart rate
  in anxiety-arousal experiment
    171 ff.
  arousal measurement and 203,
    206 ff.
  child's recognition of mother and
    213
  in cognitive-function study 224 ff.
  in sexual-response study 177 ff.
  stimuli and 220 ff.
height
  auditory-visual integrative ability
    and 46–47
  behavior and 10 ff.
  correlation with social factors 47–
    48, *47*
  as criteria of early nutritional de-
    ficiency 65–67
  and educational level of mother
    44–45, *44*, 52
  environment and 142
  factors influencing 40 ff.
  as index of malnutrition 65–67
  intelligence scores and 8 ff.
  of Japanese teenagers 142
  of Latin American children 18
  protein malnutrition and 3 ff., *4–5*
  psychomotor performance and
    16 ff., *16* ff.
  of rural and urban children com-
    pared *38*, 39–40, *38–43*
  school failure and 51, 67
height-age 21 ff., 31
hemolytic complement, malnutrition
    and 6
heredity, *see also* genes
  behavioral development and 73
  environment and 138, 153
histidene 7

hoarding, of food 53
hormones
  behavior and 99
  maternal arousal and 210
Hull-Spence theory of behavior 183–
    184
human beings
  abilty to comprehend world 149
  adaptability to stress 143–144
  behavioral development 91 ff.
  early social life 147–148
  effects of crowding on 146 ff.
  life span 94
  potentialities 153–154
  studies of primates and 70 ff., 99 ff.,
    111 ff.
  verbal learning and arousal level
    in 194 ff.
human faces and forms, in cognitive
    function study 214 ff., 224 ff.
hyperexcitability, deprivation syn-
    drome and 84–85
hypothalamo-hypophyseal mecha-
    nisms, social isolation and 134

I

imitative behavior
  arousal and 173 ff., 206–207
  emotional and cognitive determi-
    nants of 180
imprinting 112, 148, 242
impulsivity, anxiety and 245 ff.
incentive, in learning theory 160–162
incest, in monkeys 123
indifferent exteroceptive stimuli
    185 ff.
  infant distress reactions and 159
  as rewards and punishments 195 ff.
infant precocity
  in adaptive development 14, *15*
  and body measurements 16, *16*, 17,
    17
  environment and 17–18
  ethnic explanation of 16–17
  in psychomotor development *14*,
    15, 17, *17*
infants (human)
  adoption and 109
  arousal and 132
  artificial feeding of 145

infants (human) (cont'd)
  attachment behavior in 159
  behaviorial development of
    in industrial and preindustrial
      communities 9–10
    malnutrition and 9
  behavioral study of 10 ff.
  body length of *12*
  cognitive function study of 224 ff.
  compared with nonhuman pri-
    mates 97, 104
  conceptualization and analyzing
    of environment by 104–105
  deceleration response 226 ff., *227,
    229, 233*
  early experiences related to later
    development of vii, 102–104
  effects of interactions between en-
    vironment stimuli and organ-
    ismic characteristics of 106
  fixation times to "faces" *228–229,
    232*
  kibbutz and home-raised 256
  maternal care and 103 ff.
  motor development
    and chronological age 18–21, *20,
      21*
    and predictions of intelligence
      in 29
  precocity of, *see* infant precocity
  premature 208 ff.
  prolongation of infancy in 130–131
  psychological development of
    251 ff.
  reaction to facial stimuli 253
  response to visual stimuli 213 ff.,
    216 ff.
  single versus multiple mother-
    ing of 255
  visual responses 225 ff., *226*
infants (nonhuman primates)
  behavior of captive orangutan 76
  clinging behavior in 115
  developmental trends in 78–79
  human infants compared to 97,
    112–113
  infantile responses of 74–75
  maternal care of 117, 125 ff.
  onset of play and exploration in
    77–78

infants (nonhuman primates) (cont'd)
  reared with cloth-covered cylinders
    86 ff.
  reared with robot devices and dum-
    mies 83–84, 87 ff.
  role of mother and 74–75
  social deprivation and 78, *79*
  social privileges of 117
  visual preference for "mother fig-
    ure" in 254
infections
  malnutrition and 3
  social class and 65
infrahuman primates, *see* nonhuman
    primates
instincts, human behavior and 97
intelligence, *see also* intelligence
    tests; IQ
  adaptive behavior and 29–30
  auditory visual integration and
    44 ff.
  defined 29
  in studies of monkeys and apes 71–
    72
intelligence quotient, *see* IQ; intelli-
    gence tests
intelligence tests
  age and 29
  body weight and height and 19 ff.
  as measures of mental growth 66
intersensory organization
  as index of mental development
    66–67
  and learning 50
  low stature and 64–65
  in study of school-age children
    31–33
inventiveness, neoteny and *96*
IQ *see also* intelligence; intelligence
    tests
  of child and parent, relationship
    between 28
  of malnourished Yugoslavian chil-
    dren 30
isolation, *see* social isolation
Israeli kibbutzim, height of children
    in 142

J

Japanese macaques, *see* monkeys;

Japanese macaques (cont'd)
    nonhuman primates
Japanese teenagers, heights of, 142

K

kindergarten, performance in 201
kinship, in nonhuman primates 117 ff.
Koshima Island macaques, feeding
    habits of 126, 128
kwashiorkor, *see also* protein-calorie
    malnutrition
    amino acid concentrations in
      blood plasma and 7
    early growth and 18
    Gesell test performance and 24

L

language
    development of 213
      and social class 235 ff., 240–241,
        252–253
    design features of 100–101
    schema changes and 241
Latin American children, in height
    and weight studies 18
learning
    anxiety and 195 ff., *195*
    arousal level and 164 ff.
    auditory-visual integration and 51
    behavorial and verbal concepts in
      261 ff.
    benign environments for 200–201
    critical periods of 49–50
    definition of 156
    dependency drive and 253
    deprivation syndrome and 89–90
    distinguished from transient per-
      formance 189
    drugs and 190 ff.
    of feeding habits 125 ff.
    intersensory integration and 32, 50
    isolation and 205
    malnutrition and 48–49
      in rats and pigs 56 ff., *56* ff.
    of maternal behavior 208 ff.
    models and 247 ff.
    modifiability of 103
    neoteny and 94–97
    observational and incentive 173–
      175, *174*

learning (cont'd)
    performance and 198 ff.
    prolongation of human infancy
      and 131
    reinforcement and 185 ff.
    retention of 195 ff.
    schizophrenia and 136–137
    in social context 156
    social isolation studies and vii,
      162 ff.
    vocal, in monkeys and birds, 128–
      129
    to write 51
learning theory
    maternal deprivation and 162 ff.
    rewards and punishments and 160–
      162
    social and developmental psychol-
      ogists and 156 ff.
lemurs, life span of 94
length, *see* height
libido 97
light increments, in studies of rats
    189 ff.
lipoproteins, malnutrition and 5
limbs, length of, malnutrition and
    4–5
love, studies of origins of 71–72

M

MAS, *see* Taylor Manifest Anxiety
    Scale
macaques, *see* monkeys; nonhuman
    primates
Macaca fuscata, see monkeys
Macaca mulatta, see monkeys
malnutrition, *see also* diet; eating
    habits; nutrition
    adjustment to 144–145
    age and 23
    in animals 53 ff.
    auditory-visual capacity of children
      and 46 ff.
    body height as criteria of 65–67
    brain development and 49–50, 144
    developmental quotients and 26–
      28, *24–28*
    effects of 4 ff.
    interrelated causes of 67–68

malnutrition (cont'd)
  intersensory organization and 48–49
  mental development and 63
  school failure and 51, 67
  social conditions and *47*
  social learning and 66
  in study of school-age children 30 ff., *33*
man, *see* human beings; children; infants (human) ; etc.
marasmus, amino acid concentrations in blood plasma and 7
Matching Familiar Figures test 243 ff.
maternal behavior, categories of 105, *see also* maternal care; mother
maternal care, *see also* child-rearing practices; mother
  arousal and 210
  dependency behavior and 163
  females with deprivation syndrome and 90
  among macaques 119 ff.
  of premature infants 208 ff.
  research on 104–105
  sterotyped movements and 83–84, *84*
  variables during infancy 103
maternal distinctive vocalization 235 ff.
maturation
  biochemical, malnutrition and 5 ff., *5*
  problem-solving and 200
maturity
  acceleration of 142–143
  behavior patterns and 107
mental age, height-age and 19 ff., *20–21*
mental defects
  motor development and 29
  malnutrition and 30
mental development, *see also* brain; intelligence; etc.
  effects of cultural deprivation on vii
  initial assumptions on 212 ff.
  interrelated factors in 64–65
  intersensory organization as measure of 66–67
  of malnourished children 8

mental development (cont'd)
  stages of 152
mental structures, *see* schemata
mestizos, Gesell test scores of 18
metabolism, dietary habits and 144–145
methamphetamine, in learning studies of rats 190 ff., *192–193*
Mexican children
  study of auditory-visual integration in 45 ff.
  study of malnutrition in 23 ff.
  study of reactions to forms and faces in 218 ff.
mice
  early food deprivation in 53
  loss of memory in 50
Minoo–B troops 119 ff., *see also* monkeys
models
  from peer group 248 ff.
  role in child development 247–248
modeling behavior
  arousal and 207–208
  in visual stimuli study 176 ff.
modifiability, of early learning and response patterns 103
monkeys, *see also* infants (nonhuman primates) ; nonhuman primates
  adaptive behavior 75 ff.
  aggression in 123 ff.
  arousal and 79–80, *80*, 131 ff.
  behavioral disturbances in 133 ff.
  chimpanzees and 98–99, 114
  concentric organization of 118
  deprivation and 78 ff., *79*, 89
  development of 94
  dominance in 117 ff., 120–121
  dummies and, moving and stationary 86 ff., *87, 88*
  effects of isolation and social impoverishment on 132
  emotional control and 90–91
  family relationships among 90–91, 119, 123 ff.
  feeding habits of 119 ff., 125 ff.
  grooming behavior in 118 ff.
  incest in 123
  kinship among 117 ff.

monkeys (cont'd)
  maturation 117
  as playful parents 95–96
  promiscuity 18
  self-rocking in 100
  sexual performance of 81–82, *82*,
    118, 123–124
  social interaction in 117 ff.
  social isolation in 134, 162 ff.
    visual stimuli and 134
    water intake during 133–134
  socially normal, reaction to isolates
    of 135
  sterotyped movements in 98–99
mortality, of malnourished children 8
mother, *see also* child-rearing; mater-
    nal care
  and attachment behavior 158
  child's cardiac reactions to 213
  child's intellectual development
    and 28
  distinctive vocalization by 252
  educational level of, *see* education,
    of mother
  effect on social development of
    child 136
  in foster home 108
  infant response and 49
  macaque
    dead infant of 125
    dominance behavior and 120–121
    natural vs. artificial 86 ff., *87*
    teaching of feeding habits by 126
  and "nest" 74
  nonhuman primate 74–75, 77, 79 ff.,
    83, *see also* mother, monkey
  as poser of problems 200
  psychological development of in-
    fant and 251 ff., 257
  sensory deprivation of infant and
    112
  separated from children 108
  single vs. multiple 255
  vocalization to infant by 235 ff.
motivation
  cognitive development and 241–242
  deprivation syndrome and 81–82,
    81
  instinctual basis of 97
  malnutrition and 49

motor development
  predictions of future intellect and
    29
  of primate species compared 98–99
movements, stereotyped, *see* stereo-
    typed movements
muscle tissue, malnutrition and 4
mythology, neoteny and 130

                    N

Nahoa Indians, infant precocity in
    16
neoteny
  behavior and 95–96, 131
  early theories of 130–131
  and feet 95, *96*
  in humans and nonhuman pri-
    mates 100–101
  of primates compared 94–97
neurosis, in studies of monkeys and
    apes 71–72
New York, studies of middle-class
    children in 35, 45 ff.
noise stimuli, adaptation to vi
nonhuman primates, *see also* mon-
    keys
  behavioral development of 73 ff.,
    91 ff., 98–101
    compared with humans 70 ff.,
      99–101
    neoteny and 94–97, *96*
    ontogeny and 94
    organizational trends and 97–99
    sucking, grooming and, in 74 ff.,
      97, 114
    unspecific arousal system and
      115–116
  clasping in 78–79, *79*, 83
  clinging in 75–78, 115
  cultural transmission of feeding
    habits by 128–129
  digit sucking 83
  as graded series 92–94, *92*
  maturation of 117
  mother-infant relationships in 74–
    75, 87, 115–117, 125 ff.
  play and exploration in 77–78
  research on
    emphasis on deprivation and
      trauma in 104–105

nonhuman primates (cont'd)
  experimental and naturalistic
    approaches to 107
  related to problems of human
    development 101–102, 111–113
  social deprivation and vii, 90
  trends in ontogeny of 94
  vocal learning 128–129
  vocalization in 74, 75, 100–101
nuclear family, only child in 255
nurturance, dependency and 163
nutrition, see also diet; eating habits
  definition of 61
  socioenvironmental factors of 61–
    62

O

ontogenetic development, learning
    and 94–95
Operación Zacatepec 22 ff., 24 ff.
oral grasping 97
organisms, see also specific types
  changes in, dependent variables
    and 106–107
  characteristics of, interactions
    between stimuli and environ-
    ment and 106
  immature, sensitivities of 102–104,
    see also infants
oversocialization 147–148, see also
  crowding

P

pain, human attachment behavior
    and 159
paired-associate verbal-learning task
    169
parents, see also father; mother
  anthropometric information on
    31, 40 ff.
  of schizophrenics, 137
paternal behavior, of monkeys 124–
    125
Pavlovian conditioned response, in
    studies of pigs 58, 58
peers, role in child development of
    248 ff.
pentobarbital 193–194, 194
perceptual curiosity 188

perceptual discrimination tasks, so-
    cial class and 243–244, 243
perceptual recognition test, drawing
    and 213
performance
  and learning 198 ff.
  and social contact vii, 172–173
permissiveness, exploratory behavior
    and 253
personality changes, malnutrition
    and 49
phenylalanine, malnutrition and 7
pigs, study of malnutrition in 53 ff.,
    54, 57–59
pimples, picking at by monkeys 99
pitting edema 23
population control, see birth control
population density, effects of in-
    crease in 139 ff., 146 ff., see also
    crowding; oversocialization
posture, deprivation syndrome and
    83
plasma lipids, malnutrition and 5
plasticity, of macaque behavior 127
play
  in human and nonhuman primate
    parents compared 95–96, 96
  in nonhuman primates 77–78, 79
precocity, see infant precocity
preference-scale studies 186
pregnancy, infant precocity and 17,
    17, 18
preindustrial societies, infant pre-
    cocity in 10, 17, 17, 18
prepuberty period, attitude toward
    model during 247–248
primates, see human beings; non-
    human primates
prisoners, isolation studies of 182
progesterone 210
prolactin 210
protein synthesis, brain growth and
    50
protein-calorie malnutrition, see also
    kwashiorkor; malnutrition
  defined 23
  effect on animals 4
  effects on learning behavior 60
  mental development and 29–30
  in newborn pigs 57, 57

protein-calorie malnutrition (cont'd)
  studies in children with 22 ff., *22 ff.*
  survival rates and 8
  treatment of 8
psychic cost, of adaptation to urban
  environment vi
psychological tests, in study of Guatemalan children 68
psychomotor performance 13 ff.
  body measurements and 16 ff., *16 ff.*
  of infants in Guatemalan study 13–
    14, *13–14, 16*
psychomotor scale scores *13*
psychopharmacology 186
psychoses, and use of nonhuman primates as study models 72
puberty, changing age of 142–143, *see
  also* maturation
punishment
  learning and 160 ff.
  schema change and 240–241

R

race, *see* ethnic origin
ranking, *see* dominance
rats
  dietary habits of 144
  drugs and *192–194*
  effect of crowding on 146
  exteroceptive indifferent stimulation rewards and 189 ff., *191*
  malnourished
    in early life 53 ff., *56*
    learning behavior in 56 ff.
    stunting in 56, *56*
  noise and *191*
Raven intelligence test 29
reading
  anxiety and 244
  factors affecting 44–45
  lack of reflection and 247
  sex of teachers and problems in
    249
  visual-kinesthetic performance
    and 51
reflection 246
reinforcement, definition of 185
remedial action 263
  training in reflection and 246

research
  on dependency relationship 254–255
  on nature of reward 185 ff.
  with nonhuman primates, *see* nonhuman primates, research on
  on reward and perceptual curiosity
    188 ff.
  social-psychological, categories of
    156 ff.
reward
  arousal and 186 ff.
  for correct behavior 252
  elimination of perceptual curiosity
    and 188 ff.
  in laboratory 185
  learning and 160–162
  schema change and 240–241
rhesus macaques, *see* monkeys
rituals, diet and 61–62
rocking 91
  deprivation syndrome and 80–81
  distress reactions and 159
  role of mother and 83
rooting, in infants 97

S

saliva bubbling 99
schemata
  changes in
    communication and 241
    reward and punishment and 240–
      241
    role of habituation in 239–240
  definition of 214
  and density of associations 216 ff.
  establishment of 222 ff.
  nature of 213 ff.
  physical parameters of 215
  role of discrepancy in 215–216
  social class and 223
schizophrenia, etiology of 136–137
school-age children
  attitude toward "sex" of school
    objects in 248–249
  auditory-visual capacity and nutritional status of 46 ff.
  intersensory competence in 32
  methods of studying 30 ff.
  Seguin Form Board Test and 33,
    34

school-age children (cont'd)
    social isolation experiments with
        164 ff.
    visual-haptic integration in 34 ff.
school performance
    height and 67
    neurointegrative inadequacy and
        51
    nutritional deficiency and 67
    sex typing and 248
    social class and 248
Scotland, study of auditory-visual
        integrative development of
        children in 44
Seguin Form Board Test 33, 34
self-clasping in monkeys 83, 91
self-sucking in primates 91
sense modalities 32 ff.
sensitivities, of immature organisms
        102–104
sensory input, emotional develop-
        ment and 91
sensory deprivation 205
    social isolation and 112
sensory perception, see also intersen-
        sory organization
    cultural differences and 151
    receptivity in young organisms and
        102–103
separation, see also deprivation syn-
        drome; maternal deprivation
    adoption and 107–110
    long-term effects of 10
sex
    body measurements of Guatema-
        lan infants by 11–12, 11–12
    cognitive function and 230 ff.
    of infants
        maternal vocalization and 235 ff.
        reciprocal vocal interchange and
            235 ff.
        vocalization and 253
    macaque dominance behavior
        and 122 ff.
    psychomotor and adaptive per-
        formance and 13–15, 13, 14
    reading problems and 248–249
    of school-age children in study 33
sexual performance
    deprivation syndrome in monkeys

sexual performance (cont'd)
    and 81–82, 81–82
    in human males, rehearsal in child-
        hood and 91
    of isolation-reared dogs 91
    of monkeys 81–82, 82, 118, 123–124
sexual responses, in visual response
        study 175 ff.
sibling relations, of macaques 119
skin responses
    as index of arousal, 206, 207
    of subjects in sexual response study
        176 ff.
smiling
    at different ages 213
    as index of recognitory reaction 234
    in kibbutz- and family-raised in-
        fants 256
    mother's response to 136
social behaviorist position 263
social changes, technological changes
        and 265
social class, see also socioeconomic
        status
    attention and 196
    child-rearing practices and 64
    cognitive development and 224 ff.,
        241–242, 258
    goals and 241–242
    impulsiveness and 245
    language development and 235 ff.
        252–253
    nutrition and 62, 63
    reaction to facial stimuli and 252
    role of model and 247–248
    role of peers and 248 ff.
    speech development and 240–241
social communication, see communi-
        cation
social drive
    defined, 162, 182–183
    social deprivation and 205
    stress and 172–173
social interactions, of macaques 123 ff.
social isolation, see also deprivation
    aggression and 163 ff.
    arousal and 162 ff., 167, 181 ff., 205
    behavior disturbances in monkeys
        and 133 ff.
    effect on communication and 135

social isolation (cont'd)
  effects on learning and perform-
    ance and vii
  response to avoidance stimuli and
    135
  sensory deprivation studies and 205
  studies
    of prisoners 182
    of school-age children 164 ff., *165*
social learning, *see* learning
social life, of early man 147–148
social play, *see* play
social reinforcement 156, 185
social relations, deprivation and 80–
    81, *80,* 133 ff.
social satiation, anxiety and 164 ff.
social scientists
  definition of nutrition 61
  dispositional adjectives used by 157
  related to biologists v
socioeconomic status, *see also* social
    class
  environmental forces and 65
  of infants in behavioral study 10
  malnutrition and 3, 8–9
sound production, *see* vocalization
space perception, cultural differences
    and 151
speech, *see* language
stereotyped movements
  comparative studies of 98 ff.
  role of mother and 83
  social interaction and 181
stimulation
  exteroceptive indifferent, *see* indif-
    ferent exteroceptive stimuli
  maternal care and 105
  verbal, language development and
    and 235 ff.
stimuli
  arousal potential of 187 ff., *187*
  classes of, maternal care and 105
  complexity of, age and 104
  heart rate and class of 252
  interactions between organismic
    characteristics, environment
    and 106
  learning and 161–162
  noxious 102
  reaction to

stimuli (cont'd)
  age and cultural setting and
    218 ff.
  deprivation syndrome and 82, *82*
  in monozygotic and dizygotic
    twins 204
  reinforcing of, in study of rats
    189 ff.
  sexual, in arousal study 175 ff.
  visual
    age and 103–104
    infant monkeys and 254
    isolation and 134
stress
  effects of 143–144
  first-born children and 169
suburbia, compared with cities 140–
    141
sucking, in nonhuman primate in-
    fants 74, 76–77, 97
swaying
  deprivation syndrome and 80–81,
    80
  role of mother and 83

T

taboos, diet and 61–62
Taylor Manifest Anxiety Scale
    (MAS) 195
teenagers
  in affluent societies 145
  Japanese, height of 142
teeth, protein malnutrition and 4
temperature changes, newborn pri-
    mates and 77
tension reduction, *see* arousal-reduc-
    tion
Terman-Merrill intelligence scores,
    in rural preschoolers 19
timing
  and effects of deprivation syn-
    drome 86
  learning and 49
toilet training 105
toys, manipulation of 253
twins
  identical 153
  response to stimuli 204
tyrosine, malnutrition and 7

U

underground schools 149
urban environment
    definition of 139–140
    effect on man of vi
urinary creatinine, malnutrition
    and 5

V

vaccination, of malnourished children 5–6
verbal communication, *see* communication
verbal learning, *see* language
visual discrimination, measurement
    of 104
visual-haptic integration, 34 ff., *42*
visual-kinesthetic performance 34 ff.,
    39, 42
    and learning to write 51
visual stimuli, *see* stimuli, visual
vocalization
    distinctive 235 ff., *236–237*
    in humans and nonhuman primates
        compared 100–101
    by mother, social class and 252
    in nonhuman primates 74, 75
    single versus multiple maternal
        care and 255
vulnerability, of young organisms 103

W

walking
    bipedal 128
    primate development and 74
water
    attitude of monkeys toward 126

water (cont'd)
    —content and distribution in malnourished children 5
    regulation, deprivation syndrome
        and 133–134
Watsonian behaviorism 258
weaning 105
weight
    behavior and 10
    biosocial factors and *4–7*
    distribution 10, *11*
    evolution during first five years 23
    of Latin American children 18
    motor behavior and 19, *19–20*
weight-age correlations 19
wheat, in diet of monkeys 126–127
white noise, verbal retention and 194–195, *195*
withdrawal, indifferent exteroceptive stimuli and 196
writing, visual-kinesthetic performance and 51
Wundt's curve 186–187, *186–187*

X

x-rays, in nutritional studies 68

Y

Yucatan children, studies of reactions to human forms and
    faces in 218 ff., 232
Yugoslavian children, study of malnourishment in 29–30

Z

Zapotec Indians, Gesell test scores of
    18